One Day At A Time

"Look at what we've done Mel"

~

Dedicated to our beautiful daughter,

Melissa Alice Leech

First Published 2009 by Appin Press, an imprint of Countyvise Limited
14 Appin Road, Birkenhead, Wirral CH41 9HH.

British Library Cataloguing in Publication Data.
A catalogue record for this book is available from the British Library.

ISBN 978 1 906205 27 0

Contents

Foreword

I remember the first time I met Melissa Leech very well indeed. Meeting any new patient with a likely diagnosis of cancer is always a unique and momentous occasion, full of challenges for patient, family and doctor. It is usually an event that registers deeply for all concerned and is a privilege and delicate responsibility at the start of what is likely to be the start of a long, unwelcome and dreaded journey into the unknown. It begins with the bombshell of all bombshells: 'we think it's cancer....' Only those who have actually been on such a journey, either themselves or with their loved ones, have any real notion of the numbness and magnitude of such a situation. Many of us occasionally dare to ponder how we might react to such news, how we'd cope. Most of us quickly abandon such thoughts: we either think we know or would rather not know how we'd react. Even the most rational among us would rather not tempt fate by dwelling on such matters, nor think about the reality that one in three of us might be faced with such news at any point in our lives.

People are amazingly resilient however, and in their own individual way and time they rise to the battle ahead: to the unbelievable complexities of modern cancer treatments, the medical jargon, the dismay of hair loss, sickness and other side effects and the deepest urge of all: the will to survive and for some, the hardest of all: the acceptance of death. For those of us whose job it is to care for cancer sufferers we have the opportunity to learn from every single one of our patients. Some cope well, some badly. Some follow predictable coping paths, others are full of surprises.

Every once in a while, however, you meet someone who has some special effect on you: Mel was just such a person. For myself I recognised at the outset the extra responsibility of looking after a vivacious bright young woman whose hopes and dreams were starting to become reality. Having daughters of similar age, I was all too aware of the devastating effect this would have on her and her devoted family. Yet as the weeks went by, it became clear to all who cared for Mel that she was a remarkable individual. Her openness and desire to share her experiences, fears and hopes began to form a familiar part of our regular chats and daily conversations with nurses, doctors and above all her family. Her strength, courage and humour shone through in all her thoughts and were an inspiration to those privileged enough to know her. Little did we know at that time, these thoughts, hers, her family and friends, recorded as her journey progressed, would form a lasting tribute from which we can all learn so much.

This is a unique story of a remarkable person and a devoted family.

Dr Adrian G Smith MB ChB MRCP FRCPath
Consultant Haematologist

CHAPTER ONE

As Good As It Gets

"The real troubles in your life are apt to be things that never crossed your worried mind; the kind that blindside you at 4pm on some idle Tuesday . . . . ."

Mary Schmich

In April of 2007 my wife Julie and I were walking by the river. It was a beautiful evening and the sun was shinning. As we walked, we chatted about life in general and how good it was. I can clearly remember turning to Julie and saying, "Yep, perfect; it makes you wonder what's around the corner waiting to cock it up."

Julie and I have two daughters, Melissa and Rebecca. Mel was enthusiastic, sociable, and loved student life. She began a Business Management Degree at Aston University in September 2005, immediately making friends and throwing herself into student life. She successfully completed her first year and passed all her exams. Typical of her confident nature she decided to leave the Business Management Degree and study Psychology. As well as the social side of university life she worked in the campus shop and for a time mentored school children who needed a little encouragement with their studies. One of her favourite tasks was showing potential students around the university campus, answering their questions and explaining to them why Aston was the greatest place on earth to study.

In the spring of 2007, she was elected editor of the Aston Times. She was an Aunty and an International Aunty. This involved welcoming new students, both from the UK and abroad, as they arrived at Aston and helping them to settle

1

into their new surroundings. She was renting a house on the outskirts of Birmingham that she was to share with two of her friends Gemma and Milly. During the summer, she had successfully applied for a job at Branston Golf and Country Club. It was about a par four from our house and was ideal. It was ongoing and as Mel pointed out, it meant that throughout her university life she would never have to worry about finding work again. Life for Mel was perfect, and as good as it had ever been.

Becky was always the quieter of the two and her formative years were spent having her life organised by Melissa. Becky in turn could wind Mel up with her sense of humour and when she mischievously nicknamed Melissa, "Mooch", little did we know the name would stick and travel with her to Aston. I know it is very clichéd, but as well as sisters, they were the best of friends.

We had noticed at Easter that Mel lost a little weight, it wasn't a major amount and we did not think for one minute there was anything seriously wrong. Following her return from university in June, our normally healthy daughter had one illness after another. It began with a mouth infection, then tonsillitis, tiredness, night sweats, an irritating cough and a feeling of being generally unwell.

On 20 July, the four of us went to London for a weekend break to celebrate Becky's eighteenth birthday. Over the course of the two-day trip, we walked about twenty miles. On the Friday evening, we went to see The Sound of Music, whilst on the Saturday afternoon we watched the first matinee of Joseph with Lee Mead. Throughout the time we were walking, Mel was lagging behind, saying she felt tired. We all put it down to a hectic last term and Mel burning the candle at both ends. On the first day, we went back to the hotel for a couple of hours before going to see the show. Mel spent the whole two hours asleep, which at the time did not seem strange, but using that wonderful tool called hindsight, we can see it was one of the first signs that things were not as they should be.

Mel was asked by our GP to attend hospital for a blood test. She had the test on the last day of July 2007. I had time off work to accompany her. The hospital is on the outskirts of town and she became tired if she walked too far. After the trip to hospital, Mel and Becky went to see the latest Harry Potter film. A week later, the results of the blood tests came back from the hospital. Mel was anaemic. It all made sense. The initial weight loss, the various infections, the tiredness. She was prescribed iron tablets and the worry beads were packed away once more!

The first time I can remember thinking there could be more to Mel's illness than the doctors were suggesting was one evening when we walked to Branston Golf & Country Club to meet her from work. As Julie, Becky and I walked along the street we could hear coughing in the distance. It sounded like an old man of eighty who had smoked all his life. Instead, it was a young girl of 19 who had never lit a cigarette in anger. When we met up with Mel she explained to us how she had been struggling at work. She had been sick, felt tired, she was getting out of breath and when she bent down she had what she described as a "suffocating feeling" in her face.

My holiday entitlement from work was being eaten into. Hardly a week went by without me having to take a day off to accompany Mel to the local surgery. As time went on, the cough showed no sign of abating and her breathing became more laboured. She found it difficult to cope with the stairs at home and with our house having an upstairs bathroom, every trip to the toilet got slower as she fought to catch her breath. Mel would wake up in the morning and her nightclothes would be wringing wet. This was something we never mentioned to the doctors at the local surgery. We put it down to it being summertime.

Mel had planned a night out in Birmingham for her twentieth birthday. Despite the fact she'd been feeling unwell; she was looking forward to her night out. However, as we were to discover over the coming weeks and months, plans would have a habit of changing and on August 5th Mel sent out the following message to her friends.

"hey guys

Just to let you know im not gonna be able to go out for my bday afterall, ive not been very well over the summer (nothing serious or anything) but it means i cant drink or anything so im gonna postpone it till we get bk to uni and then ill be able to properly celebrate!! Sorry anyways but ill c u all soon"

As any parent will tell you, you know your own child. Whether they are six, sixteen or sixty, you can tell when they are in genuine distress. It was evident as the days and weeks passed by, Mel was becoming more concerned. The symptoms remained and the prescribed antibiotics did nothing. Both Julie and I were beginning to think there was more to the illness than tonsillitis, but we didn't know what and as Mel had no history of any consistent illness, other than tonsillitis, it was difficult to believe it could be anything other than what the GP was telling us. After a month of to-ing and fro-ing from the Practice one of the GPs realised that no amount of penicillin, paracetamol or cough medicine was rectifying the problem and with this in mind he decided to send Mel for a chest x-ray.

It was booked for Tuesday 14th August. However, by Saturday 11th August, Mel's breathing had deteriorated to such an extent that climbing the stairs to the bathroom was like scaling Everest. She'd taken to sleeping in an armchair downstairs as the breathlessness worsened. When she lay flat, the cough would start. In desperation, we took her to the Accident & Emergency department at Burton's Queen's Hospital. It was the first day of the football season and earlier in the summer, Mel and her friend Sooty had volunteered to give out freebies at Villa Park. She should have been there watching Aston Villa v Liverpool. She missed Liverpool's 2-1 win and worse still, Steven Gerrard's last minute winner. We waited for an hour in the waiting room at A & E before being taken to a side room where we were seen by one of the A&E doctors. They checked her blood pressure, her throat, her heart rate and her temperature before the doctor returned two hours later to deliver his verdict. In his opinion it was tonsillitis!

Once more, we were convinced. The way the doctor explained, his diagnosis made sense. He told us that Mel's tonsils were enlarged and this was restricting her breathing, therefore she was experiencing a constant shortage of breath. We never questioned him. He's a doctor, he knows what he's talking about. With hindsight, should we have asked him to investigate the issues regarding Mel's breathing further? He knew she was sleeping downstairs in an armchair. Would anything we might have said made any difference? We talked to him about the x-ray appointment the following Tuesday and he told us to cancel it. Julie queried Mel's earlier blood test results which showed that she was anaemic, the doctor said that this was nothing to worry about and not connected to Mel's breathing difficulties. The antibiotics he was prescribing would do the trick and Mel would be feeling much better in a couple of days. Convinced we had now got it sorted at 10am on Monday, the 13th August I rang the Queen's Hospital and cancelled her x-ray appointment.

Three days later, with Mel's condition showing no signs of improvement, I took another day off work. Mel was now spending all of her time sitting propped up in an armchair, she had little energy and her spirits were getting low. Every morning I was going into work and explaining to colleagues how I knew there was something wrong. I didn't know what it was, but I knew it wasn't tonsillitis. On the morning of Thursday 16 August I took Becky to school to get her A level results and after discovering that she had gained three A's, myself, Becky and Mel drove up to the Peak District for a picnic. We wanted to celebrate Becky's results and at the same time cheer Mel up.

We parked in Ashbourne and went for a walk around the town. The slight incline as you make your way to the market place proved a real problem, with Mel telling Becky and I to slow down, as she was getting breathless. We bought some goodies to eat and returned to the car. As well as struggling with her breathing, it hurt for her to laugh and many a time Mel told Becky and I, "Stop making me laugh, it hurts when I laugh." We drove from the town centre of Ashbourne and headed for Blore Pastures in Dovedale. We got out of the car, walked about twenty yards to a spot on the grass and sat down on our blanket. By the time Mel joined us, she was out of breath and sounded as though she had run a marathon. I knew we were getting to the stage where we had to get something done, even if it meant another dreaded trip up to the A&E department.

CHAPTER TWO

In The Company of Queen's

Sunday the 19th August was Mel's twentieth birthday and once more she was experiencing difficulty with her breathing. She was struggling to walk up the stairs and even when she was lying down her breathing was laboured. She didn't celebrate her birthday and by now we knew we had to get her to hospital and get answers. Melissa persuaded us to wait until the following day as she didn't want to spend her birthday in A & E. We were due to visit the city of Liverpool and more importantly for Mel, Liverpool Football Club in order that she could spend her birthday money in the club shop, but I knew it wasn't going to happen. We had to get her seen at the hospital and we had to make them take us seriously. At around 8.30am on Monday 20th August we set off to hospital. On the way to hospital Mel said that if they got her sorted, we could go up to Liverpool later in the day. We never got further than the Queen's Hospital in Burton on Trent.

We arrived at the Queens Hospital just before nine o'clock. The waiting room in the Accident & Emergency department was quiet. We registered at reception and waited to be called into the treatment area. We didn't have to wait long and the three of us followed the nurse toward an empty cubicle. Mel sat upright on the edge of the bed to make her breathing comfortable. We waited.

As nurses and doctors busied themselves around the department, the three of us talked, reassuring Mel, we wouldn't be leaving until we had answers. She wasn't worried and questioned whether by early afternoon we'd be walking into the Liverpool club shop at Anfield. We were interrupted by an A & E doctor. He began asking Mel questions about her symptoms. How long had she had them? Did anything in particular bring them on? What medicines had she been taking? As he talked, he listened to her chest and then to her back. He did the standard observations that we would get to know so well, they checked her temperature, her heart rate and her blood pressure. Julie had brought the results of Mel's last blood test and she showed them to the doctor to ascertain if there was any link between these and Mel's symptoms. The results were abnormal and whilst we thought they may be linked to Mel's illness, we didn't imagine for one minute they related to anything other than an infection or at worst Glandular Fever. I remember the doctor showing no immediate signs of panic, but he told us he wanted Melissa to have an x-ray.

Mel was wheeled through the corridors of the Queens Hospital to the x-ray department. As usual the waiting rooms were full and we envisaged a long wait, but we were mistaken. The radiologist in the x-ray department was waiting for us. Mel got changed into one the many unfashionable gowns that lay in a nearby basket. She was taken into an x-ray room where they took pictures of her chest from a variety of angles. It was the first of many x-rays she would undergo in the coming months, each one increasing the risk of future complications, but all very necessary. The radiologist informed us that by the time we had wheeled Mel back to the Accident & Emergency Department the results would be waiting for the doctor on screen. Gone were the days of waiting for the films to be developed and then having a sneaky peak before you get back to A & E. It is now done at the click of a button and the first time you see your x-ray is when the doctor brings it up on computer. True to their word, we arrived back in Accident & Emergency and the doctor was waiting. On his computer screen was Mel's x-ray. I knew instantly there was a problem. On the right side of Mel's chest was a huge white shadow. Lengthways, it stretched from just under her shoulder down to the bottom of her lung. There was a small patch of black near the bottom of the shadow indicating some air, but nothing like what there should be. I didn't know what it was but I remember thinking that they'd more than likely found the reason for all of Mel's symptoms in one simple x-ray. The doctor spoke to us and informed us that they thought Mel had contracted pneumonia.

I felt a wave of relief wash over me and I thought, "Yessssssss, at last, they'd cracked it". I didn't take in much of what the doctor was saying after his initial diagnosis, I was feeling strangely elated. I'd been saying for a couple of weeks that Mel was suffering from more than just tonsillitis and this confirmed it. I knew pneumonia was serious, but she was young, strong and I wasn't in any doubt that this was the first step to getting her well again. The doctor explained they were moving Mel into another bay in A & E.

I couldn't wait any longer and went outside to make some phone calls. I walked out of A & E, looked up to the heavens and said to myself, "YES!". I rang Becky to tell her. She was due at work at three o'clock that afternoon and had spent the morning in town. I called our parents, Julie's sister and my work place. I explained how the doctors had said it was pneumonia and that she was now on a side ward and they were going to make her better. I delivered the news as though it was good, it wasn't, pneumonia is a serious illness, but the total relief that they were acknowledging it wasn't a simple chest infection and there was no tonsillitis was overwhelming.

I left the hospital and went into town to get Mel some Pyjamas. Say what you like about Primark, but when the chips are down and you need cheap pyjamas in a hurry, they are in the Premier League. After picking up the new PJ's for Mel I nipped home. Becky was at home and together we 'googled' pneumonia. Thanks to Wikipedia we discovered that pneumonia was an inflammatory illness of the lung (that fits), and its typical symptoms included a cough, chest pain, fever and difficulty in breathing (every box ticked).

Whilst I'd been making my phone calls, Mel had become upset, this was her first day in hospital, she'd never had to stay in before and the reality that she may have to spend a few days in there was hitting home. She told Julie she was fed up and asked why did she have to be ill. Julie tried to reassure her, telling her that now the doctors knew what the problem was, they could set about making her better. I returned to the hospital and Julie went to get a drink from the machine in the corridor as the doctors came for more of Mel's blood. I sat and held her hand, telling her to look at me, concentrate on me and if it hurt, she should squeeze my hand. She was really brave, there was only a slight squeeze and it was all done. Julie returned from getting her drink. She'd been interrupted on her walk back by an A & E doctor who tentatively explained that they weren't certain of their initial diagnosis and they had consulted other radiologists in the hospital and they had other ideas of what the shadow may be. Nothing more was said and we waited.

In the middle of the afternoon a nurse came to see us and explained they were moving Mel to the Observation Ward. We settled Mel into her bed, sat with her and talked to try and make the time go quickly. Doctors came to Mel to gather information, some of which they'd already had and they informed us they would tell us more when they'd received the results of the earlier blood tests. We waited. The time dragged by and we suddenly found ourselves no wiser than when we'd entered the department at nine o'clock that morning. The satisfaction of finally knowing what was wrong with Mel had gone, it may not be pneumonia and we were now back to wondering, if it wasn't pneumonia, what was it?

Around five o'clock in the evening, after a day spent in A & E we were visited by a doctor who informed us that they were transferring Mel to the Assessment Ward. There were no definitive answers as to what this shadow was, so with blissful ignorance we gathered up Melissa's belongings, sat her in a wheelchair and left. We wheeled Mel to the waiting nurses on Ward 3. Mel was given her own side room, so we settled her down and proceeded to get her booked in on the ward. We'd only been in hospital a day and already Mel had had to answer the same questions about half a dozen times to different people and she was getting tired of it. There must be an easier way!

Just after tea time Mel was visited by the unusually named, Doctor Why who explained that he'd been looking at the x-ray and it appeared that something was pressing on the lung. They weren't sure what it was and there were further tests they needed to perform before they could make an accurate diagnosis. It wasn't the news we wanted, but at least with them investigating the shadow in such detail, we could be sure we'd know soon enough and Mel's recovery could begin. Following Dr. Why's visit we sat and talked. Mel had her first taste of hospital food, Julie had her first taste of hospital tea and I visited the shop for some hospital Diet Coke! We left the ward at eight o'clock in the evening. We didn't want to. Mel was scared, we were scared for her, we wanted to stay with her, but we knew we couldn't and reluctantly we left, promising to return as soon as the visiting hours allowed. We drove home, tired and worn out. We rang our parents and close family with updates, telling them the initial diagnosis of pneumonia was now unlikely and we'd know more tomorrow. It was our first full day in hospital and unfortunately, unbeknown to us at the time, it was to be the first of many.

CHAPTER THREE
Into the Care of Experts

I can't remember if I slept that night. The fact I probably did was more to do with exhaustion than anything. I wasn't too worried, my theory was that if it wasn't pneumonia, it must be something similar and therefore it would be relatively easy to sort out. It was Tuesday 21st August and Becky was due at work later that day so the plan was for us to go and see Mel at the hospital as soon as we could and then I would nip out for half an hour to take Becky to the golf club.

During the morning Mel had a bronchoscopy. This was a procedure that allowed the doctor to look at Mel's airway through a thin viewing instrument called a bronchoscope. With the problems she was encountering with her breathing they wanted to examine the airway and the flexible bronchoscope allowed them to do this. They were going to take a tissue sample for a biopsy, but they'd told Mel they weren't hopeful of doing this and their theories proved correct. There were students present, observing the procedure. The nurse was friendly and chatted to Mel to calm her fears. The doctor told the nurse to keep quiet as the students couldn't hear what was being said. Mel wasn't impressed. She talked about that bronchoscopy for months after and said that throughout all her treatment, that bronchoscopy on her second day in hospital was the worst thing they did to her.

As she wrote in her Facebook notes a couple of weeks later . . .

"I had a bronchoscapy which was horrible (but they wanted to check there was nothing actually in my lung). They injected into my neck with the bronchoscopy which was horrible and they give u a sedative but i was fairly aware of what was going

on even though i cudnt feel it! They said from that there was nothing infecting my lung but that there was something pressing down on it."

We went to the hospital for the start of visiting and sat with Mel, catching up with all that happened overnight and during the morning. Her throat was sore from the bronchoscopy and she was drinking lots of fluids. At about half past two Becky and I left the hospital and drove home. Becky got changed for work and I drove her round the corner to the golf club to begin her shift. I went home for a drink and then visited Julie's parents, Enid and Ron, to update them on what had happened in the hours since we had last called them. Julie's dad wasn't in the best of health, he had heart problems, emphysema and he was chair-bound, He had oxygen on permanent supply and Julie's mum's life revolved around caring for him. Getting to the bathroom required supreme effort. He slept in an armchair for comfort. The similarities between his and Melissa's symptoms were uncanny; the major difference was that Ron was in his mid seventies, whilst Melissa had just turned twenty.

I sat with them, I was honest but tried not to worry them. They wanted to know all that was happening, but they didn't want to hear it. They wanted the truth, but they also wanted re-assurance, a sugar-coated version. They wanted to know that she was going to be ok. As we sat talking my mobile phone rang. It was Julie. Sensing the tone of her voice I took the call outside. Julie told me that around 4pm Dr. Ahmed, Dr. Zai, Pat Holland and another member of the haematology team had converged on Mel's room.

Dr. Ahmed spoke first and Julie assumed he was the senior doctor. He told Julie and Melissa that it was Lymphoma. He questioned Mel about her various symptoms, paying particular attention to the cough and the night sweats. He said she would need chemotherapy and the disease was treatable. He explained the treatment Mel would receive at Burton, coupled with input from Birmingham and Nottingham rivalled anything available in America. I believe there is a common misconception that everything in America is better than here in the UK and that's not always the case. Dr. Ahmed was upbeat about the outlook and although he didn't mention the word "cancer", Julie knew it was serious and was trying not to cry. She didn't want to panic Melissa and was unsure what to say to her. Mel didn't seem to realise she had cancer.

As I was taking the call from Julie, I'm sure my heart stopped. My first thought was that we would beat it. I told Julie (more than once) that we would beat it. I heard a call from behind me. It was Julie's mum and dad asking for an update. Midway through the call I'd realised they were within earshot and I'd kept my reaction low key, my responses short and I'd took the rest of the phone call outside. I told Julie I'd be with her soon and re-iterated that we'd beat this disease. I turned to Julie's parents and explained that the doctor was with Mel and I was going to go back to the hospital to see what was happening. I didn't tell them the truth, I didn't know enough about Lymphoma to be able to answer the questions I knew they'd ask. I left in a hurry and drove home, walking through the front door without bothering to shut it behind me. I switched on my laptop and googled Lymphoma. The first few results didn't mention cancer, there was mention of lymphocytes and neoplasm, red cells, white cells, lymph nodes and something I had heard of, Hodgkin's disease. I flicked through the googled pages, looking for positives. I was determined we would beat it. This was the day that "sod's law" made the first of its many appearances. The one time in two days I'd left Mel's bedside (apart from the night time when I had to) and she was being told she had lymphoma.

Whilst I had been at home "googling" the word Lymphoma Melissa had been told she was to have a CT scan. This involved having a canula. A tube is inserted into a vein so fluid can be delivered or removed. Mel was ok with this, a little nervous, but she took it in her stride. The hardest part was drinking the milky liquid that accompanies the scan. It is called a contrast dye and improves the picture quality. Mel said it tasted horrible, but she managed to drink it and the scan was taken. I returned to the hospital and Julie and Melissa related all that had happened whilst I'd been out. Considering the news, Mel seemed relaxed. I couldn't work out whether it was because she was calm about the situation or whether she had not taken it all in. Whilst talking to Julie and Mel, Dr. Ahmed hadn't actually used the "c" word. Julie and I were both fairly certain it was cancer as the doctor had mentioned chemotherapy, (something that completely by-passed Mel's ears), but we wanted to be certain. The only way was to speak to one of the nurses. I went into the reception area of ward three and spoke to the Sister. I asked her if we were talking cancer and she told us we were, but it was treatable. A lot of the time we hear words but we don't actually listen. The nurse said treatable. She didn't say curable.

We went back into the side room on the Assessment ward and spent time talking to Mel. She was making plans for university and how she'd fit treatment in with university life. We left hospital at eight o'clock and on the way home called to see my mum and dad, Mel's cousin's Sarah and Hannah and Julie's mum and dad. We recounted our conversations with the doctor and the nurse and tried our best to reassure them that everything would be ok. As Julie and I were reassuring our parents and nieces, unbeknown to us at the time, Melissa was connecting to the internet on her mobile phone. She googled Lymphoma and for the first time she knew she had cancer.

It seemed like a lifetime since we had walked into A & E on the Monday morning, but it was just over 48 hours. So much had happened. It was becoming apparent that life would never be the same again. We worried, sometimes out loud, sometimes silently to ourselves, but despite our fears, the overriding message from the hospital was that our daughter should make a full recovery. Mel told us how during the night, one of the patients, an elderly lady, had come into her room and tried to tuck her in. We wondered if some of the drugs had kicked in and she'd been dreaming, but apparently this lady did her rounds every night, making sure all was well.

Visiting hours were 2pm til 4pm and 6 till 8pm. We wanted to be there earlier, to sit with Mel, talk to her, listen to her, hold her hand and to give her reassurance. As soon as the clock struck two we walked into Ward three and were startled to find Mel surrounded by nurses. They were from the fertility clinic and were talking to Mel about the possibility of freezing her eggs for the future as the chemotherapy would affect her fertility. Having her eggs frozen would result in her giving herself hormone injections and travelling to Birmingham Women's Hospital to have the eggs harvested for future use.

It was one of those topics that had to be talked about there and then. Mel was twenty years old, she didn't have a steady boyfriend, but here she was being told she would most likely be infertile within a few weeks and a decision on whether she could ever have children had to be made within the next few days. Melissa loved children; she worked in a nursery for three years and had never been in any doubt that one day she would have children of her own and her initial reaction to the meeting with the fertility nurses was that she wanted to have her eggs frozen. At one point we were asked to leave as the fertility nurses needed confidential information. She didn't want us to leave, but we had to and we made our way to the relative's room. We had tears in our eyes. This shouldn't be happening. It was all moving too fast and there was too much information to take in. I wanted a pause button. I needed to stop everything whilst we absorbed all the information that was being thrown at us, but there was no pause button and we were fast forwarded to the next group of experts.

Within half an hour of the fertility nurses disappearing, Dr. Adrian Smith and Dr. Zai entered the room. Dr. Smith was to be Mel's haematology consultant and she took an instant liking to him. He had a very relaxed manner and after the rollercoaster ride of the past two days it was welcome. He was accompanied by the softly spoken Dr. Zai. She too endeared herself to the three of us, like Dr. Smith, she was understanding, compassionate and best of all, positive. Dr. Smith explained to us that he thought it was Hodgkin's Lymphoma and after treatment it would all just be a bad memory. The reasoning behind his theory was that Hodgkin's was the most common type of Lymphoma found in people of Mel's age. He also talked to Mel about the fertility, saying that if it was Hodgkin's then chances were fertility may not be an issue. He explained about the "egg freezing" procedure, the pros, the cons and the chances of success. Mel's mind was slowly changing. Dr. Smith went on to explain that even though his thinking was erring toward Hodgkin's he wasn't going to guess, as guessing was never clever in a situation like this and in order to be certain of his diagnosis they needed to perform a biopsy. He checked Mel's neck and also under her arms for any sign of swollen lymph nodes. If there were any swollen nodes then they would be used to obtain the required biopsy and the doctors could then be certain of Mel's condition. Unfortunately, after examining Mel he could not find any swollen nodes. He went on to explain that their only option was to obtain a biopsy from the tumour and this meant cutting into Mel's chest. This wasn't a procedure they could perform at Burton and Dr. Smith explained that Glenfield Hospital in Leicester carried out the necessary thoracic surgery. Dr's Smith and Zai left the room. We talked through all that had happened during the afternoon. We were exhausted but there was no time to rest. A nurse came in and told us that a bed had become available at Glenfield, it was reserved for Melissa and we would be leaving for Leicester within the hour.

CHAPTER FOUR

To Glenfield and Back

The drive from Burton to Glenfield took an hour. Melissa began to get concerned. This was all new and events were occurring at an alarming rate. She should have been looking forward to Fresher's week and nights out with her friends, not worrying about being transferred to a hospital in another county. Sensing her anxiety I enquired about the possibility of Julie travelling in the ambulance with her. I would then drive over to Glenfield and meet them. It was agreed. I set off to Glenfield. I had been driving for about twenty minutes when my mobile phone rang. I parked in a lay-by and answered it. There had been a change of plan. The ambulance wasn't insured to take passengers and Julie could not travel with Mel as originally thought. Mel was in tears, the technicians in the ambulance were brilliant and calmed her, one of them travelled with Mel in the back of the ambulance and this made the journey seem quicker. Throughout her life, Mel had never been one for change. She would tackle anything as long as she knew what was happening and she had a plan to work to. She was never at her best when plans suddenly changed.

My own worry at this point was that Mel would be alone when she arrived at Glenfield, so I wasted no time in getting back to Burton to pick Julie up. We arrived at Glenfield Hospital at about seven thirty in the evening. As we arrived the ambulance carrying Mel pulled up. The anxiety that was with her at the start of the journey had disappeared and she was chatting to the ambulance staff. We had been told Mel would be taken to the Critical Assessment Unit, but instead we were directed straight up to the thoracic ward and shown into the side room where Melissa would be staying. After settling Mel into her new surroundings we left the hospital and drove home.

It was 10.30pm. The drive from hospital to home throughout Mel's illness would become a time of reflection. We would go over the day's happenings, picking over all the information. We would re-examine any positives, dissect the negatives and try to predict what may happen next. We would then phone close relatives to inform them of what had occurred in our rapidly changing life.

Whilst we were driving home, a ward doctor took all of Mel's personal details again. They then took blood gases. These are taken when the doctor' suspects an oxygen/carbon dioxide imbalance in the blood. A blood sample was collected from Mel's radial artery (located on the inside of the wrist, below the thumb). The blood gas test was painful and for the first time Mel was becoming anxious when having injections. On Thursday 23 August, she was due to have a biopsy. The doctor removed a sample of tissue from Mel's chest. This should assist in diagnosis, they only removed a small sample. Mel was "nil by mouth". Anyone who knows Mel will be aware that "nil by mouth" and Melissa are not compatible. Melissa loved her food and her" hog feasts" of ham and cheese cobs with ham and crisps on the side with possibly a piece of Scotch egg were legendary amongst her family and friends. It was a long day. With Becky at work, I would drive over to Leicester in the morning, spend a couple of hours with Mel before taking Becky back to Burton in time for her shift at work and then I'd drive back to Glenfield. Mel needed us with her and it was important for Becky to be at the hospital as much as she could.

She was informed during the morning there had been a change of plan and they were going to send her down for an ultrasound scan so that they could perform one final check of the lymph nodes in Mel's neck to see if there were any that could be used for the biopsy. This would save them having to go into her chest cavity. There weren't any so they had no option but to take her down to theatre and perform the biopsy. Mel's doctor at Glenfield was Dr. Nakas, he spoke English in a Greek accent and was funny, friendly and endeared himself to Mel very quickly and after a day of "nil by mouth", Mel took a lot of endearing to! Every time he walked past Mel's room he poked his head around the door and asked how we were. He told us the biopsy would be done that day and not to worry. At five in the evening, Dr. Nakas entered the room and he wasn't happy. He apologised to Melissa, saying that he wanted to perform the biopsy that evening. He was prepared to stay late into the evening to do it, but his staff weren't, so it had to be put back until tomorrow. Julie told him not to worry as he we could see he was doing all he could and he replied, "But it's my job to worry, I am a surgeon, Melissa is not just a number, she is Melissa".

He told Mel he would put her at the top of his list and the biopsy would be done first thing in the morning. After being "nil by mouth" all day, Mel was hungry and never before has hospital food been eaten with such enthusiasm as she cleaned her plate of sausage and chips. We stayed with Mel for the rest of the evening. She was anxious, but nowhere near as anxious as she would have been had she not had the brilliantly funny and caring Dr. Nakas waiting for her the following morning. We made sure that we arrived at Glenfield Hospital early on the Friday, we went into Mel's room and it was empty. No bed and no Mel. Dr. Nakas was true to his word and Mel was having her biopsy. Mel described what she remembered about the biopsy in her blog . . . .

"The procedure itself was fine, I was nil by mouth for a day I think which was hard! I also had to have a cannula fitted which was a bit painful but nothing major and they tried to insert a bigger one into my wrist but it hurt me too much so they did it after I was asleep! All I remember then is them giving me the mask to breathe in anaesthetic and I was gone! I woke up, high on drugs and asking if the x-ray in the corner was mine! I was also desperate for a drink but had to wait for a while, I also asked for more morphine which I was later sick from! I also threw up from the anaesthetic and I was pretty groggy for the rest of the day!"

Julie and I went for a walk. We talked over all that had happened since Monday and tried to predict what may happen in the following days and weeks. We tried to guess whether it was Hodgkin's or Non-Hodgkin's Lymphoma and as usual we trawled through all that had happened during the summer, questioning whether or not we should have realised what was happening. We returned to Mel's room and as we sat there we heard one of the nursing staff talking to someone outside. A few minutes later the person left and the nurse came in and told us that someone had been asking after Mel. The nurse thought that he was a student friend. We left the ward and caught up with Tim just as he was leaving the hospital. They lived on the same corridor in their first year at university and he lived in Leicester. He had heard about Mel via Facebook and had come to see her. We stopped and chatted with him for a while.

Just after lunch they wheeled Mel back into her room. The biopsy was done. They had inserted a chest drain, which was standard procedure when they enter the chest cavity and she had a lovely wound to freak Becky out with. She was drowsy from the anaesthetic and drifted in and out as the afternoon passed by. I drove back to Burton on a mission.

When we were told that Mel had cancer we immediately told our family. Mel also asked me to call her close friends and explain to them what was happening. It was difficult enough for us to take stock of what was happening, but as a twenty year old, the last thing you expect is to be told one of your friends has cancer. One of the hardest calls of all was to Mel's oldest friend Claire. Melissa and Claire had been friends since Primary School. They had always kept in touch and although they didn't live in each other's pockets, they were close. Claire was devastated and it was no surprise when she asked to visit as soon as she was able. On that Friday, I drove back to Burton, picked up Claire and we made our way back to Leicester to see Mel. Mel told us that she was relieved it was all over. As we drove home that night we recounted the day's events and speculated as to whether Mel would be discharged from Leicester and sent back to Burton the following day. The results of the biopsy weren't due until early the following week and we were in the dark as to what would happen when Mel was sent back to Queen's Hospital.

Our first question when we arrived at Glenfield on the Saturday morning was "When is Mel going to be allowed back to Burton?" I hated being so far away from her, particularly at night. You're left with a feeling of helplessness. You want to be there. I couldn't (and still can't) bear the thought of her being upset and us not being there to comfort her. Mel tried her best to freak Becky out with operation stories. A nurse came to check the wound and for the first time we saw where they had taken the biopsy from. On the right side of Mel's chest, just above her breast, was a cut about three inches long. Above that was a small hole, about the size of a five pence piece, this was the entry site for the chest drain. I told Mel she looked like she'd been stabbed and shot! We were told by ward staff that Mel would be allowed to go back to Burton when the chest drain had been removed. Following on from Mel's description of the biopsy in her blog, she also recalled the removal of the chest drain,

"I had my chest drain removed, something which was very painful, as soon as she started pulling until she finished I screamed! Loudly! My mum and sister had to leave the room!"

It was the first time Julie and Becky had to leave the room... it wasn't to be the last! I sat with Mel and held her hand as they removed the chest drain, trying to calm her, but to be honest the best I could do was to let her cry out. As well as the pain from the chest drain removal, there were probably other frustrations that were released. Mel was still distressed when a few hours later the ambulance technicians arrived to take her back to Burton.

CHAPTER FIVE
A Room with a View

When we arrived back at Queen's Hospital in Burton Mel had been taken to Ward Seven. We walked onto the ward and were shown to an open bay. The first thing I noticed was that it was full of elderly ladies, some sitting up talking, some reading and others fast asleep. Mel was the youngest in the bay by at least thirty years. We didn't need to ask where she was, we looked across the room to the far corner and there she was, sitting on a bed crying. She kept saying that it wasn't fair, why did she have to be ill. She wanted to go home. A nurse explained they had to give her an injection in her tummy. Mel wasn't moving around much and this injection would prevent blood clots. The nurse wasn't aware it was the first time Mel had had these injections and she forgot to mention they stung, not when the needle was going in, but about five seconds after. Mel screamed again. If they'd been able to walk, some of the old ladies would have scarpered and any constipation on the ward would have been sorted in an instant! It was an awful time for Mel, she had been taken from her young, care free, student life and thrust into this new world of illness, injections, medication and constant examination from doctors and nurses. She cried after the injection and she cried again when they told her she couldn't use her mobile phone as it may affect equipment in an adjoining room. Her one remaining link to family and friends had been taken away. She sobbed her heart out and all we could do was hold her and let her get it out of her system.

We realised the bed she was currently sat in wasn't adjustable. For someone in Mel's condition this presented a problem as she needed to be propped up with more than a couple of pillows. She was breathless and lying down flat was

23

impossible. I asked the Ward Sister if she could be moved to a side room and the Sister agreed it would be for the best. Julie's brother Ray, his wife Nikki and their children Katie and Lee came to visit. For a while the tears stopped and we talked over what had happened during the last three days. After they had gone the Ward Sister came to inform us that they were moving Mel to a side room. We gathered up her belongings and they showed us to the isolation room, which was part of the haematology suite. The en-suite room was very spacious; it had an adjustable bed and a TV. There was a reclining chair in the corner. We closed the door behind us and it felt like we were shutting out the rest of the hospital.

The stress of the day had got to Mel and although she was thankful she had her own room, she remained tearful. The nurses gave her oxygen and nebulisers to assist her breathing. Throughout the evening she was unsettled. She didn't want us to go, asking us to stay "just a bit longer" each time we prepared to leave. Becky had bought her a red "Squishi" cushion for her birthday and as we left the hospital at around ten thirty that night, Mel lay on it, trying her hardest to block everything out. Julie was upset. I tried to be strong. Even at this early stage in the illness we dealt with our emotions in different ways. We were all unanimous though in wanting Mel's treatment to start as soon as possible and for her to start feeling better.

On Sunday morning we arrived at Queen's Hospital just before 10.30am. As we were to discover over the coming months, finances can take a battering when you have, or are looking after someone, with a long term illness. There are the obvious problems, such as time off work, but travel to and from hospital can become expensive, as can hospital car parking fees. At the Queen's hospital it costs £5.00 a day. There are concessions, but we weren't told about these, so we tried to park as cheaply as possibly, sometimes using the adjoining streets. Annoying for the residents, but understandable if you are a patient. We walked to Ward Seven, not knowing what to expect, but concerned about how Mel's emotions would be holding out. We needn't have worried. We walked into her room and she was sat up smiling. She was talkative and hungry. She wanted yogurts, lots of yogurts, but Mel only liked the smooth ones, so we set about finding some. It was her first food craving, more would follow but for now we were on a yogurt quest. That Sunday was the closest we had got to having the "real" Mel back since she came home from University. We made enquiries and were told that she had been prescribed a course of steroids. It was Mel's first experience of steroids. There are many side effects and in Mel's case they initially came in the form of hunger, yogurt cravings, and a "feel good" factor. The swollen face, or "moon face" as it is often referred to, came a week later. The haematology consultant, Dr. Ahmed, told us that he expected the steroids to break down and crumble the tumour. This in turn would release the pressure on Mel's airway and right lung. He went on to tell us that if the steroids didn't shrink the tumour, the chemotherapy was effective and would do the trick. Days in hospital are never pleasant, but after the week we had had, it was nice to see Melissa happy, positive and feeling relatively good. She was on oxygen and had the use of nebulisers as and when she needed them, but on that particular Sunday, at that particular time, she was in good spirits...even if they were steroid induced.

Monday the 27th August arrived and with it the realisation that it had been a week since we had taken Mel into Accident & Emergency. The hospital had the weekend feel to it as it was a Bank Holiday. We usually spent our Bank Holiday Monday's watching Burton Albion. It had been the most emotional week of our lives. Each of the last seven days had brought new challenges. We each had our own way of dealing with Mel's condition. I was adamant that we would beat it. Yes, it was cancer. No, it wasn't going to be easy, but we would beat it. Melissa was young, she was strong and her outlook on life was positive. There would be many tests of our resolve over the coming months and we were about to face the first. Waiting.

We waited to get to hospital in the morning. Some days we waited to leave hospital at night. We waited for doctors, for nurses and most of the time we waited for news. I'm not criticising the doctors or nursing staff, but as a patient or carer, the hours can seem like days and a week can seem an eternity. Our first experience of waiting began on that Monday. We were waiting for the results of the biopsy. It was due "early this week" and it was Monday which meant that "early this week" was here, but with it being a Bank Holiday, we doubted we would know anything that particular day. Even so, when you are waiting your heart skips a beat every time a doctor or nurse enters the room. You think they are here to give you the news you are waiting for now. They're not of course, the delivery of news, good, bad or indifferent is given by the consultants, but we were new to this game and were naive enough to believe that something as serious as a result of a biopsy may be given by a nurse or doctor on the ward. Never was the word patient more apt.

Mel had visitors that day and her spirits were boosted as she sat talking to Sooty, Laura and Mand, three of her friends from university. Julie and I went for a coffee in the nearby canteen. After Mel's friends had left, we returned to the ward and spent the rest of the day talking and watching TV. We left the hospital in the evening and for the first time in a week felt ok about going home and leaving Mel alone.

On the Tuesday we arrived just after ten o'clock hoping that today would be the day we discovered the true identity of Mel's type of Lymphoma. Mel was in good spirits and they were heightened as we arrived with a fresh supply of yogurts. She had always had a healthy appetite, but this was in a different league and it was totally random. We would be sat having a conversation and suddenly, she would ask, "Can you just get me a yogurt please?" After finishing it off, she'd say, "Mmmmm, I really enjoyed that, I'll have another".

Each day now had its own routine for Mel. She was woken up by a nurse at 6am to have her "tummy injection". The Clexane injection was given in order to prevent blood clots forming within blood vessels. As Mel's tumour was also pressing on her veins, this injection helped thin her blood. I used to try and distract her in order to take her mind off it and in later months we tried applying an ice pack, which although didn't take the pain away totally, did help. What didn't help was having the injection administered at six o'clock in the morning. Going to bed knowing she would be woken in the early hours with a painful injection didn't aid her sleep. Mel's other barrier against her blood clotting were a pair of stunning white stockings. They were so tight I could hardly get my fingers underneath them to roll them onto her legs. There were blood tests every day and the kindly ward doctor would call a couple of times to ask how she was. She had her temperature, her blood pressure and her heart rate checked at regular intervals.

Mel decorated her room in the hospital with pictures of her university friends, cards and presents from well-wishers and of course the obligatory Liverpool memorabilia. She sought to make it as homely as possible and having familiar items around her helped. A few months previous I bought a portable DVD player. I took it in for Mel and it enabled her to watch her own DVD's. She would put it on her table with a stack of DVDs before we went home and they would help to keep her occupied in the hours we weren't at hospital. The days began to merge into each other. Tuesday, Wednesday and Thursday all passed us by and still there were no results from the biopsy. Each consultant's visit came with an apology and as they left the ward we tried to convince ourselves that "no news was good news". The waiting was unbearable. We wanted the treatment to start. The sooner it started, the quicker Mel would feel better and the quicker we would get her home. The steroids had helped ease her breathing and they'd sent yogurt sales through the roof, but other than that it felt that we weren't getting anywhere. We'd been to the hospital every day and as well as ourselves and Becky, there was a constant flow of visitors. Laura and Phil, two of Mel's friends from school came to visit as did Claire. Mel used her mobile phone to good effect, keeping in touch with everyone and this constant communication set the tone for the months ahead. She loved keeping in touch with her friends, there were occasions she felt envious that they were going about their normal daily lives, but Mel fed off their stories to keep her own spirits up, believing that it wouldn't be long before she was back at uni with them.

CHAPTER SIX

Suspicions Confirmed

We had to wait until Friday for news on the biopsy, but that wasn't conclusive. Dr. Smith came in to see Mel and after chatting for a couple of minutes about football, he explained to us all that they were almost certain Mel had Non-Hodgkin's Lymphoma. However, they were not a 100% certain and more tests had to be done in order for them to be sure. Our first thought was that this uncertainty would delay Mel's treatment, but Dr. Smith went on to explain that they were going to give Mel Rituximab, an antibody drug that works alongside chemotherapy.

He told us that the Rituximab could be used regardless of the specific type of lymphoma Mel had, hence they could go ahead with the treatment straight away. I sat with Mel whilst she had yet another cannula inserted. The nurse came into the room. Julie and Becky went out. I sat on the bed, holding Mel's hand and talking to her. We'd talk about anything. Liverpool, The Bill, Burton Albion. Anything that would help her to focus on me and not the needle. As the nurse inserted the needle I would feel the grip of Mel's hand tighten round mine. No fingers were ever broken but there were a couple of times I had to stifle an "ouch". There is always the possibility of an allergic reaction to Rituximab and with this in mind the first dose is always administered slowly, over a number of hours. Mel was given some medication to help prevent any possible reaction, particularly sickness. As the Rituximab was given, Mel's obs were checked constantly for signs of change. At first it was every fifteen minutes, then every half an hour until the bag was empty. It took seven hours in total. Every trip to the toilet was a military operation as the drip was unplugged, the wires lifted from the floor and we'd slowly help Mel to the en-suite. Julie would go into the toilet with her and they would sit chatting before she had enough energy to return to her bed.

There had been talk of allowing her home over the weekend. It was suggested she could come home and then return to hospital later that evening. Her room on Ward Seven would be kept for her, so if, at any time she needed to return, she could do so. We arrived at hospital early on Saturday morning, hoping that Mel had not suffered any reactions to the drugs and praying she'd be able to come home. We were not disappointed and after liaising with the nurses and ward doctor we were able to sit Melissa in a wheelchair, wheel her to the car park and take her home. We discussed with the staff at the hospital about bringing her back and they agreed that as long as there were no problems, she could return to hospital on Monday. She had been in hospital for almost two weeks and although we were still not a 100% certain of the diagnosis, we were happy that the treatment had started and most importantly of all, Mel had felt some benefit from it. It seems strange to say we had a great weekend, especially with Mel having been diagnosed with cancer the previous week, but after all we had been through in the last couple of weeks, it felt great. I cooked Mel cheese and potato pie on Saturday (her favourite) and we watched Sky Sports Soccer Saturday. Mel was glad to be home. She knew she had to return to hospital on Monday, but she was determined to enjoy the weekend. The time was made all the more sweet for her as Liverpool scored against Derby . . . again and again and again. Six times in all and as her consultant, Dr. Smith was a Derby County fan, Mel was almost looking forward to returning to Ward Seven on Monday morning!

On returning to the hospital after our weekend leave, we waiting all morning. Lunchtime passed and then in the afternoon we were visited by Dr. Smith and we were told that Melissa had Diffuse Large B Cell Lymphoma. He was upbeat about the prognosis, saying that they were looking to cure her and the chemo would start on Wednesday. He said to us, "There may be times when things move very quickly and there may be other times when it appears we're doing nothing. Just trust us." We did. He went on to tell us that Diffuse Large B Cell was a common type of Non Hodgkin's Lymphoma and it was aggressive. He must have seen the look on our faces, as he quickly explained that the aggressive nature of the disease was good as it generally responded better to treatment.

As Mel explained in her first blog entry . . .

"NHL is a cancer of the blood. The lymphatic system is a crucial part of the body's immune system and helps to defend against infection and diseases. In Non Hodgkin's Lymphoma, the lymphocytes (white blood cells) start to grow abnormally and multiply in ways they shouldn't. This then forms swellings throughout the body, most commonly in the neck and armpit (lymph nodes) though my tumour is in my chest."

Dr. Smith then explained Mel would have R-CHOP chemotherapy every three weeks. This was three drugs, Cyclophosphamide, Doxorubicin and Vincristine along with Prednisolone, which is a steroid. This was accompanied by the antibody treatment that Mel had had on Friday called Rituximab. As Dr. Smith departed for a meeting we were told that Mel could return home and then come back for the chemotherapy on Wednesday. Mel returned home feeling better than she had been when she entered hospital a fortnight previous, but she was still poorly. Julie and I were still off work, as Mel needed constant care and monitoring. I planned to go back to work on the 10th September. Could life be any more stressful? A daughter with cancer and a new job. Another task we had to perform that week was to move Mel's stuff out of her house which was situated on the outskirts of Birmingham. It was obvious that it wasn't going to be possible for her to live away from home so Julie and I made the forty five minute trip to Erdington and emptied the room. It was a sad time as we knew how much Mel was looking forward to moving in to her new house but she took it in her stride and looked on the positive side.

On Tuesday 4 September, she wrote on her Facebook Wall . . .

"Just to let you all know, save writing to everyone, that im home from hospital now! for good! my results came back and they know now its a non hodgkins lymphoma - high grade type which means its faster growing but thats good cos the treatment attacks it better and quicker!

i just have to go in now for chemo and antibody treatment every 3 weeks or so as an outpatient. Ill be missing freshers week as still pretty weak at the min but i am much better than i was a week or so ago! ill be back at uni in october but probably commuting from home for term one but ill be back soon enough getting drunk im sure!

Just thought it was easier to write that once instead of 10 times on everyones wall! hope it makes sense and thanks for all the messages and texts since ive been in hospital - they really have helped! :) xxxxx"

We returned to the hospital as planned on Wednesday. Before going to the appointment, we went to McDonald's for our dinner. Prior to having the chemotherapy we talked with Dr. Zai and Pat Holland and they explained about the risk of infection and how we had to do all we could to avoid it. This meant no take away food and no eating out. Only home cooked food from now on. Mel didn't argue with that. There were other rules too, she had to avoid people with coughs and colds, make sure hands were kept washed and that she had her own towels and flannel. They talked further about the treatment itself, explaining it would be given every three weeks. Initially they were going to give Mel the chemotherapy and then she would be allowed home, but as it was her first session of chemo, it was decided that Mel should stay in hospital overnight, so we returned to the same room on Ward Seven and waited for treatment to begin. She was taken to the chemotherapy unit and met Wendy for the first time. Wendy was brilliant and Mel felt at ease with her straight away. Wendy talked about hair loss with Mel and explained about wigs. Two were ordered, a red one and a brown one. The treatment began and within an hour she was back on the ward. My sister Karen visited in the evening and we all sat around chatting in what was now becoming known as "Mel's room". All that was missing was a plaque on the door!

Later that evening Mel had issues with her cannula and the fluids they were administering stopped. The cannula had to be replaced and a doctor was called for. Julie and Becky had had a lift home with Karen at about ten o'clock in the evening. I waited with Mel until she had settled down and left at quarter to midnight. During the night Mel was sick. She also suffered tingling and numbness in her fingers and she was tired. They administered more anti sickness drugs and they made her high. She rang me at 2am and we had a conversation in which she told me about everything that had happened since I'd left the hospital. These conversations would happen many times over the coming months. Mel would call me at some unearthly hour and talk constantly for about twenty minutes. Gradually her conversation would grind to a halt and the call would end with me saying, "Are you tired now Mel?" She would reply, saying she was and I would suggest that she went to sleep.

The other reaction Mel suffered to the chemo was a swollen face. The swelling subsided over a few hours and never returned. Dr. Smith gave us information on Mel's type of lymphoma and also the web address of Cancerbackup (www.cancerbackup.org.uk)We left the hospital feeling positive and determined to enjoy some quality time at home before Mel's next appointment on 24th September.

THROUGH MELISSA'S EYES (PART ONE)

"Ok, hey everyone, im not sure if this is the right thing to do but i figure its the easiest way of letting people know whats going on and lets face it we're all friends right!! Plus my phone bill is gonna go thru the roof the amount of texts im sending lol!

Basically ive had a pretty shit summer, and this is why...

I've just been diagnosed with non hodgekins lymphatic cancer, diffuse large b cell type. But im gonna be fine!!

I came home from uni in June and after about a week had a mouth infection which then turned to tonsilitus, i never felt right after the tonsilitus and although i went to work at my holiday job i struggled to carry on. I was also disganosed with anaemia after a series of blood tests and glandular fever was also suspected, i also had a really really bad and persistant cough, at the doctors i was prescribed antibiotics, inhalers and sent for a chest xray at the hospital. I eventually had to stop work as i was sick while at work n was struggling to breathe n my cough must have annoyed everyone!!

Just before the chest xray date my dad took me up to a and e as my breathing had become really bad,it was the first saturday of the season - i remember cos i was in a and e wishing i was watching match of the day n gerrards winner against villa!!! It was so bad i was sleeping downstairs propped up in a chair as i couldnt lie flat for coughing and i could barely get upstairs to the toilet without being out of breath. i was also sweating loads in the night and was just generally exhausted. And as you know i had to cancel my birthday celebrations cos i was ill.

At a and e they did all the usual stuff but they concluded that it was tonsilitus and my tonsils were blocking my airways even though i had no pain in my tonsils and they told us to cancel the chest xray n that i didnt need to be admitted to hospital. They prescribed a weeks worth of antibiotics and sent me home. however there was no real improvment, so we went back. (the day after my 20th birthday!).

This time they took bloods and they did a chest xray. Once they saw the chest xray they suspected phemonia but soon said that actually they didnt know. I was admitted to hospital that day and the next day was told they suspected it was lymphoma, most likely hodgekins, that this was a type of cancer but it was 100% treatable.

I had a CT scan and also a bronchoscapy which was horrible (but they wanted to check there was nothing actaully in my lung). They injected into my neck with the bronchoscapy which was horrible and they give u a sedative but i was fairly aware of what was going on even though i cudnt feel it! They said from that there was nothing infecting my lung but that there was something pressing down on my lung.

Basically after all the tests they said what had happened was that the lymphoma had formed in my chest and had collapsed my right lung which is why i cudnt breathe properly!

I was also told it was a big tumur - football sized it was called which was a tad scary but i was reassured that it was 100% treatable. i was then sent to Glenfield hospital in leicester to have a biopsy on my chest as there were no other lymph nodes that were infected that they could get a sample from (if i had had a lump in my neck or armpit it wud have been much easier to get a sample but i didnt) i had an ultrasound at leicester to check for any additional swellings anywhere else but they didnt find anything either.

So i had the biopsy. I have a lovely scar on my chest now and one where i had to have a chest drain for 24 hours (which *bloody hurt when it was pulled out - ill admit i screamed from the second she started pulling to when it was out!!). i threw up from the anaethetis and i dont remember much of leicester if im honest but ah well! I was barely eating either (no suprise due to minging hospital food)!*

i was taken back to burton on the saturday (i had been in hospital almost a week by this point). i was given my own room at burton which was good, i did kick up a stink when i got there when they started injecting me so maybe they thought id scare everyone else on the ward!! once back at burton i was on oxygen and nebulisers as my breathing was still quite poor,i also had to have some VERY painful stomach injections for 10 days after my biopsy as i wasnt moving around much and these prevented blood clots - they did them at 6am everyday! - i also had to wear some sexy stockings too! i had blood tests every day, one day i had to have two cos they couldnt do it the first time - not nice!! But i was put on steriods n these helped my breathing alot in the last few days of last week as well as an antibody treatment called rituximab and i was feeling much better by last weekend. The steriods also increased my appeitie - im addicted to yogurts and cant stop eating!! unfortunley they also make your face abit bloated so i look a lil chubby at times! :S but that will go hopefully!

On tuesday we were told officially that i had Non - Hodgekins lymphoma, high grade (fast growing but thats better as treatment can target it more effectively) diffuse large b cell type. I was allowed home from the hospital on Tuesday night officially though i had been allowed out for the afternoon on the saturday and sunday. (2 weeks after first being admitted).

I had my first chemo session on wednesday afternoon and had to stay overnight in hospital again. I also have the Rituximab antibodi treatment with the chemo usually too (but id had that the previous friday when they thought they knew what it was so i wont have that again till my 2nd session - the treatment altogether is known as R-CHOP).

The chemo was ok, im not a fan of needles but the venflon they gave me for chemo wasnt too bad (although it stoppped working in the night when they had to give me fluids n i had to have another one in which i wasnt very happy about!!!) and i was sick in the night but the anti sickness drug they gave me made me high so there was an upside!!! my face also really swelled up - i cried when i saw myself in the mirror as i looked so fat but it went down within a few hours after they gave me an antiallergy drug, they werent sure what caused the swelling, maybe just an allergic reaction but they said it was nothing to worry about and hopefully wont happen again!

so now im at home and waiting till the 24 th september which is my second dose - n yeh thats freshers week!!! :(so i wont be around to be an auntie but i may pop up to freshers fair on the sunday to grab some freebies n say hey!i shud be in uni the first week of lectures providng everything goes ok!

Im carrying on at uni but ill be commuting from home and no longer have my house in erdington. The main reason for this is that im close to brum anyways and with having to go into hospital its just easier to be in burton. they did offer to transfer my care to brum but i know the doctors n staff at burton now n feel more comfortable carrying on with them.
The uni r gonna help with my course. Ive had to give up my job in the shop at uni n i was editor of the paper but im now only going to write for them as i cant commit to it as much. Im also prone to infection in the second week after chemo so have to be more careful about where i go n what i do but i shud be able to live a normal life as much as possible.

Once my breathing starts improving which should happen quite quickly ill be able to go out more n i might even start driving lessons this year as ill be saving money by living at home. So im trying to stay positive n ive been told that ill be fine, n it will be able to be treated so thats good!

Ive got to have 6 initial sessions of chemo n then maybe some more if needed followed by radiotherapy if i need it but i wont know that till much later on.

Theyve said my hair will defintely fall out and it will happen within the next 3-4 weeks but at least im prepared. I had my hair cut today so its fairly short so that when it does come out it wont be so bad. Ive ordered some wigs as well that the hospital helped with so im fully prepared for when it does happen. It was weird getting my hair cut today knowing that it wud be gone within the next few weeks but like i said, leasts im prepared! Ive had great support from all my family n all you guys too which has really helped, n the hospital have been really really good. The nurrses were great, a coupl were lfc fans so we got on well! though my consultant was a derby fan so wasnt too pleased last weekend!!! and one nurse who came to give me an injection was a united fan - i was pretty scared of her!! lol

Its not been an easy summer n its definetley not been an easy last 3 weeks but im home now, i know whats wrong with me n i have a plan of action for this year! and fingers crossed by final year ill be out there again with everyone falling off my chair in einies and doing generally stupid things!!! in fact i can still drink but not while im on the steriods n probs best to avoid nightclubs when im prone to infection so it will be a bit more limited though im sure ill find some time for a lil drinking session one week!!!

But yeh thats about it. I thought if i wrote a note then people knew and that way it saves me writing everything out loads of times.

I hope that explains stuff and im sure ill c u all soon enough!!!

and again thanks so much to everyone whose been texting n leaving me messages on here - its been really really helpful and its gotten me thru some tough days!! and to laura, mand sooty and gemma who came to c me - seriously i really really appreacited it!

xxxxxx"

CHAPTER SEVEN

Just Being Normal...(well sort of!)

Mel was at home and for the first time in a while things were looking up. Her breathing had eased, she could walk further and she had revised her plans for university, saying that she could possibly return in October. On the Saturday we drove round to Branston Golf Club and sat looking out across the 18th, drinking coffee and tea.

With Mel settled, it was the right time for me to return to work. On the Sunday morning I checked my wardrobe and realised that I needed some new work attire. I decided to take a trip to the huge George department at the Asda store on the outskirts of Birmingham. Melissa asked if she could come with me for a drive, she had been cooped up for so long, she wanted to get out, get some fresh air and maybe buy some clothes herself. She just wanted to do something "normal".

We went into the store and Mel disappeared into the ladies section whilst I chose my shirts and trousers for work. I paid for mine and stood looking for Mel. She suddenly appeared between two aisles with an armful of clothes and a huge smile on her face. The next thing I remember is Mel saying she felt a bit dizzy and before I knew it, she started falling towards the floor. I managed to grab her and support her arms and the clothes we were both carrying fell to the floor. Two shop assistants came over, asking if we needed help. They picked up the clothes and put them on a nearby trolley. I asked for a seat for Mel and they brought a stool over. I lowered Mel gently onto it but she couldn't support herself. I stood behind her to support her back. I talked to her, whispering words of comfort. I asked the staff for a glass of water and they immediately fetched one. The assistants asked me if I wanted them to call First Aid, but there was no point. I knew what the problem was.

Suddenly, Mel's head fell forward. I tilted it back and offered her the water. She wanted it, but couldn't speak. She was a dead weight, she was conscious, but had no energy at all. I had to get her out of Asda so I asked for a wheelchair and then asked the assistant to support Mel for a minute. I went to the checkout and purchased the clothes that Mel had wanted to buy. It may sound strange, but I felt it was important, that despite this horrible experience, we should be able to salvage a positive from our trip. We'd set out to do something normal, to buy clothes and I was determined that was what we were going to do. With the clothes paid for, I lifted Mel into the wheelchair and we went back to the car. Once in the car, she gradually came round and by the time we had driven the half hour back to Burton, she was back to normal. I arrived home and Mel was laughing as she told Julie and Becky all that had happened. Whilst she was telling them the story I phoned the hospital. They said we should take her in, so after a morning in Asda, we spent an afternoon in the Queen's Hospital, Burton. Her obs were done, they took blood ran a few tests and then allowed her home. I had been frightened. To have your daughter sat there so lifeless, unable to communicate, even for such a short time, scared the life out of me and for the first time I realised what we were dealing with. It frightened us both and it made me realise just what may lie ahead. If we had thought it was going to be plain sailing now Mel was out of hospital, I now knew that wasn't going to be the case.

Melissa recounted the experience on her blog . . . .

"On the Sunday me and my dad decided to go to Birmingham to the big Asda and also to collect some things from my house I had there. While in Asda I tried on numerous clothes and was feeling fine. Once I had picked my clothes I went to find my dad, as soon as I saw him I started to feel a bit weird, my breathing started getting worse and things started to spin, I managed to get over to him but as soon as I did I collapsed. My legs gave

way but luckily my dad caught me, but I had no control over my own body. I was always conscious but for about 5-10 minutes I was all over the place, I couldn't even speak and people were asking if I wanted water and although I did I couldn't say anything and I couldn't even lift the cup to my mouth. I was gotten a wheelchair and managed to sit down but my head kept falling all over the place and I had no control. It was one of the scariest experiences of my life and I think my dad's too! Anyway eventually I recovered and we were able to get home though we had to go up the hospital to get me checked out but I was fine."

We never did find out what caused Mel to pass out, it never happened again. Theories were suggested by doctors and medical staff, but it was totally a one off.

Following the Asda incident, Mel did a rethink on her plans for university. Up until that point she had thought about commuting to Birmingham from Burton, but she now realised that commuting was not going to be possible. Our biggest concern was that it may happen again and the possibility that there would be no-one there to help or understand frightened us. We travelled over to the university to discuss the possible options. Mel wanted to carry on with her studies and various options were discussed, including the recording of the lectures and then playing them on DVD. The university were brilliant and Mel left for home knowing that all things being equal she would be able to continue with her course, studying from home. She resigned herself to the fact that she would not be able to take up the position of editor of the Aston Times, but as she said at the time, she could still contribute.

Following the "Asda" incident I returned to work and things settled down. Sophie and Matt visited and brought a card signed by loads of Mel's friends and like the calls and texts it kept her spirits up. Before long it was the 24th September and Mel's appointment for her second round of Chemotherapy had come around. I tried to organise my work around Mel's appointments, sometimes getting into work at 7am, working until 11, going to the hospital with Mel and then returning back to work whilst Mel had her chemo. I would then leave work and pick her up from the hospital. Tiring days, but what mattered most was that Mel was as calm as possible. We had cause to visit A & E the previous day as problems with Melissa's breathing surfaced again. It had been three weeks since her chemotherapy and although there had been an improvement, it seemed we were now back to the point where we had first entered hospital back on 20th August. The treatment was brought forward a day as they wanted to get the second round of chemo going as soon as possible. The consultant also told us that as Mel's breathing had deteriorated they were going to give the chemotherapy every two weeks instead of every three. I wasn't sure this was a good sign. Did it mean the treatment would be over more quickly, or did it mean they were concerned it wasn't holding and they were throwing more at it? I sat with Mel as Wendy inserted the cannula and the second course of treatment started. As the chemotherapy was now to be given every two weeks this meant that Mel would have to have GCSF injections to increase her white cell count. Usually the white cells would recover themselves but two weeks isn't long enough for this to happen. The GCSF injections are subcutaneous injections usually done into the fatty layer of skin around the tummy. Mel had the option of doing them herself or having the district nurse to do them, for five days before each round of chemo. Mel opted for the nurse.

One of the side effects from chemotherapy is hair loss. Taken from her blog, here is Mel's take on hair loss and how she dealt with it. . .

"I have to say when I was first told I wasn't particularly bothered about it, I thought that I'd be able to try loads of different styles of wigs and saw it as a positive thing as much as I could. I picked 3 wigs from a catalogue and I was feeling ok about it.

However as the time when it was likely to come out got closer I got more apprehensive, I started researching on the internet about how it fell out and how long it took and would I just wake up one day and find all my hair on my pillow…I couldn't find too much information, people tended just to say ' I lost my hair' but no details.

Anyway one night I sat there and I ran my fingers through my hair and a few strands came out in my hand. I knew then that it had started and I was a little bit upset I have to say. It makes everything real when your hair comes out. Anyway over the next 2 weeks I lost the majority of my hair. Whenever I brushed it a fair amount would come out, I went in the shower twice a day sometimes to wash it and get it out. My mentality was that once it was out, it was done and it would be easier to deal with it. I had been told by the nurse to do this as it would be easier. I had my hair cut short so it was easier anyway and I would stand over the bath and just pull at my hair. It came out in clumps…. When I was losing my hair, it used to stick out and not fall back into place! It also was sore when it was coming out, like I'd left it in a ponytail for too long and tried to take it out. it just stuck out at all angles and wouldn't lie flat!

In a way it was funny, weird as that sounds, me and my mum had quite a laugh literally pulling my hair out! Crazy as that sounds, made it easier anyhow. Anyway for a long time I had a covering of like baby hair, I wasn't bald though you could see my scalp and I would always wear something to cover it if I went out. But in the last few weeks I have finally lost the last bit of it and now have almost like a skinhead! Some like stubble is growing I think, but I have virtually no hair now, I look bald for the first time! Which was really weird at first, I didn't like it but I'm used to it now and don't care!

With regards to my wigs, before I lost my hair I thought I would want to wear them all the time and I would hardly ever take them off but when the reality came I found them too itchy, they made my head sweat and I wasn't all that keen on them. The first 3 I ordered, 2 of them were fine but the 3rd one I didn't like so I swapped it. At first I didn't like trying my wigs on, I found it weird but it was ok once I got used to it and I did go out in them a few times. However now I have pretty much given up with them. I wear headscarves, bandanas and Buffs which are like pieces of material that you can fold into different styles and wear on your head. They are so comfy and look pretty cool too! Alternatively when I'm sat round the house and if it's a bit warm especially I'll wear nothing on my head! Go for the natural look. I'm not ashamed of it, I was a bit apprehensive about showing people but I've decided now that I shouldn't be really and everyone has reacted fine and stuff so its ok! I know I look different but I can't help it!!"

The second session of chemotherapy seemed to have an immediate impact on Mel's health. There was the usual tiredness, and some sickness but it was nowhere near as bad as the initial dose. Within a couple of days she was feeling so much better and the difference was incredible. On the following Saturday we took Becky to Durham. We packed the car full of Becky's stuff, leaving just about enough room for the four of us and we travelled up the motorway. Mel was wearing her favourite red wig. She sat chatting with Becky in the back of the car, Julie was in the front and I was driving. It was a proper family day out. It was how it used to be and it was how it would be again once this dreadful disease was beaten. As we travelled up the motorway Mel suddenly became hot. She wound her window down, bent forward, removed her wig and sat back. At that point Julie turned round, saw the open car window and Melissa's bald head, put two and two together and made five. She cried out for me to stop the car, because Melissa's wig had blown out of the window. Mel, Becky and I knew it hadn't. We were just about in Durham before we stopped laughing. We unloaded the car at the university, Mel and I wound Becky up a little before we settled her into her room and headed for the main building. Mel was her usual chatty self. It was so good to see and again a reminder of how good this RCHOP chemotherapy was.

The following day, with Becky at university, we took Mel over to Aston to see some of her uni friends. It was the day of the Fresher's Fair, something Mel would have been heavily involved in. Julie and I went for a walk, whilst Mel met up with friends, played pool in the Guild and albeit in a gentle way, managed to do some of the things she would have been doing had she been at university. She visited the shop where she had worked the previous year and after a couple of hours I received a call on my mobile from her to say she was ready to go home. It had been a tough experience for her. Seeing her friends enjoying the university life that she so much wanted to be a part of was heartbreaking. When we arrived home Mel was tired. It was only six o'clock in the evening, but the two hours spent at uni had worn her out and she went to bed. She slept through until the following morning. We sat and talked the next day and Mel came to the decision that she would have to take a year's leave of absence. There was no way she was going to be able to study and deal with this illness. I spoke to the university and explained the situation and they were understanding. Since being diagnosed, over a month earlier, Mel had tried everything to ensure she could continue with her course and the university had helped her too, but it was time to be realistic. Her plan now was to recover from the cancer, and start the second year of her course next October. Not being able to carry on at university was hard for her, but instead of sitting around and letting it get the better of her, she enrolled for a home study course in A level law. That, she said, would keep her going until she could return to uni next October.

THROUGH MELISSA'S EYES (Part Two)

"just thought id write a lil update on things as they stand seeing as i havent seen anyone for a while!

Had my second chemo and rituximab treatment yday (if ur really confused now n r thinking 'wtf?' read my previous note first lol), it was meant to be today but my breathing had become really bad again so they wanted to 'crack on' as the doctors put it lol. apparently 3/4 of my right lung wasnt working (that was on sunday/monday i think) and they think it was pressing on some airways n stuff which was causing me more aggro and pain.

already i can tell the difference, the pain is almost gone and i can get up and down the stairs for one thing! its crazy how fast this stuff seems to work! the tumur is in my chest and in between treatments they do start to grow back but not as fast as before so eventually the chemo will beat it but thats why i had started going all breathless again. i was sick again after chemo :(and im sooooo tired today but hopefully by tomorrow il start to feel more normal. already feel better than i did this morning!

Their gonna do my treatment every 2 weeks now for a while to try and really get it shrunk down so my lung starts to inflate again and i can breathe and therfore do more than sit in a chair and go on facebook all day! means it'll be finished quicker too hopefully! Means i gotta inject myself for 7 days from thursday to increase my white cells so im ready in time for the next chemo in 2 weeks (if it was 3 weeks my white cells would grow back at naturally in time but we need to hurry them up this time!) so that shud be interesting! the nurse is coming on thurs to show me how to do it! :S but if i dont do it myself i gotta wait around every day for the nurse to come n it means i wudnt be able to come out to uni n stuff so im gonna learn to do it myself - ive been told its pretty easy! :S

My hair is almost all gone now :(but it wasnt as stressful as i thought it would be, bit weird but almost funny too! means im wearing hats and wigs and stuff now but its all good, ive got plenty of different styles to play around with! short n long and all

47

sorts! ooo and i hav some funky new glasses - 2 pairs actaully - gotta love specsavers 2 4 1!

But yeh on the positive side i'm coming to uni on sunday all being well for freshers fair so i shall c whoever is around! come say hey if u see me! missing freshers week like crazy - soooo wish i was there but hopefully ill be there next year n stuff so all is not lost! soon as i get this breathing malarky a bit more normal ill be able to come out n do much much more!! but coming out sunday shud be fine!

and thats my life at the min, hospitals and needles! fun fun fun! and anyone at freshers week have a drink from me!

cya all soon
love and hugs xxxxxxxxxxx"

CHAPTER EIGHT

Wishing, Hoping and Praying

With the decision made to take a year out of university, we discussed financial support for Melissa. Due to a delay in her application and subsequent illness, Mel had not received her student loan. We contacted Student Finance and informed them that as Mel had now been diagnosed with cancer, she was taking a year out to recover from the illness and therefore she would not be applying for her student loan. Despite the fact that she was feeling better, she still struggled with her breathing, so Julie rang the benefit agency on Mel's behalf and spent a good half an hour completing a telephone interview in order to apply for financial support.

The third round of RCHOP was given on the 9th October and for the first time there was no sickness to follow. They had tinkered with Mel's anti-sickness drugs and the cocktail they had concocted had worked. Its contents were noted for next time. In the days that followed the tiredness subsided and Mel came as close to being her old self as she had been in a long time. She had a visit from her uni friend Sooty a few days after the chemo, he stayed all day and they cooked pizza for lunch. It doesn't sound that exciting, but in the context of how Mel had been over the previous six weeks, it was stunning. After they had eaten, Mel did what she had been threatening to do for a long time, but never got round to . . . she set Sooty up on Facebook! The following day we went to Westfields shopping centre in Derby. Mel loved it and she walked round for a couple of hours enjoying all the new shopping centre had to offer. She went into town with a friend and they went to the pub. There was such a difference, it was a far cry from how things had been over the last few months. We suddenly felt positive. It looked like we had finally begun to make inroads into beating this disease.

Mel felt so much better and made plans to visit her friends in Birmingham that week. She wanted to get out of the house. Facebook messages were exchanged and she decided she would go on the Wednesday. Much as she wanted to see her friends, when Wednesday arrived she was too tired and had to postpone her trip. We tried not to get too disheartened, but there seemed a distinct possibility that her symptoms were returning and it had only been just over a week since her last chemotherapy.

Mel had her next pre-chemo check on Monday 22nd October and as the day grew closer her breathing began to deteriorate, the effort in getting upstairs worsened and her temperature, whilst not going sky high, yo-yo'd somewhat. Her appetite had gone, she had no energy and to top it all Liverpool had stopped winning! On the Sunday evening her temperature started to rise, but didn't go above 37.5. On the Monday morning, we had the appointment at the hospital for Mel's pre-chemo check. Her temperature was taken, blood count analysed and despite her being tired and breathless, she was allowed home, to return the following day for her chemotherapy.

We drove home, had tea and prepared for a normal Monday night in front of the TV. During the evening however, Mel's temperature continued to go up and down. It passed the magic 37.5 mark so we called the hospital and they advised us to go to A&E immediately. After doing all the customary checks, they decided the raise in temperature was due to the chemotherapy. At one point Mel's temperature hit 38.9, but they gave her paracetamol. We now know that giving paracetamol to Mel was bad advice as anyone on chemotherapy with a raised temperature may have an infection, which could be extremely serious if left untreated. The chemotherapy kills off the good and bad cells and therefore renders the immune system almost ineffective. Paracetamol brings the temperature down and masks any infection. They told us they didn't want Mel around the hospital due to the risk of infection. We were there just under four hours before we were sent home, at around 1am.

When we returned on the Tuesday morning for the fourth round of chemo, Mel's breathing was worse than ever. There was immediate concern amongst the doctors and nurses regarding her biopsy wound and she was referred to a surgeon. It was infected. The doctor cleaned and dressed it and then she was admitted to Ward 7. Her usual room was occupied so we were shown to a small side room. Later that morning, after another round of tests and an x-ray, her conditioned was diagnosed as pneumonia. Pneumonia at anytime is bad enough, but with a rapidly deteriorating immune system it was the last thing we needed. On top of all that, Mel's usual consultant was on holiday, but the haematology consultant, Dr. Ahmed stepped in and took over her situation. She was immediately prescribed antibiotics, a drip was set up and they were administered four times a day. She looked poorly, her breathlessness was back, and she didn't have the energy to get to the toilet from her hospital bed, which considering she was in an en suite side room was not good. The only positive we could take was that the x-ray Mel had had taken showed the last round of chemo looked to have shrunk the tumour by around twenty five per cent. We stayed with her all day, reluctantly leaving her bedside at about half past nine; we knew the next few days were going to be a real test. We arrived at the Queens Hospital on the Wednesday morning to find Mel in tears. A nurse had upset her and she was inconsolable. She explained in her blog why she was upset . . . .

"One nurse told me that I needed to find a way of coping, things were going to get worse before they were going to get better; that I didn't need my oxygen and my breathing was due to me panicking! By the end of that same day I was being monitored by high dependency unit staff and they were pretty certain I had pneumonia so I'm guessing she felt a bit of a fool! She really upset me and I have never quite forgiven her! All the other staff were brilliant and Dr. Ahmed was fantastic."

After Mel had explained what had happened I went to find the ward Sister to complain. The nurse was asked to apologise to Mel, but never did. It was the only time we ever had to object to a nurse's behaviour. About mid morning Dr. Ahmed came to visit. Doctors huddled around Mel's bed, offering advice, listening and deciding where to go from this point on. We sat by her bedside all through the day and into the evening. I wanted to cry for her, she was twenty years old for God's sake; she shouldn't have to be dealing with this. You could sense the concern and it was heightened when they told us that overnight, Mel would be monitored by the High Dependency Unit. She wasn't moved to the unit itself as they were fearful of infection and Mel's inability to fight it.

At about eight in the evening I ventured out of the ward to make a phone call and after I'd finished, Dr. Ahmed and Pat, the McMillan nurse specialist were coming out of the ward. I asked the consultant a question, I can't for the life of me remember what it was, but he took me through a series of doors into his office. We then talked for about three quarters of an hour, he showed me Mel's x-rays, he told me the seriousness of the illness, that they were doing all they could for Mel and the fact she was young was a positive for her, however, we should prepare ourselves for fact that she might not make it. It was that serious. He explained that we should take things one day at a time, and just see how she responds to treatment. He was hopeful that as youth was on her side, she'd pull through, but there were no guarantees and we should be aware of the gravity of the situation. I didn't know if he was talking about pneumonia or the cancer. I presumed the pneumonia. I should have asked, but I didn't. I was in shock, but I had to keep being strong. Should I tell Julie what he'd told me? Should I tell Becky? Should I tell Melissa?

It was at that point that "One day at a time" truly sunk in. It's one of those throw away lines that are said daily, but never actually mean anything. This time, it was being said by Dr.Ahmed and we knew, the only way we were going to get through the pneumonia and ultimately the cancer was to take life "one day at a time".

After speaking to the consultant I went back into the Ward, sat by her bed and held her hand. She was barely conscious and I had never seen her looking so ill. I just wanted to reach inside her and grab whatever it was that was causing her pain and rip it out of her. I wanted her to be back to Uni, to get drunk and say stupid things. I wanted family days out. I wanted to take her to football matches again, there were just so many things I wanted her to do.

As the clock ticked and tocked its way past ten o'clock that night Julie and I left the ward and went for a coffee. We walked into the chapel, sat down and prayed. Our tears came soon enough. I just asked God to look after her and get her through this, to make her better. It was the first time I'd talked to God and I knew it probably wouldn't be the last.

After visiting the chapel we went back to the Ward and sat with Mel. Both Julie and I decided that we weren't going home and we stayed at the hospital all night. Julie sat in the armchair by Mel's bed, and I tried to rest on the recliner that was outside her room. I didn't sleep though, all through the night, they checked on Mel and I heard every visit. I heard the old man on the ward get up and go wandering in his pyjamas till the nurses caught him and put him back to bed. I think I must have heard every noise on the ward. The snoring of the patients, the low chatter of the nurses, the spoon in the mugs as they stirred their tea and coffee. At seven o'clock the following morning, with Mel fast asleep we went home, got into bed and for two hours we slept solidly.... before waking up and returning to the hospital for another day of wishing, hoping and praying.

Mel was still very poorly and when we arrived at hospital, Dr. Ahmed was already there checking on her progress. He was brilliant and his care and compassion was incomparable. The day passed Mel by as she slept for most of it. In the evening, her cannula developed a problem. They only last a few days and Mel's was beginning to wear out. Despite sleeping for most of the day she managed a smile as "dishy doctor" entered the room to try to insert a new cannula. Julie left the room and I sat with Mel and tried to take her mind off what was happening. Following days of antibiotics, blood tests and other forms of injection, Mel's veins were shot to pieces and after two attempts, "dishy doctor" had to give in and fetch the Senior House Doctor. He was very apologetic as was the SHD when his attempt was unsuccessful. Melissa was getting more and more stressed by the minute. An "expert" from A & E was called for and her two attempts also met with failure and she burst a blood vessel along the way.

At this point, with Mel close to breaking point, I stepped in and said that it had to stop. Melissa cried and told me that she couldn't do this anymore. I knew she didn't just mean the injections. The sister on the ward agreed. Holding Mel's hand and fighting back my own tears I asked the sister if the antibiotics could be given orally and she left the room to speak to the consultant at home.

I sat with Mel holding her hand and calming her down. In due course the sister returned to say that she had spoken to Dr. Ahmed at his home and unfortunately the antibiotics had to be given intravenously and therefore a new cannula had to be put in. Dr. Ahmed asked to speak to me on the phone, so I left the room and Julie came in and sat with Melissa. As I reached the nurses station up the corridor I heard a scream and an almighty crash. I thought that one of the nurses had dropped something, but after speaking to the consultant I returned to Mel's room and I was told Mel had screamed and then, summoning up what little energy she had, she kicked the end of her bed in frustration and anger.

I sat down on her bed and in a calm controlled voice explained that they had to do it. Julie had already said the same. We knew the importance of these drugs and somehow we had to reach a compromise and find a way for them to be administered. The sister returned, bringing with her a small tablet to sedate Mel. She explained how this tablet would make her a bit woozy and then one of the anaesthetists from theatre would come along and insert the cannula. These were the experts. I returned to the chapel and prayed that they would get it in. Within an hour the tablet had taken effect and when the anaesthetist arrived to put the cannula in Mel's wrist she welcomed him with open arms...literally! She held out her hands and told him to take his pick. After the cannula was in place she turned to the man and said "You are amazing, really amazing, I know that sounds really sarcastic, but I'm not, you are amazing."

No doubt he had seen the sedatives in action before and he left the room with a smile. As the sedative continued to do its stuff, Mel talked of apologising to the Ward sister and wanting to kiss and hug dishy doctor for his earlier efforts, saying it wasn't his fault her veins were rubbish. The happy talk had returned, albeit drug induced. With Mel high on the happy side we left the hospital at quarter to midnight, fourteen hours after we'd first arrived.

Mel's condition settled down and improved slightly. The treatment that Mel had received thanks to her "amazing" anaesthetist worked well. We spent the weekend at the hospital, arriving at 10 in the morning and staying for 12 hours or so. On the Saturday night we all sat and watched X Factor in her room, with some of the nurses popping in now and then for updates. Mel and I love watching The Bill too, so earlier in the week I'd copied current episodes and old UK Gold episodes onto DVD and we watched some of those.

The following week Mel gradually improved, the smile was back and it was noticed by Dr. Ahmed, who told her that her smile made his job so much easier. Dr. Smith returned from holiday and Mel's treatment was once again in his hands along with Dr. Zai. The only major decision that particular week was whether or not to give her the next dose of chemo. Obviously, chemo reduces your immune system, which with her having pneumonia wasn't good. However, the delay in chemo also gives the tumour chance to fight back. It was a difficult choice, but they decided to go with it and on Tuesday 30th October she was given the Rutuximab and the following day they wheeled her up to the chemo unit to see Wendy, one of her favourite nurses. The fourth session of chemo was completed and a CT scan was ordered. She also made an appointment to see the psychologist at the hospital and received an aromatherapy session which she thoroughly enjoyed. It took Mel a long time to recover from the pneumonia, not just physically, but emotionally too. For a long time she would worry that every temperature rise signalled its return. We shared those fears. The emotional experience of nearly losing Mel rocked us all.

THROUGH MELISSA'S EYES (Part Three)

"Hey everyone
Just a quick update on whats cracking really....and im bored and this gives me something to do....so yeh anyway...

Treatment is ok. Had my third dose yesterday, it was all fine and went according to plan, and i got extra anti sickness pills which actually worked so no being sick this time! woohoo! apart from being tired i actaully feel ok. My breathlessness is about the same, still not doing a whole lot but im getting ther slowly, hopefully this time will be the one where i notcie a proper difference n i can start actauly doing more than sitting round the house with the occasional trip to the supermaket or uni lol. Enjoyed freshers fair a coupla of weeks ago but i got home n slept from 6pm onwards till the next morning, totally knackered me out n iwas pretty tired until the tuesday. Made me realsie that trying to carry on with my course was gonna be really hard. Spoke to my head of school and she said she thought the best option was to take a leave of absense n so did i. with trying to get into uni being an added pressure i dont really need. plus trying to keep on top of coursework, practicals and exam deadlines is hard enough when im in uni never mind trying to work totally from home. It just wasnt gonna happen. I'd rather start my seciond year when i can do it properly and have a proper year of uni rather than a shitty stressful one! so i'll be back in september to carry on with my course (i swear ill be at uni forever at this rate!). Plus we wdont knoww hats gonna happenw itht his cancer malarky, it could be that my treatment is done by christmas or it could be that it carries on and with not knowing it makes it much harder to plan so i thought screw it, lets just focus on getting better n then next year i can properly enjoy myself (and do my course as well!)

so.....im at home but i plan on visiting, certainly in the next month or so anyhow, so if any of u fancy a random visitor lemme know! n if anyone fancies a trip to burton their more than welcome!

Im also doing an alevel course to pass the time, cos although sitting on ur arse al day watching tv sounds great it gets really boring really quickly, esp when u dont do anything else and i thought my brain might stop working unless i di something so im doing a home learning alevel in law. shud be interesting anyway. and it'll pass the time.

so thats about it, oh and i have to have injections most days next week to keep my white cells up so im ready in time for my next chemo....fun! i ould do them myself but after seeing the nurse do it i thought i'd leave it to her! not very easy to do yourself! but im kinda used to them now anyhow! neber thought id say that! and i have this weird numbness in my fingertips - so weird! lol but all a normal side effect of chemo im told.

So yeh thats my life, hopefully ill be much more active soon! if it wasnt for this bloody lump being in my chest id be doing soooo much more! have to be arkwrad i guess! got a bitch of a cough as well, apparently its the tumur moving and pressing on airways etc and its cauring irritation which is casuing e to cough! so bloody annoying!!!

anyways thats all! and i still have hair - not much mind but a sprinkling, not that id go out without some form of hat/wig cos i look like a freak without them but lol yeh im not bald yet!
I was getting much better, even went out shopping in Derby n out with some friends in Burton about 5 weeks ago after my 3rd lot of chemo.

Then i got really unlucky n picked up what turned out to be a pnemonia infection. Was in hospital for 11 days and it was pretty shit, was pretty ill n it wasnt very nice. Had major problems with breathing and also had issues with getting in canulars in my hand (5 attempts failed - very painful before the 6th one worked!) but i was put on antibiotics through a drip n after a few days they started working n i gradually improved. Was let out about 2 weeks ago now. Am still really really tired and weak and am still recovering from it but am better than i was when i was in hospital n thankfully my breathing is much much better now. Had a CT scan while in hospital n they can tell from that that the tumur is shrinking so thats good news.

Having a PET scan tomorrow (Friday) to determine exactly how much tumur is left n how we go on from here with treatment n how much more ill need etc etc.

i had my 4th round of chemo when i was in hospital (though a week later than planned cos of the infection) and my 5th is due next tuesday all being well. I still have the injections some days n they make me feel crappy too with aches and flu like symptoms but the actual injection is not that bad - just the side effects!

Im back on a 3 weekly cycle now so thats good news, least it means i get longer in between sessions.

Thats about it for now until after the PET scan results.

Hope uni is going well for everyone. am missing it like crazy!
Anyways, im off to have a nap!
love&hugs

Hope uni is going good for everyone! misss uuuuuu!!!

xxxx"

CHAPTER NINE

Scans and Plans

With so much having happened, I needed an outlet, some days I didn't want to talk, other days I could talk forever. It was at this point, on 1st November, I decided to start writing a blog. What follows are those blog entries . . .

Thursday 1st November

I've decided to write this blog so that when my daughter is better I can look back and take stock of all we've been through and the journey we've had . . .

Another day, and as my Facebook profile says, "Another day on the set of Holby City". It's nine weeks since we first discovered my eldest daughter had Lymphoma.

Friday 2nd November

Yesterday saw an improvement, Mel was alert and full of beans. This could be steroid related but all the same, it was good to see. They talked about the possibility of letting her home for the weekend. All a far cry from a week ago when we wondered if we'd be bringing her home at all. The planned CT scan was put back 24 hours.

She managed a little trip out to the hospital shop this afternoon and as we were returning we were stopped by one of the porters who asked how she was getting on. You know you're spending too much time in hospital when staff recognise you. At 5.45pm we brought Mel home. Still very weak and tired, she was just glad to get away from the hospital and is looking forward to a decent night's sleep. The amount of stuff we carried from the ward is amazing. Tablets, potions, lotions, pills, syringes, dressings, you name it, it was there!

The consultant said that his preliminary findings on the CT scan were that the lymphoma tumour and the pneumonia were decreased in size and that was a good sign.

Saturday 3rd November

Today is like a normal Saturday, Mel didn't wake up till midday. Becky has returned from Uni and is full of stories of drunken nights out and new friends made.

We went to Morrisons this morning to get some supplies as we'd not shopped for two weeks. We ended up buying all the things the "experts" tell you not to buy, sweets, cakes, sugary stuff, you name it. Mel has to eat this sort of diet in order to build her up and regain her strength. She's also booked in for another session of Aromatherapy.

Julie is worried about what the doctor didn't say, rather than what he did, but as I explained, he was very positive, but cautious as he's not the x-ray expert. My plan now is to enjoy each day as it happens, make the most of the good times and get through the bad.

Sunday 4th November

Becky returned to University. Mel is perky today. She ate well which is a good sign. There was a nervous moment when she complained of feeling hot and before you could say "sizzle" we'd whipped out the thermometer and taken her temperature. It was 36.2 degrees and the panic subsided!

Monday 5th November

I went back to work today and I was exhausted. At times it's difficult to concentrate. Julie stayed at home and nursed Mel. The District Nurse called to administer Mel's "G" injection. This injection is to keep her white cells boosted.

With it come side effects that make her bones ache. Sort of flu like symptoms, but without the runny nose. The emotional side of things seem to be affecting Mel at the moment, the realisation that for a while things aren't going to be normal.

Tuesday 6th November

Julie walked to the doctor's surgery this morning to register Mel at our local practice. After explaining her condition, situation and current state, the first question asked by the receptionist was "Well, can she come down to the surgery for a Health Check?"

Julie asked the people from the Income Support Office, what Mel was expected to live on when they told her Mel wasn't entitled to income support. Apparently, because she's taken a year out of Uni they won't pay income support as she's still classed as a student.

It's all about government departments ticking boxes. They haven't the brains to realise she's taking a year out because she has cancer, not because she's going on a working holiday to Peru or touring the outback! Our question couldn't be answered, so we have a twenty year old girl, with cancer, recovering from pneumonia and not entitled to benefits. The matter is now in the hands of our MP.

Wednesday 7th November

Mel continues to improve but she is tired and lacking in energy. The nurse arrived this morning to give her the "G" injection and to dress her biopsy wound. I received a call from my MP. Like us, they thought it common sense that she should be able to claim something, but quite what, remains a mystery. Julie chased up a claim on Mel's behalf for Incapacity Benefit, but she's not entitled to this either. She needs to be incapacitated for 26 weeks. In the meantime I guess she's meant to live on fresh air and the goodwill of passersby!

Thursday 8th November

A slight concern this morning as Mel's temperature passed the 37 degree mark. The hospital was called, blood taken by the district nurse and within a couple of hours her temperature was back to normal.

Our letter of appeal for Income Support has been drafted. We've not heard any more from the MP's office.

Mel's white cell count was "reasonable" but not high, so she needs the "G" injections tomorrow. The side effect of this is bad headaches as well as aching generally. Because she can't have paracetamol whilst her temperature is raised we've resorted to using "Kool and Soothe" which are cool strips that sit on your forehead and sooth away your headache. They don't take Mel's away, but they do ease it.

Friday 9th November

A couple of days ago I mentioned that the Income Support people said Mel wasn't eligible for any money for a variety of reasons. The district nurse called today to dress her wound and explained that she would need it dressing next week. She gave us a prescription to take to the chemist so this evening we went along to pick it up. On it were six items.... times that by six pounds ninety five for each item and you realise that's .... nearly forty pounds.

Mel, who isn't getting any money from anywhere... is expected to pay forty pounds for medical supplies. Of course, we will pay it. There is a financial strain on us, but the alternative is to turn round to our daughter and say sorry, we're not buying the things you need to stop infection in your wound. We could apply for an exemption certificate, but from what we've been told, the chances of Mel obtaining one is minimal, and involves a mountain of paperwork

Saturday 10th November

Monetary issues continue to cause us unnecessary stress. We have enough dressing supplies to last us for a week, so that's how long we have to sort it out. How does someone who isn't entitled to any money, who has no money and who has no realistic chance of earning money in the next few months afford anything, be it food, clothes or prescriptions?

Mel's had a good day. She was visited by two friends from Uni and two of her cousins. She said it was good to chat about normal things. We spent the evening trying to think of the worst Christmas present anyone could buy her..... Hair straighteners were top of the list!

Sunday 11th November

Mel's friend Claire visited, as did my Mum and my sister who had just flew in after six months abroad. Despite it being a good day, we never switch off.

This morning Mel had bouts of coughing, the cough was very loose, but immediately our thoughts turn to the summer and the cough that preceded the diagnosis of cancer, or the cough that accompanied the pneumonia. Are the symptoms returning? Is the tumour growing again and this is just the start of the coughing? Thankfully, it subsided, her temperature was normal. By half past seven the effects of a few visitors began to show as she began to feel tired. She complained her breathing was poor and again we're left worrying if it's lymphoma, pneumonia or just the effects of what for her has been a busy day.

Monday 12th November

Our emotions are going through the mill at the moment, I know Mel is a lot better than she was two weeks ago, but she seems poorly and is emotionally fragile too. Her constant headaches are a concern, but her temperature remains ok. I want a positive sign, something to raise mine and everyone's spirits, particularly Mel's.

CHAPTER TEN
Fighting Lymphoma and the Government

Tuesday 13th November

As last night progressed, Mel's temperature rose higher and higher, peaking at 37.4 degrees. She felt unwell, had a headache and we began to fear the return of the pneumonia.

I went into work early today, Julie phoned the hospital and by midday we were making our way back up to the Queen's Hospital.

Mel had a blood test, her obs taken and was sent for a chest x-ray. Within half an hour we were joined in the waiting room by her consultant, his assistant, and two others. They explained that they'd looked at the x-ray and the signs were positive. It seems the tumour may have gone down in size, but in order to be certain they want to carry out a PET scan. PET stands for Positron Emission Tomography.

This is a fairly new type of scan developed in the 1970s. It can show how body tissues are working, as well as what they look like. It will give them a clearer picture of how the tumour is reducing and from the results they'll decide whether to carry on with the same type of chemo or maybe change to radiotherapy. All in all, it was a positive afternoon.

Wednesday 14th November

Last night was a good night, we played music and before she went to bed Mel sat on the sofa singing karaoke to High School Musical. Earlier in the evening she'd been communicating with some other Lymphoma sufferers on the official Lymphoma site. Last night a few young people emerged and being able to chat with others in a similar situation helped a lot.

The appointment for the PET scan is on Friday at 1pm. The scanner itself costs £4.2 million pounds to set up and each scan costs between £750 and £1000. No expense spared on Mel!

The day ended with another scare; Mel's temperature is again on the rise, peaking at 37.9 degrees at 9.15 this evening. She's feeling tired, achy and has a pounding headache. Is it the return of pneumonia? Is it the 'G' injections? Is it the chemo? We don't know. What we do know is that our choices are simple. We take her up to A&E or we keep her at home for the night and ring the consultant in the morning. If we go to A&E, we have to drag her out into the cold night air and sit in the A&E department for three or four hours or they keep her in overnight. Alternatively, she stops at home, we check her temperature in the morning and then ring the consultant for advice.

Talk about a rock and a hard place. It's so hard knowing what to do.

Thursday 15th November

Following the temperature scares, I decided to get Mel to go upstairs and get ready for bed, calm down a little and then we'd take the temperature one more time before deciding what to do. It was 37.3 degrees, so our choice was made. We stopped at home, and this afternoon (Thursday) we called the Chemo Unit for advice. According to the chemo unit, it is feasible yesterday's aches and pains (and the temperature rises) could be as a result of the 'G' injections or as Mel refers to them..... 'Bastard things'.

Today she rested. She keeps complaining of nagging pains. This of course worries the life out of us, but they subside and I wonder if she mentions them just to check our reaction time to her pain :)

For the first time since I started my new job, I couldn't settle at work this morning. I assume it's because of the uncertainty of last night. Julie felt the same and was trying to predict various outcomes and scenarios, so this evening I had to re-enforce what I've said many times before. We take one day at a time. We enjoy the good days, get through the bad and deal with things as and when they happen.

This evening Mel became agitated about tomorrow's scan. Following her recent "cannula experience" the thought of needles puts her on edge. The thought of catching pneumonia again plays heavy on her mind and I had to stress the importance of living in the here and now. It took an hour to calm her down,

Friday 16th November

Mel had her PET scan today; it took us an hour to get there. The building on the City Hospital site was only opened last year and the first patient to receive treatment there was a 20 year old student, with Non Hodgkin's Lymphoma.

Mel was taken to a room, asked the usual round of questions and then given an injection which took an hour to go through her body. The scan was then taken and took half an hour.

She came out with the customary plaster on her arm and a smile.

Mel's clinical McMillan nurse rang about five-ish to put back Monday's appointment by 24 hours. They hope they will have the results by Tuesday and they can then decide on the next course of treatment . . . the waiting begins!

Saturday 17th November

We're over half way there, and we're going to win
We'll beat it, defeat it, we'll never give in,
From start to finish, I've been by your side
Lifting you up when your spirits slide,
I held you close, wiped away your tears
I was there to reassure, calming your fears
And I'll be there to catch you, if ever you fall
To ease your pain, I'd do anything at all,
I'll make you smile, when things don't seem funny

Fill your glass half full, make rainy days sunny
Hold your hand for comfort, help your spirits rise
Re-ignite the spark that shines in your eyes
I love you so much, and I know life isn't fair
I just want you to know, I'll always be there.

Sunday 18th November

Saturday was a quiet day, Mel got up around midday and spent an hour or so on the phone to her friend Rachel. Julie and I nipped into town.

Despite it being a good day, Mel has no energy; she can't get up the stairs and back with being short of breath. She spent most of the day feeling nauseas and there was of course the customary headache. Added to this, her body is now playing tricks on her by making her think she may be having a period, something she hasn't had since August, so she gets all the customary side effects from that. That was on the physical side. On the mental side, she carries around the worry she is going to get pneumonia again and she's worried that her appetite isn't what it should be.

As head cook in the household, I'm starting to give her smaller portions. It will do her good to empty her plate.

Monday 19th November

Mel didn't get up yesterday (Sunday) until about one o'clock and we all lazed around all day. I was up at half six, the rain battering down on the conservatory roof outside managing to keep me awake. Julie got up about ten, saying she slept mainly because for the first time in a long time she felt relaxed enough to.

My sister visited in the afternoon, she was the only visitor we had all weekend.

I'll be glad when tomorrow is over and we know which direction we're heading. I'm trying to stay positive, because, logically if you compare how she is now to how she was three months ago, the signs are all good. My fingers.... and toes.... are crossed!

Tuesday 20th November

We got to the hospital for half past nine, sat waiting for three quarters of an hour before being informed that the scan results weren't back and there'd be no treatment today.

It seemed to sum up our lives at the moment. Waiting... waiting... and then nothing. We are now waiting for a phone call from the hospital, Mel had a blood test whilst she was there. She's now developed thrush, so it's another medication to add to the ever growing list.

For the first time today, I felt that work was getting on top of me. I felt the stress and pressure of it all. Everyone is being nice, considerate and helpful, but I wonder if people do understand what it's like. Watching your daughter gasp for breath when all she's done is walk upstairs to the toilet. Seeing her appetite diminish. Looking at her sat on the sofa not having the energy to walk to the end of the drive let alone anywhere else. Seeing her tired out and ready for bed at nine o'clock in the evening... the time she'd normally be getting ready to go out. It is heartbreaking and I wonder what we've done to deserve this.

Today is November 20th. Three months since Mel was diagnosed.

Wednesday 21st November

Another day waiting for the phone to ring.... but the only call I got was at half past four this afternoon. It was Julie asking me to go straight up to the hospital to pick up some more medicines for Mel, this time to treat her latest ailment, thrush.

As the days go by, we tend to worry more. The no news is good news theory doesn't cut any ice. We begin to wonder if there's something they're not telling us, a problem that they're trying to sort out before giving us the news. It's almost four weeks since her last dose of chemo and that's an additional worry.

We received a reply from the Benefits people today. The reason Mel cannot claim income support is because the law says so. It doesn't make any provisions for someone in her situation. We are now left trying to claim Disability Living Allowance, which if we're successful means we can then claim the Income Support we were originally turned down for. Needless to say, this evening, I left a message on my MP's answer machine. We were supposed to hear from the Labour MP by the end of last week and still, like everything else at the moment.... we're waiting!

Thursday 22nd November

Today we received a phone call from the hospital telling us to be there tomorrow (Friday) at 11.30am and the results should be there.

I've had a response from my MP's office, saying that the Minister was contacted on the 21 November and he should have a reply for us by the end of this week, beginning of next. That's what they said last week. The letter included a line which said, "I do understand your frustration, but your daughter's case is being worked on."

They don't understand my frustration at all. With respect, they haven't a clue!

Friday 23rd November

The meeting with the consultant went ahead as planned today and the news wasn't good. The PET scan showed that there are a large number of active "bumps and lumps". Dr. Smith first words were "I'm worried."

When normally positive consultants are worried you know you have problems. The RCHOP chemo worked to a certain extent, but it not working anymore. Mel is probably about 30% better than when she first went in three months ago, but the chemo has stopped working.

The doctor explained that he'd been in touch with other experts at Derby and Nottingham and they have decided to give Mel a higher dose chemo. This is called I V E. He stated that if the RCHOP is equivalent to Gas Mark 4, then IVE is

Gas Mark 8. This I V E has to be given in high doses over a period of time; therefore she has to stay in hospital for at least four days whilst it's administered. There will be two doses of this, an x-ray to check how it's progressing and she will have to endure what is called a stem cell transplant. Providing all is well and the tumour is reduced, some of Mel's own stem cells are taken and stored before she has a real blast of high dose treatment. After the high-dose treatment, her stem cells are then returned to her body through a drip into her veins (bit like a blood transfusion). We sat there in the consultant's room listening to all the latest news on Mel's lymphoma and how they are hoping to beat it. There were tears from Mel and Julie as I tried to stay strong. I'll save my tears till I'm on my own.... it's a man thing!

Julie went to the doctor's this evening and got a certificate for a month off work.

The lady rang at 4.30pm to tell us we have to be at Derby at 9am on Monday.

So begins another journey.....

THROUGH MELISSA'S EYES (Part Four)

"A few of you know this already as i told u over the weekend but for the few of you who don't i was gonna write an update later in the week but given the chance i thought i'd do it now.

Some of you know that ii had a scan a week or so back. The scan results came back last friday n it wasnt the news i expected.
Basically there is still alot of active tumur in my chest, more than they thought and the RCHOP chemo i have has essentially stopped working. so there scrapping that now. So not the greatest news.

The plan now is that I've gotta have a stronger chemo called

IVE but they dont do it in Burton so gotta go Derby hospital for that n its an inpatient treatment as its done over a few days so will be in hospital for that.

The plan was to go into today and stay in but after going in this morning nothing is booked for me to have done until tomorrow so after taking bloods and just getting everything ready they said to go home and rest, save waiting around in hospital all day doing nothing.

So now i go in tomorrow morning for about 6 or so days. First thing i have done is to have a hickman line (central line its called as well) fitted in my chest as having this chemo through my veins in my hand wouldnt work as my veins wouldnt cope with it. once its in though i can have all injections and chemo through it inc blood tests so itll be much easier. its just the bit where they fit it that im crapping myself about! though i have been reassured its not as bad as it sounds! i bloody hope so!

I have two lots of this IVE chemo about 3/4 weeks apart (im hoping i avoid christmas in hospital but dont know yet!)

After that i've gotta have whats called a stem cell transplant (this time in Nottingham hospital) which i dont know the details of but i know it involves taking my stem cells outa me usng like a dialysis machine,then giving me a very powerful blast of chemo (stronger than the IVE) which kills my remaiing cells but then my others r put back in and stimulate the growth of lots of new cells. this is all done in hopsital and i think ill be in for about 4 weeks. i'im assuming this will be in january sometime but i dont know yet, it could be later.

The chemo im having next week is pretty strong though the effects are pretty much the same as the last lot, only more pronounced. i didnt lose all my hair with RCHOP (i only have a covering left but still!) but i think it will all go now.

So yeh thats as far as we've got so far. Hopefully this treatment will really shrink it down n hopefully totally get rid of it. im hoping anyhow. was pretty shocked n upset when they told me as i was expecting positive news and got the total opposite. pretty nervous about going in to have this all done but it'll be worth it all if it gets rid of this bastard thing!

With me being in a new hosptial im not sure about using my phone but feel free to text me n stuff but i may not be able to reply.

Anyhow sorry for the longest message ever but thought i would let u all know what was happening.

Thanks xxxx"

CHAPTER ELEVEN

One Week in Derby

Saturday 24th November

I went to bed at about 11.45 on Friday after we sat talking to Mel for an hour about what had happened. She remained upbeat, but it's not possible to tell whether it was the Temazepam talking or how she felt. She talked about university. We talked about crying, we chatted about the Hickman line, which in truth is her biggest worry, though she said, once it's in place she'll be ok. A Hickman line is a tube that goes into the chest and directly into one of the major blood vessels. The end of a central line hangs out of the chest and is usually sealed off with a cap. Instead of having cannulars, everything that needs to be taken can be done through that.

The rest of the family have been told of developments. Julie and I try to remain positive, Julie spent a good two hours on the phone last night to her sister and friends, talking things through, explaining what would happen.... and what could happen. I keep emphasising the need to take one day at a time, I keep trying to be strong for everyone, keep my tears to myself and try to put smiles on faces.

Sunday 25th November

Unbeknown to us at the time, Mel started yesterday with tears. She says it ultimately made her feel better and sort of "got it out of the way". The reason for the tears? She'd had a good dream, in which she wasn't ill, she was out with her friends and she went out for dinner with Lee Mead. Of course, she woke up and ok the Lee Mead bit was the icing on the cake, but she realised that days out with friends etc were a long way off. During the night there were pockets of coughing, the same coughing that used to accompany the tumour in the early days and a sure sign that it's on its way back.

I started the day with tears.... I decided to go for a walk. I found myself being drawn toward St. Peter's Church. Whilst walking I had my MP3 player on. There are over 2600 tunes on this player and I always have it set to play random tracks. I have mentioned before, that a certain song is giving me strength. It's by Josh Groban and is called Don't Give Up (You are Loved). Whenever I have "down" moments I play this and it lifts me. As I was drawn toward the church, the above mentioned song started on my player. It was totally random. I kept walking toward the church and as the track ended and the music faded I walked through the gates of the church.

It gave me an incredible feeling. I sat down, the tears flowed, but they weren't tears of sadness or of joy, just tears, this feeling came over me at that moment that whatever happens, good or bad, we're all going to be ok. I walked back home. My biggest fear of this illness not giving us a happy ending is that I'll never see Mel again, but that fear was allayed yesterday.... I know that whatever happens we're all going to be ok.

Mel chatted with some people on the internet who had endured the same treatment as she will and that helps a great deal.

The day ended with Mel having taken one of her Temazepam tablets. The last time I saw her she had a container in one hand, a funnel in the other and she was sat the wrong way round on the toilet trying to work out how she'd collect her wee the following day and laughing and cursing whilst she did it....

Monday 26th November

I read an interesting article in The Times last night before I went to bed. A prisoner serving time for drug dealing had been awarded £500 compensation. The reason for this was that he was handcuffed to a prisoner officer six times whilst attending hospital for treatment for Lymphoma.

I now know where I've been going wrong. Forget going through the right channels, talking to MP's, civil servants etc., all Mel has to do is sell drugs to some lowlife, get caught, make a claim after treatment and she'll get £500! That's £500 more than she's getting at the moment!!

We arrived at Derby Royal Infirmary at 9am. The hospital is busier than Burton. We were told what would happen over the next few days. Mel will have her Hickman line fitted on Tuesday and then be given fluids, before having her chemo on Wednesday and the following three days. If all goes well, she should be allowed home next Monday. We were given a list of leaflets on the treatments and procedures and sent on our way.

This afternoon, Mel's tears flowed. Having read the leaflets and possible side effects she became upset. Her ability to have children is all but gone. At present she has a short covering of hair, but again, this will disappear once the new fierce chemo kicks in.

Finally, she read that a possible long term side effect of the chemo is getting other forms of cancer in the future. It was too much for her to take and she let it all out in tears. We tried our best to console her and in time she stopped crying and went back on her computer to read the experiences of others in her situation. It was a tough afternoon, but we got through it and we move on to see what tomorrow brings.

After watching Coronation Street, we talked some more until she took her sleeping tablet. It took longer than usual for the Happy Talk to kick in, but before long she was once again in a world of her own and fell asleep after saying she was going to buy a telephone system off her friend Claire, in order that Claire could get her fifty pounds bonus....

A lot of people have been asking how Mel is coping with everything.... she posted the following on the McMillan site this afternoon . . .

"ive not written on here before but im hoping it might help.

i'm 20 and i was at uni (taking a year out) and i have non hodgkins lymphoma,Large B cell type and the tumur is in my chest. i have had 4 cycles of RCHOP but its stopped working. When i was told i was shocked and upset.

Now I've gotta have a stronger chemo called IVE but they dont do it in my local hospital so have to go to a different one for that n i have it over about 5 days as an inpatient. I go in tomorrow morning and have to have a hickman line fitted which i am terrified about!!! although i know once its in ill be glad cos no more canulars but the getting it fitted part is scaring me so much!!!

I have two lots of this IVE chemo about 3/4 weeks apart (im hoping i avoid christmas in hospital but dont know yet!)

After that i've gotta have a stem cell transplant which im also scared about but trying not to think about yet as its a while off.

Hopefully this treatment will really shrink it down n hopefully totally get rid of it. im hoping anyhow. was pretty shocked n upset when they told me as i was expecting positive news and got the total opposite. pretty nervous about going in to have this all done but it'll be worth it all if it gets rid of it.

but im so scared and im just worried about all the side effects and the whole being in hospital and i dunno it suddenly all just got a whole lot more serious!! i mean it was serious before i guess but i was coping with the RCHOP n everything....i had pneumonia a few weeks bk too and ive not long got over that! I can't stop crying at the slightest thing.....i am trying to be positive but im finding it soo hard at the moment. Sorry i just needed to let it out a bit.

Mel x"

Tuesday 27th November

We made our way over to Derby, booking in Ward 10 at about ten to nine. Mel was placed on the ward with four others. She was welcomed by them all and like the nurses and other staff at the hospital, all were friendly and helpful. After being admitted she settled down and went to have her Hickman Line fitted at about quarter to eleven.

She returned at about quarter to one and explained to us how her Hickman Line was fitted.

She didn't escape a final cannula as one was inserted to administer the sedative. The first time they tried to insert the Hickman Line; they discovered her vein wasn't big enough, so the team performing the procedure was sent out to find a smaller line. The first one was taken out, a second, smaller one inserted and all was well.

We spent the afternoon chatting to the other patients on the ward, discovering in the process that one of the ladies had been told the doctors could do no more for her, but the treatment she was having would prolong her life by a couple of years. Her wish being that she lived long enough to see one of her children married.

The registrar arrived mid afternoon to obtain Mel's consent to administer the chemo and in the process explained the side effects, possible problems and also their plans for the future. It was a lot to take in and our emotions went on a rollercoaster ride as they talked of a series of side effects, none of which were nice and some which were just too frightening to contemplate.

When they tell you what should/could happen it sounds so simple, but if we've learnt anything throughout this illness, it's that things are never simple. We know that over the next few days, Mel's health is going to deteriorate and she will become sick. It's not going to be nice.

The evening ended with the three of us sat round Mel's bed discussing her plans for the future.

As we left the ward at eight o'clock she was laughing as I'd stuck a "£6 off" sticker on Julie's back. As days go, today was a good day.... we enjoyed it!

CHAPTER TWELVE

A Drop of the Strong the Stuff

Wednesday 28th November

Just after midnight I received a text, it said "Please can you bring my Skins DVD and my brown wig"… it was Mel, she was having trouble sleeping.

We arrived at hospital at 2pm and Mel was in good spirits. Her chemo hadn't started but she'd spent the morning chatting to the pharmacist. Mel is far happier when she knows what is happening and Derby Royal Infirmary seem good at this.

Just after 2pm we were joined by the clinical nurse specialist who explained about the treatment and what they were hoping to achieve. Basically, the initial blast of chemo is referred to as a "salvage" session. They are looking to salvage the situation with this new IVE chemo. The strong chemo is used to "induce remission". After the second blast of IVE a scan will be done, which will hopefully reveal the tumour has gone. At this point, the stem cell transplant should be started. The doctors are looking at this procedure to cure Mel's condition, but have stressed there are no guarantees. Should the stem cell transplant not work, then the Bone Marrow Transplant option kicks in. With this current treatment Mel will be at her most vulnerable for the risk of infection between day 7 and 14 (today is day one). At that point her white cell count will be virtually nil and we have to be careful. The MCN explained that most infections come from the skin so it's important to keep hands clean, washing them often and not putting them in her mouth. So she'll have to stop biting her nails!

We'd been back on the ward about five minutes when suddenly Mel's mood changed and she became quiet and tearful. Again she asked the question, "What if this treatment doesn't work". After talking to her for a while it emerged that last night, the lady who has only two years to live had spent the evening talking about her condition, her husband's suicide, the illnesses she'd endured apart from the cancer and the fact she was dying. I told Mel that that lady's situation was different to hers and the two couldn't be compared. Mel calmed down and smiled as she rubbed her head and some of her hair fell out. "Bloody ell" she said, "this stuff doesn't mess about"

Thursday 29th November

I phoned our local MP's office this morning. Despite the fact that I wanted to shout and scream at them, I didn't. In this day and age of instant communication taking four weeks to respond to someone with no financial support is pathetic.

Following that phone call I contacted the Disablement Living Allowance office. I thought that maybe if I explained my twenty year old daughter had cancer and no financial support they may, just may, give some priority to her claim. Alas, the answer is no, the only way they can speed the claim up is if her illness is terminal.

My third and final phone call of the morning was to the Benefit Advice Line where an advisor talked "at" me for ten minutes, telling me that Mel's future financial support depended upon the result of the Disabled Living Allowance claim. If that's successful we can then try again for Income Support, but of course that takes eight weeks to process. When I managed to get a word in edgeways and ask her what Mel was to do in the meantime, she talked about getting a form for an emergency loan benefit... or something like that. Finally, I asked her what happens if we're refused DLA, the answer was simple. We then get nothing!

This should be simple. Coping with a life threatening illness is stressful enough, but the government want to make it harder. I felt drained and wanted to cry.

Before going to visit Mel we called at Primark to get her some new pyjamas, God Bless Primark!

In between visiting times I called work and after enquiring about how things were going and how we were coping, I was asked if I'd any idea when I'd be returning. My reply was easy. The day after Mel comes out of hospital. At the moment if I went in to work I'd be as much use as a one legged man in an arse kicking contest, my concentration levels would be zero. One of my favourite sayings has always been, "It's only work, it's not real life" Never has this been more true!

Our emotions yo-yo from one extreme to the other. We live in the present all the time but can't help thinking of the future. Although Mel's responding well to treatment, we won't know for another eight weeks if it's working.

When we went back, Mel gradually woke up and talked solid for nearly two hours occasionally tugging her hair to check how much was coming out.

Julie and I left the hospital at eight o'clock. We'd been home about half an hour when I received a call from Mel to say her Hickman Line entry wound had been cleaned up and redressed and that Julie would freak out when she saw it tomorrow!

Friday 30th November

Today was a horrible day. The chemo kicked in overnight and by the time we arrived at the hospital Mel was tearful, tired and aching all over.

The afternoon was spent trying to convince her that it will all be worth it in the end. We spoke to the doctor's who said they had been concerned about her temperature, but had screened her and there was no infection. We later found out that the whole ward had been screened due to a suspected bug. The hospital was on Amber alert and every bay on the ward was being given a "deep clean". Mel was moved from Bay C to Bay D on the ward and I told her that if she moved any further she'd be on E bay and we'd have to put a bid in to see her!

Throughout the day we had to keep reassuring Mel as through teary eyes she told us "she couldn't cope anymore" and "why have I got this". Of course, I can't answer the why question and all I could do was to tell her again, to get through the bad, enjoy the good and in the end it will all be worth it. I hope I'm right.

It's awful seeing my girl so ill. She has no energy and is in pain and aches so much. The chemo is destroying her body, before they attempt to make it better and it's painful to watch. As a dad I'm supposed to be able to fix anything, but at the moment I feel useless. I want to fix things for her, but I can't and it's just horrible. I know I use that word a lot, but it just describes things so well. Horrible, Horrible, Horrible.

Last night I emailed David Cameron about Mel's financial plight. His private secretary replied this morning, showing concern but stating he couldn't do anything because my case was being dealt with by another MP but he offered his sympathies. Whilst I didn't expect anything to happen I was impressed with the speed of his reply.

We got home from the hospital at about 8.30 this evening completely drained. I sat down and Julie came and sat on my lap. She cried and we hugged until the tears stopped. At ten to ten I received a text, Mel had started being sick.

Saturday 1st December

I'm now sat here in the armchair, waiting for the clock to tick round to the time we can go and see her again. Another day to get through, another day of pain for her, of watching her in pain for us. I wonder when it will stop.

Julie is still in bed. Whilst she's sleeping she's not thinking and when she wakes it's less time to have to sit and think about the day ahead. I can't sleep. We had tickets to go and watch the football today. Burton Albion v Barnet in the FA Cup. It's the second time we've planned to go and not made it. We said earlier in the week we're going to get season tickets next season.

I know we'll get through this, I sometimes think about "what if the chemo doesn't work", but I believe it will work so I never have to dwell on that thought long enough to worry about it. We have to believe it is going to work, even in the darkest times, we have to believe. If I didn't believe it, I'd struggle to go on.

I composed a list of inspirational songs this morning to play when I feel the need. At the moment I'm listening to You'll Never Walk Alone. It goes against all my instincts as an Everton fan, but I'd swap my allegiance to the Reds now if I thought it would make Mel better. I just want my old Moochie back. This is the worst time of our life.

She's so unbelievably tired. There was a problem with her Hickman Line in the morning that caused her to be breathless, but it was sorted out by the nurse. Most of the time we sat watching her, holding her hand and passing her water to sip. She ate nothing.

Her bed was taken away and steam cleaned during the afternoon, a result of the suspected bug on the ward. Signs were up everywhere reminding visitors and staff to constantly wash their hands. The first series of chemo that Mel is receiving should be completed tomorrow (Sunday) and there is talk from the nurses that she may be allowed home. At present, she is in no fit state to come home and I think she may be allowed to leave because as her white cell count goes down, she is more prone to the infection that is sweeping through the ward. We have questions to ask before we leave.

The visiting ended today and we left with Mel struggling to get comfortable, she goes from hot to cold, has dark rings round her eyes and again was asking why it had happened to her and how long it would be before she stopped having the awful side effects.

We got home and the house over the road had been decorated with an endless stream of Christmas lights. .... I've just realised it's December.

Sunday 2nd December

Mel's Facebook status summed things up. Mel is ... Feelin' Crap. I texted her this morning as usual just hoping that I may get a positive reply. A "feelin' better" maybe, but it didn't happen. The reply was "I feel awful, being sick". I'm running out of things to say. I keep trying to tell her that it's for the best, but when she's being sick every five minutes, has a permanent headache, got no appetite or energy it's so hard to keep convincing her that it's "for the best."

I'm due back at work either tomorrow or Tuesday and whereas part of me wants to go back, another part of me is thinking I must be mad. At the moment, my mind is all over the place. I can't think straight. Both Julie and I have said we're drained and have no energy. I feel I am on alert all the time; I watch my phone, waiting for a text or a call. If she needs me, whatever the time, I need to be there.

Our trip to Derby was interrupted by a call from Mel telling us that they were allowing her home now her chemo had finished. She was very weak and I think the decision to allow her home was due more to the "bug alert" at the hospital, rather than her being well enough to leave. We went over there, collected her belongings and her tablets (about 15 packets in all) and brought her home.

Once indoors she sat in the armchair and checked her Facebook. I made her cheese on toast; she took one bite and started heaving. The sickness remains. She then started crying. She says that sometimes she wonders if it's all worth it, she feels guilty for thinking that but she's been in so much pain, she just wonders if it's worth it. She told me she couldn't ever imagine being normal again and that's why she questioned whether it was all worth it. I reassured her that it was and it was all part of making her better. Like her online friend Alan said, the ends justifies the means. He should know, he went through exactly the same.

I went out to the shop and whilst I was out Mel talked to Julie about the possibility of the chemo not working. She was very matter of fact and reiterated what she'd told me earlier about wanting to be normal and wanting a quality of life. She is so strong it's untrue. It was almost as if she was telling us she wasn't afraid of dying.

I'm sure life isn't meant to be like this. It hurts so much.

CHAPTER THIRTEEN

December Arrives...Financial Support Doesn't!

Monday 3rd December

Apart from coughing a lot, Mel had a quiet night and got some much needed rest. She slept in our bed, whilst Julie and I slept downstairs. Julie had the sofa and I had the cushion and bean bag on the floor. My phone went off a couple of times in the night as Mel needed help.

Prior to her going to sleep, we spent an hour sat on the bed with her, just talking about all manner of things. She kept grabbing the bucket as waves of nausea washed over her, but she wasn't sick and even managed a slice of marmite on toast before she fell asleep. We watched Match of the Day 2, had a call from Becky and just sitting there watching Mel laugh and smile as she talked to Becky was special.

When I last spoke to her she had just noticed that the hair on her knuckles had fallen out and she was itching all over. I don't think it will be long before the rest follows. She says she's happy for the hairs on her legs to go and hopefully not return as she says it will save her a fortune in razors and waxing products. We talked about football and her desire to marry Fernando Torres and still keep Stevie G as a bit on the side, we chatted about DVDs she wants to watch, before I gave some of the hair on her head a gentle tug and out it came. She smiled; fell asleep and I felt that for the first time in a week.... I'd got a bit of my old Moochie back.

The hospital rang this afternoon and we have to go in on Friday morning so she can have some blood taken and have her Hickman Line looked at.

Work tomorrow!

Tuesday 4th December

Following the previous evening's sleep on the sofa and armchair we made ourselves more comfy last night by utilising the cushions from the conservatory furniture and making ourselves a double bed on the floor. It took us back to when Julie and I started going out together and Julie stopped at our house. I'd sleep downstairs and Julie would sleep upstairs in my bed. When everyone was asleep she'd creep downstairs and join me.... ah, a bit of romance amidst all the troubles! We told Mel this and it made her smile. She also said she wants our bed for at least another night!

This morning the district nurse came round to take some blood. I may have explained before that our arrangement is, I sit with Mel during needle times and Julie sits with her during sick times. Of course, when one of us is away, we have to cover the other's duty. The district nurse asked Julie to hold some tubes for her and pass them to her as she took Mel's blood. There were only three, but apparently by the time the nurse was ready for the third tube, Julie was on her way to passing out and was herself being sick. As she disappeared into the bathroom, Mel jokingly told the nurse she'd gone to pass out as she didn't like needles. Within seconds Julie verged on passing out and she was grabbing Mel's sick bucket and using it to its full potential. The District Nurse had to abandon Mel and concentrate on sorting Julie out. The first I knew of it was when Mel phoned me at work, laughing as she told me the story!

Mel is now entering the neutropenic stage which means she is at great risk from infection. We have to visit Derby on Friday and then on Monday (10th) Dr's Smith and Haynes will discuss Melissa's case and decide when the next high dose of chemo is administered. She will have blood tested several times over the next few weeks and the results of these tests will be discussed before her next course of treatment.

There is some hair clinging on for dear life on her head, legs and arms, but the hair on the toes and fingers has all gone. She looks cheeky when she smiles at the best of times, but even more so at the moment!

This evening we all sat on the bed, myself and Julie eating Mel's Cadbury's Snaps before we all watched Never Forget, the Take That Musical. After that had finished Mel went online to speak to her new found friends on the Lymphoma Association (www.lymphomas.org.uk) and McMillan websites. As I came downstairs she was sat up in bed, singing along to Never Forget, she managed to wave her arms three times to the music before they collapsed to her side. I told her it was the most exercise she'd had in six months!!

Wednesday 5th December

Mel is still breathless, has the occasional cough, but other than that she's bright and bubbly.

The appetite continues to improve. The range of foods Mel likes isn't great, but what she does like, she is eating plenty of. Chicken and Oxtail Soup seem to be the favourite at the moment... though not in the same dish!

Mel spent the day adding her own group to Facebook. It's called Mel's Fight against NHL. Some refused to sign it at first as they thought it was a rebellion against the National Hockey League.

The evening came to a close with the Temazepam kicking in and Mel trying to do funny voices whilst sitting on the toilet hoping the Lactulose would take effect.

Thursday 6th December

Mel is continuing to get stronger each day. She is still camped in our bed and we sleep on cushions on the floor.

A letter arrived regarding Incapacity Benefit. They want a certificate from the doctor's called a MED 4. We've already supplied a MED5, but now they need a MED4. To get a MED 4 Mel needs to visit the doctor. This is at a time when she's at most danger of infection, can't walk up the stairs without being breathless and is just coming off five days of intensive chemo! They also sent us a form to fill in with some fantastic questions in it. Questions that they've asked before, but want to ask again. It wouldn't be so bad, but they've already turned us down for this benefit!

Julie didn't shout at the benefit people, but she let her feelings be known on their stupid forms, telling them that there was no way on earth that Mel was going anywhere near the doctors. It was almost like they wanted proof of her illness (which they'd already had) and as Julie informed them, she wished we were making this up, we wished it was a fraud. It would have been a damn sight easier to deal with.

Finally, the third letter to arrive was from the Disabled Living Allowance people. They can't make a decision on whether Melissa is entitled to this financial support until they get a reply from her consultant regarding her condition. We've already told them her condition. We've already supplied them with a letter and sick note giving those details of her illness. They want more. Why does everything have to be so difficult?

Friday 7th December

Mel's appointment was to have her Hickman Line flushed through (they have to do this when it stands idle for a certain amount of time) and to have some blood taken. We also had to pick up some Hickman Line stuff so the District Nurse could flush the line and take blood from it and also get some more mouth wash to keep Mel's sore mouth at bay. We arrived at the hospital, were ushered into a room and no sooner had Mel sat down than she was asked by a Health Care Assistant to go and sit over the other side of the room. She sat down and the HCA started to try and take blood.

Mel started crying; saying the whole point of the Hickman Line was that she didn't have to have needles in her veins. The HCA replied by telling Mel that she wasn't qualified to take blood from the Hickman Line and it had to be done by a sister. My first thought was "bollocks", they'll never get Becky to come down from Durham to take blood, but then I realised what they meant.

Enter the Lead Sister. Mel tells her that she's here to have her line flushed as well as have some blood taken from it. Mel is then moved back to where she was originally sat and the process begins. I am asked to leave the room by the sister, which upsets Mel. Julie had already legged it after the needles appeared.

We sat in the waiting room, I knew Mel would be upset and I couldn't do anything.

There were issues regarding her next appointment to have blood taken. We wanted it done at Burton (5mins down the road), but couldn't because the appropriate paperwork hadn't been completed by Ward 10 at Derby when Mel was discharged. Mel told the sister that it wasn't fair that she was being made to pay for their mistake and the upshot was that our next appointment is at Burton next Friday.

As well as the appointment for blood tests, Mel will have an x-ray done to see if the first session of High Dose Chemo has reduced the tumour. When they say things like that, it hits home how ill she is. This last week she's been tired, but she's eating better and this morning she did walk from the haematology unit back to the car. It has helped, she is showing signs of being better, but it's the x-rays that give information on how the chemo is hitting the tumour.

More letters today. The first to say they stand by their decision not to award Mel any Income Support and the second to say they stand by their decision not to award Mel any Income Support and the decision has now gone to an appeals committee. Name your dates people.... see you there!

There was one interesting note at the bottom of the decision sheet . . . I quote,

"Miss Leech is not a lone or foster parent; is not a refugee and is not a deaf student or disabled student, I therefore finally submit that the claimant is to be treated as a student during a period of study and is not entitled to Income Support."

Damn, if only she'd been a single parent or a refugee she'd have income support!

Following her exertions at the hospital, Mel spent the rest of the day in bed..... Our bed! It's obvious that she rests better in our bed, so for the time being we've forfeited our room and we're sleeping downstairs. We've got the air beds out of the shed. I'm a light sleeper and I find that every time you move whilst lying on them they make a farty sound! I can see me being kept awake by farty sounds all night! My other fear is that one of the cats will puncture the air bed and in the middle of the night I'll be sent whizzing round the lounge in the dark on an inflatable bed!

Saturday 8th December

Last night was a sleepless one. I went out into the cold night air and blew them up.... I wish I'd blown them up with dynamite. They are the most uncomfortable things ever created. I'm sure they are only popular because students use them and after a night on the sauce, they'd sleep on anything. Anyway, we gave it a go and pushed the two single airbeds together. Every time I moved, so did the beds and consequently I kept falling into the crack between the two beds. Tonight we are reverting back to plan A.

Before we fell asleep Julie shed a few tears. I re-iterated my thoughts about taking one day at a time, enjoying the good days and getting through the bad. I think what brought it on was the "forthcoming x-ray". If I'm honest, they worry me, but I focus on the here and now and I'll deal with any issues if they arise. The problem with x-rays from our point of view is that they are the definitive answer on how the treatment is going. As I've said before, Mel is eating and resting well, is positive and as well as she has been for a while. The x-ray will give the consultants an idea as to what is happening. It's strange because we know the x-ray will bring good or bad news and whilst Mel is seemingly so well we don't want anything to come along that could spoil it. It's difficult to explain, I suppose what I'm saying is that sometimes, ignorance is bliss.

Becky texted Mel this morning, it's snowing in Durham!

Sunday 9th December

Mel spent the day downstairs, ate two hearty meals and, one evening headache apart, was ok. Her group on Facebook continues to gather members and that helps to keep her spirits up, as do the people on the Lifesite.

Julie and I reverted to the cushions on the floor last night with a double duvet and we had a better night's sleep. At least when we did wake up, we weren't cold.

Mel woke up this morning with stomach ache and generally had a bit of a misery on her. She went onto her computer and spoke to a couple of people on the Lifesite about their problems, reassuring them in the process. Her only issue is the Hickman Line rubbing on her nipples! I suggested nipple caps! I don't know if they've been invented, but if not there's a market there and I might approach Dragon's Den. Something along the lines of a small thimble... there's a future for them I'm sure!

I don't feel Christmassy at all at the moment. We could be spending ours in hospital, we could be waiting to go into hospital or we could have been in and come out with Mel recovering from another round of 24/7 - 5 day chemotherapy . . . oh for a normal family Christmas!

Monday 10th December

Today was conference day between Dr. Smith of Burton, Dr. Haynes of Nottingham and all the other important people who are responsible for Mel's care. They communicate via webcam and discuss individual cases

THROUGH MELISSA'S EYES (Part Five)

"Being me at the moment - i wanted you to see whats its like, what im feeling and thinking and it helps me write stuff down too. gets it off my chest.

Generally it's a bit shit! But being me at the minute is very different to me normally. I'm still me, in the sense that on good days I'm still loud and bossy and sing way out of tune but my lifestyle is almost the total opposite to everything I'm used too and it has been for a while now.

My day usually starts around 9am with my mum coming to wake me up so I can take the tablets I need (usually between 3 and 4 at the minute), I then usually drift back off to sleep until the district nurse shows up (this happens most days but she doesn't always need to come) to give me, at the moment, my GCSF injections used to help my white cell count increase in order to help me have the ability to fight any kind of infection. The injection itself doesn't bother me anymore but I suffer a lot with the side effects which is mainly aching in the lower back and upper part of my legs and can get VERY uncomfortable and painful. I usually take some form of painkiller for these but before I do I have to take my temperature as paracetomal can mask temperature and as my temperature is one of the obvious signs of infection I need as accurate reading as I can get. If its raised or higher than normal I tend to stay off the painkillers but usually it isn't a problem and I can take them though they don't take the pain off they help ease it a bit.

The constant fear of infection is something I have almost gotten used to. When you have chemotherapy it kills all the good cells as well as the bad ones and you are very prone to infection during days 7-14 especially. It means being extra careful about things and not shutting yourself off from the world but being extra careful about anyone who is near you coughing or sneezing and about what foods etc you eat. No takeaways is what im told. After having pneumonia this scares me a lot more than it ever did before though the fear is easing as time goes on and I get more confident but I will always be wary when I am going through that period. Your mouth tends to get a bit sore too but my mouthwashes have controlled this this time though I've had it bad in the past.

After the nurse has been I stay awake for lunch, at the minute this is usually chicken or turkey as I have a weird appetite! Eating lots of soup as well but I can't stand chocolate, tea or biscuits. I also eat a lot of toast and I still like my cheese. But not sandwiches. It has to be on toast. After that I usually go back upstairs to bed and rest for the afternoon, I sometimes watch a bit of TV or more often than not spend an hour or so on the internet on facebook and various sites or sleeping if I'm particularly tired.

About 5 'O Clock I have my tea, usually soup, and my dad gets home. The evening is spent watching a bit of TV, downstairs if I can and maybe going on the computer again. I go to bed depending on how I feel. Some nights this can be as early as 8pm, other nights I might stay awake to nearer 11.

The nights usually pass ok, I sleep alright, sometimes I take a sleeping tablet to help me get off as constant thoughts going round in my head about various things can hinder me getting off to sleep.

This is all since I have come out of hospital from the IVE but my lifestyle before that was also very limited, I did get dressed most days and spend the days downstairs and didn't spend as much time sleeping but I didn't go out very much, I didn't have the strength and my breathing has always been really limited because the tumour is pressing on my left lung and ha more or less collapsed that lung. With the RCHOP not working the tumour has obviously grown back a bit and so my breathing has never got totally back to normal. The most I've done since being diagnosed is go to Derby shopping for one weekend, I went with my mum and dad and I did well by all accounts to walk around for as long as I did as my breathing was still recovering. I also managed a trip into town on my own to meet a friend. However by the next weekend I was in hospital with pneumonia and have never got back to the state where I can do that kind of thing.

Just getting up and walking to the shop is not an option, my life revolves around my tablet taking, my resting, my hospital visits. I obviously do have a laugh and a joke and stuff but in reality things revolve around the above.

I now have a central line, also known as a hickman line fitted in my chest. This means I have two wires hanging down my chest, It doesn't freak me out any more and I'm used to it (and its great cos it means less needles) but when you sleep at night your aware of the fact that you might lean on it though this is getting less and less of a problem as I get used to it more and more. When I have a bath I have to wrap a small bag around it to keep it dry. I have to make sure it is clean and kept sterile and it has to be flushed once a week.

I also have to take my temperature a couple of times a day and if it gets above 38'C I ring the hospital immediately as it's a potential infection. A few weeks ago my temp kept hitting the 37.5 – 37.8 mark and it scared the hell outa me. Nothing was wrong though. Just one of those things I think. But the pneumonia scared me. I'm careful with everything now, not to the point of obsession but I always wash my hands and any visitors that come into the house, if they have a cough or cold have to stay clear of me and avoid contact, in fact if they are really ill it's best they don't come.

Everything I used to do has been taken away from me, I cant just nip out to the shop or go see my friends at the minute, I feel much better than I did a week ago but compared to a normal person im a million miles away. I know that. I cant walk very far at all without being out of breath. Coming up the stairs does my breathing in though I can walk around on flat surfaces much easier.
Having this cancer has made me realise how much I took for granted and how much I want my life back but also that its gonna take a while, it wont be a case of treatment ended, all better,

go get drunk. Its gonna take me a while to get my confidence back, I don't even know what I want to do next year, I always intended to go back to uni but you cant plan anything because u just don't know what is going to happen. If everything goes to plan I may well be there. But the future is something I look forward too but I don't plan in too much depth, I'll know when I'm ready what I want to do.

Spending time in hospital is also pretty shit, sleeplessness is awful esp when you most need it and the boredom is pretty crappy too. But you do get used to it.

I sound very negative in this but I want people to understand what its actually like for me at the minute. I am positive and I'm keeping going and despite not doing much I still have a laugh and I still joke around about silly things but at the same time I am limited and with the stem cell transplant coming up I know im in for a very rough time. Ive been told infertility is almost a certainty with this treatment, something I cant even begin to properly think about because I need to focus on getting through the next few months first and if I thought about that I might not be able to stop thinking about it.

Sometimes I feel fine and I feel really happy and positive and other times I wanna cry all day but I have to just take one day at a time and try and get through it because even though sometimes it is hard, it will be worth it and believe me I've had moments when ive doubted that but ive always believed I will get through this. Im scared shitless that this treatment wont work but I have to believe it will because if I don't I would just give up and I cant do that because really I do want my life back and I want to be able to go out to the shop and feel normal and healthy and chat with my friends. That's why I have to get through this. The not knowing if things r working is very scary but you just have to pray that it is. I'm very reliant on my mum and dad to do things for me and that in itself is going to take some getting used to, being independent again.

When I first got diagnosed I was told that there was a very high chance of curing this cancer. I still believe that is true despite the setbacks ive had but it still scares you shitless of the possibility that it might not. Being in hospital with pneumonia was the scariest thing I've ever experienced, I couldn't breathe and was constantly on oxygen, they had the high dependency unit monitoring me one night and I was almost taken up the High dependancy unit, the reason I wasn't was because it was an open ward and I was at risk of infection. I don't think I realised at the time how ill I was but I pulled through that and got back to being me again so I can do it with the rest of this bastard thing.

So despite this seeming a negative post it isn't, its just so you can understand my life and what its like. I am positive and im still Liverpool and football mad and I'm addicted to X factor, in fact these things r even more important cos they r sometimes the highlight of the week!! Except when lfc lose of course.

Finally, this is long I know and if u've read it thank you because it musta taken you ages. I do read and appreciate all the messages on the wall but I dont always have the energy to reply to each one but I do appreciate them and I do read them all I promise.

Thank you and apologies for all the spelling errors!!"

CHAPTER FOURTEEN
It's Results That Matter

Tuesday 11th December

There's still no word from the hospital so it looks as though the x-ray will be on Friday. Mel's condition is much the same as yesterday, although this evening she was a little tearful, worrying about whether the chemo was working. Until the x-ray confirms it, all we can do is look at the situation with some logic. She's better than when she went into hospital, her breathing, whilst not the best is better than it was. She's gone seven days without infection and the nights sweats have stopped. At the moment that's what we cling on to.

Wednesday 12th December

A letter arrived from our MP today telling us to try things we'd already tried and gave us information we already knew. They told me that rules are rules and that's the law. THE LAW IS WRONG!

What I wanted to hear was that they appreciated it was wrong and would take steps to change the law. But no, the law is right, having no financial support for three months is the way this government treats cancer patients!

They suggested we contact the Local Education Authority who can, at their discretion, continue to give Mel her student loan. Of course, if she gets her student loan she forfeits all chance of income support and has to pay the loan back at the end of the term with no chance of working to assist in paying it off (like a normal student). This means that she gets penalised for being ill. They wouldn't offer her a loan to repay if she wasn't a student. It is disgusting. Her other option is to give up university altogether. She is considering it! Thank you government, you're all heart!

I intend to take this to the highest level. There needs to be a change in the law. I have read the report from the Income Support office and basically if Mel was a deaf, disabled, single parent from Eastern Europe she'd have no trouble getting benefits. But as she is a single, well educated, cancer sufferer from England she gets nothing.

Thursday 13th December

Becky arrived home late last night. When the Stem Cell Transplant was talked about, the doctor explained that if that didn't go as planned they may look at giving Mel a Bone Marrow Transplant. For that they need a donor and the obvious place to look first are any siblings. Becky is our only other child, so after we'd plied her with tea, sat her down and I asked the question. I explained the situation and the fact that the doctor wanted a blood sample so they could see if Becky's Bone Marrow matched that of Melissa's. I told her that the chances of a positive match were only 25% and if there wasn't a match, then they would look to the Donor List. She asked questions about procedures and we answered them. We all went to bed about half past twelve.

In the early evening we decorated the Christmas tree. Becky kept eyeing the box of Roses and paid healthy attention to Mel's Advent Calendars. Mel still doesn't fancy chocolate. She can eat cheese and potato pie and polished off a plate load for her dinner.

We received a call from the hospital, it was Pat to say that Becky's blood test for Bone Marrow compatibility would be next Wednesday at 9.30 am. She also told us Mel would be having her x-ray tomorrow as well as having her Hickman Line flushed. They don't know yet when she is to be admitted to have her next lot of high dose chemo.

Mel is in good spirits and I am remaining positive. I try to apply logic to each situation. The constant waiting gets to you. You're waiting for information and for signs that things are heading in the right direction. At the moment we're waiting to see if we'll be spending Christmas at home or in the Derbyshire Royal Infirmary.

Friday 14th December

Mel had an x-ray and blood taken.

We got to the hospital around half ten and went to the chemo unit to have Mel's Hickman Line flushed. Mel walked from the car park to the chemo unit, but was tired by the time she got there. She also walked to the X-ray department, but needed a chair to return. As we were waiting for the blood results, Mel had a bit of a wobble and had to sit down.

The sister took her to a side room and did her obs. They were ok, but again it was a stark reminder of how little she can do. Whilst we were in the consulting room, the Clinical Nurse came to fetch the Sister. They were gone for about fifteen minutes before returning with the doctor. They had a chat with us about Mel's general condition and we were allowed home. Our short appointment lasted four hours! I took Mel and Julie home and went back to work.

It's difficult to know what to expect and a million thoughts are buzzing in our minds. We wondered if the Doctor, Nurse and Sister had already seen the x-ray results, we wondered if they knew whether it was working.... but if they did why didn't they say so.... they talked about getting radiologist reports... is that a delaying tactic? Surely they can tell. Mel saw the x-ray briefly but didn't think it looked any different.

We're due some good news, we're desperate for good news. Next week we should have the x-ray results and we'll know whether the first session of chemo has worked. I went to my works Christmas meal this evening. I enjoyed it to a certain extent, but my mind, as it is so often these days, was elsewhere.

Saturday 15th December

Sometimes it's difficult to know what to write, particularly at the moment as Mel's condition doesn't seem to change from day to day. She's bright and reasonably bubbly. Her appetite is good and it's helping having Becky at home. Her liking of chocolate hasn't returned. She's nervous about the Liverpool game tomorrow, a defeat for the Pool could put her back a month!

Sunday 16th December

There is nothing more likely to make Mel feel under the weather than Liverpool losing to Manchester United. She's not taken it well, but as we said, it's good that it still matters. She swore a little, shouted a lot and if she'd have had any to tear out, she'd have tore her hair out too.

Julie and I went for a walk this morning and talked, it's strange how when we talk, we realise that a lot of the time, thoughts that come into our heads, that we think are unique to ourselves, but aren't.

The beauty of the weekends is that you don't clock or phone watch. During the week, I'm constantly watching the clock, waiting for a call from Julie for an update on how Mel's doing or a call from the hospital with news or appointments. At the weekend, we're free from all that (unless there's a sudden change in Mel's condition).

This weekend Mel and I laughed till we cried (at the contestant on Family Fortunes who when asked for a type of nut answered "cheese"), but come tomorrow it's back to watching and waiting, it is almost like the week interrupts our good times at the moment. We want to know what's happening, we need to know, but if it's not good news then maybe we're better as we are. At the moment we can escape, albeit for a short time, from chemotherapy, stem cell transplants and bone marrow matches. We can enjoy normal things.

Mel's appetite is good, but she's limited in the food she likes. At the moment, it's still chicken. We are running out of ideas of things you can do to liven up chicken.

We went wild today and had a change from chicken..... We had turkey!

Monday 17th December

The McMillan Clinical Nurse rang today to ask how Mel was after Friday's wobble. There was no talk of x-ray results and again you begin to wonder whether that's a good thing or not. In the past, results from x-rays have come fast and furious, but this time there seems to be a delay. Maybe it's just the way we're thinking, but you can't help worrying can you?

Mel and Becky spent time in the conservatory this morning, just talking and listening to music, I wish I'd been there to see it. I sometimes feel that by being at work I'm missing out on things. Things that in the past I'd taken for granted.

No replies to emails from James Plaskett MP or Janet Dean MP. Mel apologised to Julie, Becky and I last night for not buying us Christmas presents. It sounds dramatic to say she can't because she has no money, but it's the truth.

This evening we sat in the bathroom whilst Mel had a bath and talked about her symptoms. The only blip seems to be when she lies totally flat. It makes her cough, but she says things seem to be moving inside. She said she'd like a call to say whether she's going in before or after Christmas.

Finally, Mel's weight has gone up.... I'm not sure what it is, but it's up on what it was before.... it must be the chickens!

Tuesday 18th December

Mel, Becky and Julie are playing Mouse Trap. They asked me to play, but, I like to sit and watch and listen to them, it's great to see, normal, in fact, if Mel didn't have a head like a badly shaved cat you'd never know there was anything wrong with her!

I'm struggling at the moment to complete a full week at work. My mind is all over the place. Someone came in to the office today and asked if I was looking forward to a week today. I wondered what they meant, until I realised a week today is Christmas Day.

I received a call from the McMillan Clinical Nurse this morning from Derby. He rang to organise Becky's blood test to see if she's a match for a possible Bone Marrow transplant should the need arise.

We're booked in for 9am tomorrow. This is a pressure at the moment, I don't like being off work, I feel like I'm letting people down. Stupid isn't it, but that's how it makes me feel.

Last night we tried a new tact with the floor sleeping. We got the mattress off the top bunk bed and dragged that downstairs and put it on the floor to sleep on. I don't think I'd sleep anyway at the moment, but it was as comfortable as it could be. My big fear was rolling off the side and cracking my legs on the coffee table.

Wednesday 19th December

Another day waiting for calls that you think will never come and when they eventually do, they tell you nothing. I rang the hospital this morning to see if there was any news on the x-ray taken last Friday. She will call us in the morning.

Mel woke up this morning saying she'd had another bad dream. A couple of nights ago she dreamt of treatment and hospitals, last night she dreamt that her treatment didn't work and she was told there was nothing they could do for her. This made her anxious, hence the call to the hospital.

First thing this morning I took Becky to have her blood test to see if she's a match for Mel's bone marrow. She nearly fainted and had to sit down afterwards. She said she saw black dots in front of her eyes! I have this technique now; I call it my hypnotic technique... I could see her going a bit white so I say to her "Look into my eyes", when she does this, I talk to her and before you know it, it's done!

We'll know in a couple of weeks if Becky is a match.

I wish we could get an update from the hospital, not knowing is torturous, a million thoughts go through our minds and we can't settle... and the longer it goes on, the harder it gets....

Thursday 20th December

A letter arrived from the Incapacity Benefit people telling us that Mel's sick note had run out and they needed a new one. Despite not being eligible for this benefit until March, they still need sick notes from the doctor. We had sent one over a week ago dated 11th November and covering Mel for six months. Julie rang them up and was told that "if the doctor doesn't examine your daughter, then we can only accept a note for a month.... it's the law"

Julie explained that with Mel's blood count so low it could be potentially life threatening to take her to a doctor's surgery, to which the person on the end of the phone said we should get the doctor to visit.

As Julie pointed out... to say what? It's Lymphoma, it's cancer, the doctor isn't making it up!!! I wish he was! Today is four months since Mel was diagnosed. She still hasn't had a penny in financial support! Julie asked to speak to someone in higher authority and the six month note was accepted!

Speaking of calling back, the hospital let us down today with their lack of communication. Up to now they've been brilliant, but there seems to be a lack of information coming through at the moment and it's worrying. The promised morning call with news of Mel's next appointment and x-ray result never materialised and we were left waiting all day. I'm sure they don't understand how it affects Mel, the last time she was made to wait for results, it was bad news... you can guess what she's now thinking.

I put a call in to the unit at 4pm and at 4.30pm they called back telling us to go to hospital at 11.30am in the morning to see the consultant Doctor Smith. To say our emotions are being stretched is an understatement. It's this situation again of "we want to know..... But do we?" If it's good news, why didn't they just tell us? I also feel bad for chasing up the hospital. Maybe it would have been better to have left things... maybe ignorance is bliss!

Mel doesn't seem as well today. Her cough has returned and seems to be rattling on her chest when she's breathing. She also says her energy levels aren't as high and she has a headache. It could be the lymphoma returning, it could be stress, it could be the chemo... it could be that she's overdosed on chicken. I think she may lay an egg over the weekend!

She wrote on her blog this afternoon before the hospital called......

"I had my first lot of IVE at the begining of the month and it did wipe me out, i was sick and extremely tired. The side effects are wearing off now, the main one i have is tiredness and i sleep alot of the day. i had an xray last week to check the progress of the chemo.

However im now expecting to hear when im going in for my next lot of treatment, last friday in clinic we were told it wud be this week, we had heard nothing by yesterday morning so we rang the hospital and spoke to our nurse. By 5 o clock we had heard nothing back so we rang again. She said she was sorry but she hadnt been able to get hold of the doctors all day and could she ring in the morning.

Its now 3 o clock and we;ve heard nothing. I'm getting increasingly anxious and nervous, i want someone to tell me the dates for my next chemo and if its going ahead, i just want someone to tell me whats going on and what the plan is.... ive been told nothing yet about the stem cell transplant, i am expected to get an appointmnet with someone but goodness knows when!!

My doctors have been really good so far but i hate all this waiting!! Last time i was made to wait for results for longer than we thought it turned out that the RCHOP had stopped working! so im scared soemthing bad is waiting for me this time too!! I mean i feel ok but i did last time too. And i have a bad cough which is scaring me as that can be due to the lymphoma or it could be a chest infection (though i dont think it is as my temp is normal) so i really need them to ring!!!!

anyway i just wanted to vent my feelings a bit, i know noone can tell me what i need to know but it helps to write it down sometimes.

im in hospital tomorrow to have my line flushed so we have said that if no-one rings us today we will start asking q's then and ask to speak to a doctor. I just hope its good news."

Amen to that!

Friday 21st December

We sat up last night talking with Mel, she was anxious about the meeting with the doctor. Not even the temazapam could relax her as she talked and cried over what he might or might not say.

We went over a hundred scenarios, but always come back to the same conclusion.... we don't know what's happening and we're only guessing. It was past midnight before Julie and I went downstairs to our mattress on the floor.. ... ... it was after 3am before sleep finally won and we drifted off. Before that, I'd got up and made myself a drink, listened to Mel coughing, listened to music and fought off a string of negative thoughts that hammered into my head.

Since diagnosis we've had four months of things not going our way. It's time the balance was redressed.

Whilst walking across Tesco car park I saw a woman walking with her daughter, about the same age as Mel, they had a trolley stacked to the brim and were laughing and joking. It made me think of how our Christmas was meant to be this year. Both the girls coming back from uni, full of stories, parties, dressing up and maybe, just maybe they'd squeeze in enough time to talk about their courses. They'd both be working at the Golf Club, earning money to supplement their loan, they'd have been into town together Christmas shopping, buying presents for friends and family. They'd have taken time out to visit their nannies and on Christmas Day we'd have visited family before tucking into Christmas dinner.... Reality isn't quite the dream!

We'll make the most of it, but at the back of our mind will be this horrible, horrible disease that has taken over our lives. Every cough, headache, tired spell will be watched, knowing that if things take a turn for the worse we could be spending Christmas in hospital. It sounds like I'm negative, it's not negativity, it's reality and if the last four months have taught us one thing, it's to prepare for anything!

We went to see the consultant, Dr. Smith. After asking about Mel's general health and breathing he told us that the latest IVE chemotherapy hadn't worked and both he and his Nottingham counterpart Dr. Haynes were worried.

Because her lymphoma is rejecting all forms of chemo given so far, they're going to try another cocktail called GEM P. Dr. Smith went on to explain that administration of this chemo is out of Burton's range and that Derby aren't totally happy giving it, so we're now being put under the auspices of Nottingham and the renowned Dr. Haynes. Dr. Smith explained that he wasn't sure about this type of treatment so in order to find out more about it, he switched on his computer. It is strange when your consultant explains the treatment by googling the name of it.

The idea is to reduce the tumour to such a size that they can then take healthy stem cells and do the transplant. They're also rushing through the results of Becky's blood test. Another option open to them is to blast with the super high dose chemo which will cleanse her system completely before performing a bone marrow transplant. Radiotherapy is a possible option but in someone of Mel's age, it increases the chances of breast cancer in the future so they're reluctant to do this.

Another option is called mini beam which we don't know a great deal about. We thought that the IVE chemo was Mel's only chance, but it seems that's not the case. They're basically throwing everything they can at this stubborn tumour in order to get rid of it and the aim is still to cure her.

Mel is down at the moment, she knows it's not good. We're waiting for a phone call to tell us when they want her to go into Nottingham. He inferred it will be sooner rather than later, but it won't be today.

I took Mel out this evening for a drive around the town and the suburbs to see the Christmas lights. It got her out of the house and we chatted about the day's events. She admitted it hadn't sunk in yet and the time for tears hadn't arrived. I told her that when she was ready to talk and cry to do just that, not to hold anything in...

Saturday 22nd December

Mel's "lymphoma cough" is on its way back and getting worse each day. The tightness in her throat which restricts her breathing is returning, a sure sign that the tumour is making an unwelcome return.

In addition to the problems with Mel, Julie's dad is ill. He's been ill for some time, but soldiered on year in year out, but at the moment he's not too good at all.

Aunties and cousins visited Mel this morning and that helps. It also gives her an opportunity to freak out her cousin Sarah by showing her the Hickman Line. Hannah's not too keen either, but it keeps Mel amused.

She's asked later if we can go for another drive out. Julie and I talked this morning, we're not under any illusions as to what lies ahead, but we agreed we have to keep strong and stay focused. I think up to now, if Julie's wobbled I've been there to support her and vice versa. Our problems will arise if we both wobble together!

Sunday 23rd December

We went for a drive again last night. We didn't talk about the illness or any imminent treatment, we chatted about football, houses with lights on their frontages and other 'normal' things.

We watched Match of the Day and Mel went to bed just after midnight. We set up our bed downstairs. This morning Becky and I went for a bike ride to see my parents and to wish my mum happy birthday. Mel woke up at 12.30pm with backache, shortness of breath and chest pains, saying that she felt the same as she had done prior to going to hospital back in August.

The suffocating feeling that she gets in her neck is there all the time. We know that within a week or so, without the new treatment, she will get worse and we can understand why the doctors want her back in sooner rather than later. She took two codeine tablets to ease the pain in her back and settled down with Becky on the sofa to talk all things university (past and present). Becky is currently checking out Mel's injection holes in her hands and is impressed with her veins! She is asking questions about cannulars and every answer is met with Urggh! Julie's dad isn't too good. He should be in hospital, They're calling the doctor in the morning.

Going back to Mel, we're not sure at the moment whether she'll have her treatment as an outpatient or inpatient at Nottingham. Mel said she wasn't bothered... she knew she needed treatment and had to be back in hospital. It's a sure sign that things aren't good at the moment.

CHAPTER FIFTEEN
Meeting Dr. Haynes

Christmas Eve

I don't know where to start today; last night Mel went upstairs and sat on her bed alone so I went to keep her company. We chatted about the impending appointment with Dr. Haynes, football, Christmas TV and took bets as to whether Julie and Becky had fallen asleep downstairs (They had!).

This morning I'd been at work an hour when my mobile rang. It was Julie. Dr. Smith called to say that Dr. Haynes wanted to see us as soon as possible at Nottingham. I left work at half nine, got home for ten and got to Nottingham City Hospital for quarter past eleven.

Dr. Haynes went through everything in fine detail. He stated that the chances of the original chemo (RCHOP) not working were 15%. The chances of the second chemo (IVE) not working was 30%. With every set of chemo that doesn't work, the chance of cure diminishes. Like Dr. Smith on Friday, he stated they were worried. He talked through the type of lymphoma it was and gave it a name, which, though he said a couple of times, we didn't catch. *

It's more prevalent in ages 40 and under and also in women. About seven out of ten people who contract this form of Lymphoma are women.

He introduced us to Faith, his Lymphoma Clinical Nurse Specialist and then explained how they plan to proceed. Firstly, they will administer the GEM P. The chances of this working are 50-50. If they can reduce the tumour to a certain level, they can then take the stem cells required. The only way they can cure Mel now is via a bone marrow transplant. The chances of complete cure are now only 20 - 30%. Becky's match results are awaited and ideally it would be hers that are used.

The stem cell transplant now serves to keep Mel in such a state that they can then complete the Bone Marrow Transplant when a donor is available. With Mel's type of lymphoma, there are only 12 people worldwide who have ever got to transplant stage.

They offered Mel the option of starting her treatment straight away or waiting until after Christmas. She opted for the latter. Dr. Haynes told us not to go away without hope, he assured us everything that could be done would be done and we were in the hands of one of the best Lymphoma units in the world. When Mel went to get weighed, Dr. Haynes re-iterated to Julie and I that he was worried, the odds were against us, but everything possible would be done.

With Mel back in the room, he then went on to explain the type of care we could expect. Palliative care was mentioned, but at the moment they are trying to cure the lymphoma. Other detail was gone into, some of which went over our heads as we struggled to take in all the information.

He prescribed Mel some steroids. She has to take twenty at a time for four days. This will help to reduce the symptoms she is struggling with. They took a blood sample and Mel and I went up to the pharmacy to meet Julie. As we went to leave the hospital, we were called back as the blood results were worrying. They took some more, debated about giving Mel a blood transfusion before letting us go home, with the firm instruction that if she took a downward turn we were to go back to Nottingham City Hospital immediately. We were booked in for 9am on Friday when Mel will have a blood transfusion and the first lot of GEM P chemo.

We drove home and on the way back rang parents and sisters to update them. We also told Becky what had gone on. Becky bombarded us with questions, most of which we answered, some of which we couldn't. After leaving the hospital I rang work. I am having two weeks off. I've tried to keep going through this, but the time has come for me to give in.

This evening Mel and I went for another drive. We didn't talk as much, but I let her know that whenever she wanted to talk, whatever the time of day, she only had to say. If she needed to cry she should. By nature she is a very positive person so there is no need to keep telling her to be positive. We always knew this was going to be difficult, we never imagined for a minute it would be this hard.

* Mel's Lymphoma is Mediastinal Sclerosing Diffuse Large B Cell Non Hodgkins Lymphoma.

Christmas Day

We saw the 25th December in and sat up for a further two hours talking with Mel. She'd taken the twenty steroids in the afternoon and consequently she was wide awake. We talked of what had been said in the afternoon. We all agreed the set up at Nottingham, Dr. Haynes and his staff, on first impressions, were superb. There were tears as we discussed the percentages. The reality of the situation is slowly sinking in.

I awoke on Christmas morning at about quarter to eight and woke Mel. She ate her marmite on toast and then knocked back the twenty steroids. The ones she took yesterday have begun to take effect. The breathless issues had subsided and she was able to lie flatter in bed.

We came downstairs and opened our presents before Mel went upstairs and got changed. We spent the morning making and taking phone calls before I disappeared into the kitchen and cooked the Christmas dinner. We all had full plates and Mel ate most of hers. Her appetite and her liking for chocolate have returned.

Cousins and aunties visited and prior to that we nipped round to see nanny and check on granddad. Julie's dad had improved a little, the doctor popped in to check on him this morning. People often complain about the NHS, but we have come to realise they do so much for people, a lot of it unnoticed.

It's been strange, I've enjoyed Christmas Day, but it's been hollow. I'm trying not to think of this time next year, but I can't help it. It's the fear of the future I suppose. We've had four months of bad news, it's difficult to see a change in fortunes... but that's not to say we don't remain hopeful.

Boxing Day

Just before ten o'clock last night I was sat in the conservatory reading when Mel came in and asked if I'd take her out in the car for a while. She wanted a break from the four walls. We got in the car and drove round for an hour. She had written an update for her own Facebook site and she wanted to talk about what she'd written. Being Mel, she was very wary of upsetting people, but at the same time wanted them to know the truth. We talked through certain things and when we arrived home, we sat up for a couple more hours chatting away.

Mel had her mass intake of steroids this morning and then asked if Becky and I were going a bike ride, maybe we could ride over to my mum's house and relieve her of some soft centred Cadbury's Roses.

About five minutes after getting in from the bike ride, the phone rang, this time it was my brother in law...

Something you hear a lot of is "These things are sent to try us." We had something else sent to "try us" today. Julie's dad passed away. He'd been struggling this morning and Julie's mum called the paramedics. They took him to hospital and within half an hour he'd passed away. He'd been ill for some time, but fought on for years, defying the odds and the doctors. If there is any comfort to all this then although his quality of life wasn't great in the last few years, he did have his family around him. I took Julie to the hospital and she joined her mum and sister.

In the afternoon, Julie's mum came and sat with us. I went upstairs about quarter to six and found Mel sat on the edge of the bed with her arm around Becky. Becky was crying. The reality of the situation had hit her and she isn't sure at the moment about returning to university in January. She sat on the bed saying it wasn't fair, which we can't argue with. The three of us sat and talked. I told her that ultimately it was up to her and whatever she decided we'd support her. We realise how difficult it must be for her.

Mel and Becky spent some time sorting out their music on their computer and talking to friends on the internet. They were sat next to each other laughing and joking and messing about and for a brief moment I could almost believe things were back how they used to be. They've always been close and rarely fall out. We may not have got everything in our lives right, but we brought up two beautiful girls who over the years continue to make us so proud.

After taking Julie's mum home we watched a bit of TV and I chatted with Julie about the day's events.

In terms of life's Christmases, it's not been up there with the best!

THROUGH MELISSA'S EYES (Part Six)

"Now bear in mind this will be long considering how long I ramble for but its honest and it the most recent things we know.

PLAN FROM NOW

The plan now is to have a new kind of chemo, called GEM-P. The drugs in it are different to what I've already had. The good thing it's done as an outpatient so I won't have to stay in hospital. It's done over 2 weeks on day 1, 8 and 15. On day 15 I stay in for 24 hours so I can have fluids but it's only a day so that's fine. After that they will do a PET scan and access things again. The GEM-P chemo has a 50% chance of a response from me. That's me, not a general estimate as

I've not responded too much so far! I go in on Friday 28th for this. I will also have a blood transfusion on Friday 28th as my counts were low on Monday. This just goes through my line and for me is no big deal – just a case of sitting in a chair and being hooked up to a drip for a few hours. If the GEM-P doesn't work but they can collect stem cells as a result that is a positive although not as positive as if it all works! A stem cell collection is just like collecting blood which then goes through a machine – takes out my stem cells and puts everything else back into me. No pain – just boring as it takes 4 hours and you can't be unhooked! This will be done after the 2 week cycle I think.

My only chance of a cure now is a bone marrow transplant using someone else's bone marrow. Ideally this would be my sibling – in my case my sister Becky but we are waiting on the results of the test at the min. It's safer and less risky if it's a sibling but there's only a 1 in 4 (25%) chance of her being that match. If she isn't a match we go to the national database and search for a match from the people who donate their bone marrow. There's a 50-50 chance we'll get a match from there. The Doctor said it was likely we will get a match that way. In the meantime they could give me a stem cell transplant using my own cells or if they can't collect any from me for a number of reasons use someone else's. This wouldn't offer a cure and I would almost certainly relapse but it would buy them time to find a donor if Becky isn't a match. They can also use different kinds of chemo and high dose chemo which would blast my tumour but would destroy my stem cells and at the min they don't want to do that but they are options open to us at a later stage.

That's essentially the plan. Basically they are keeping their options open and seeing what happens. When I was first diagnosed, like I said before my chance of complete cure was 80-90%. That has now dropped to 20% and can go up to 30% if I can have a transplant but even with the transplant there is no guarantee that I will fully recover. But there is hope. The odds aren't in my favour particularly and the Doctors are worried. The odds have dropped a lot. However like they said it isn't hopeless and there are still things they can try.

At the moment they are still aiming to cure it. If you get to 5 years in remission (no sign on cancer in the body and none for the previous 5 years) they can class you as cured. If they can't get a cure they can offer what they call palliative care which is treatment to control the disease for some time, essentially different types of chemo etc - eventually the disease will overcome this and that is when they turn to just controlling any symptoms I have which is essentially a terminal prognosis. Scary stuff. Lets hope we never get here. I guess though u never know. I could be cured, I could not be - It's a gamble. And it is something you think about – you cant help it.

That is essentially it. That's the honest truth and I know it seems very negative and its not good news obviously. It's probably not hit me yet really. I've cried a lot but I think the steroids are kind of helping me keep my spirits up at the min. Also I am being positive, I'm not being negative all the time but its very very hard to be positive 100% of the time and I am trying! Seriously and I do believe and hope this treatment will work and give me a cure.

POSITIVITY

Although I absolutely 100% appreciate all the messages from people please try not to say 'Keep positive or keep your chin up' because I hear this everyday from lots of different people and I already know this and to be honest it gets to the point where I get annoyed and I really don't want to get annoyed with people especially when its not their fault. If you've said in the past don't think I've been offended – chances are I haven't – it's just that nowadays its something EVERYONE says and it gets *irritating! I need to be honest with people because that's the only way I can be. If you don't know what to say tell me! I would much rather hear 'I don't know what to say' than something that doesn't make sense or nothing at all. And if u feel too uncomfortable saying anything that's fine. I'm not going to get offended or anything!*

UNI
Come September I honestly don't think I will be back at Uni and I don't honestly know if I'll go back at all. I have no clear plan yet because I can't plan ahead at the min. I don't know what is around the corner. I will of course come to Aston and visit people even if I don't return to my course - symptoms permitting of course. Its for a number of reasons really: one – I don't know at what stage my treatment will be at, even if I do get the transplant and all goes well it will take me a good while to recover from that and two – after everything that's happened, its made me think and I'm honestly not sure if studying for another 2-3 years if what I want as much as I used to. As much as I love the social life I don't think I'm doing myself any favours by going back just for that if my heart isn't in the degree and what I'm really there for. That's just my initial feeling and its nothing to do with the people – in fact you are all my best friends and I couldn't have done this without you all. But nothing is set in stone and I could just as easily turn up and carry on I guess – u never know either way! I know it will be hard for some of you to understand my reasoning for this but to be honest unless you have been in this position I don't think anyone can really understand much of what I'm going through right now. And that's me being honest.

OTHER BITS

On another note a bit of my hair is still clinging on though not much! Lol got some nice headwear for Christmas though which is great. My eyebrows are thinning like crazy but no big deal and I have virtually no eyelashes! Nice! I have stripy nails – with white lines on them – a result of chemo!

I had a nice Christmas day in the circumstances and the steroids are making me eat more – I've eaten chocolate for the first time in about a month! I'm still staying in a lot apart from the odd drive out with dad and I'm watching a lot of football! Normal then hey!

And I'm staying positive as much as I can and its not always easy but I'm trying I promise!!! I am scared and worried – esp when Doctors themselves say they are worried but I'm trying to carry on.

THANKS

Anyway if you've come to the end of this, thank you because I know it's an essay but its all stuff that needed to be said. I had a nice Christmas and thanks to everyone who has joined this group, left messages and everything cos I do appreciate it I promise!

So I go in on Friday and apart from the odd day ill be home for the next 2 weeks….so speak to u all soon…..

Thanks again
Love Mel xxxx"

CHAPTER SIXTEEN

The End of the Year

Thursday 27th December

I went to the doctor's this morning to get a sick note for work. As I explained last week, things have got so intense now that something needs to give way. I can't keep going to the hospital, keeping strong and concentrating on work too. I need to support Julie too.

The District Nurse visited us this morning and put us in touch with the local hospice's charity fund. We explained our situation and she gave them a call. They'll call us back after the holidays. She brought with her a male student nurse whom Mel described as "the fit one", so that brightened her day.

During her dinner, Mel had a bad coughing fit. It took her five minutes to recover. She finished her dinner but was quiet afterwards and we became concerned. She told us she was ok, just tired. Any sudden change of condition is a cause for concern. We'll keep an eye on her this evening...

Friday 28th December

I mentioned yesterday that Mel went very quiet in the evening; I could tell something was bothering her, so I asked her if she wanted me to take her a drive out. We'd been driving about ten minutes, before she opened up and told me she was worried about Becky not going back to University in January. She was also worried about Julie and how she was after her dad passed away, she was overwhelmed by the messages of support she'd received from her friends and finally, she said she was scared.

To hear your daughter say she's scared is horrible. What can I do? I can't tell her it will be alright because we both know that may not be the case. I didn't know what to say, I told her I was scared too. She talked of the statistics and her chances of 20 - 30%. I told her that when those figures scare me I try to break them down. Three in every ten people are cured. Of the seven that aren't, some will be older people, others will have other health issues and chances are the three will be the young and healthy with the ability to fight and be strong. Mel is a fighter and so strong.

Much as I wanted to, I couldn't and wouldn't make promises that I couldn't keep. I told her that whatever happens we're there with her and we'll do whatever we can to help. It seemed to help and we talked about going shopping and maybe even fixing up a football match. It was a tough evening, but it makes me so happy that she feels she can talk to me.

Mel spent this morning and part of the early afternoon having a blood transfusion. She slept some of the time and when she was awake she wasn't very talkative. She seemed down. Her Chemo was administered in the afternoon. The hospital gave us our next appointment and left it open as to when they take the stem cells. It may be day fifteen (11th January) or they may take them the following Monday (14th) or leave it a week and take them on the 18th January. They leave it open so they can harvest them at the best possible time.

Mel was given her tablets before she left. There are ten steroids a day for five days, plus other pills that Julie and Mel know the names of. It never ceases to amaze me (and the doctors and nurses) how they remember them all. After tea Mel was tearful again, so I asked her if she wanted to talk. We went and sat on the bed and for nearly an hour talked and cried. She admitted that it was getting to her. The unfairness, the wanting to be normal again, the wanting for the treatment to work this time. We talked about it all. I told her that if this treatment is going to be the one that works (and there's no reason to think otherwise), she's taken the first steps on the road to getting better today. Gradually the tears dried and there was even a hint of a smile.

It's been a tough 24 hours.

Saturday 29th December

Mel currently starts the day with 10 steroids, then there are a couple of other "morning" pills to knock back.

As with all chemo, you're never sure which side effects you're going to get and the lethargy this morning could be attributed to that. She wanted some music to listen to in order to help her relax so we went a drive to Byrkley Garden Centre to pick up a couple of CD's. By the time I got back to the car she was saying she had pains in her chest and in her back. I took her straight home. We took her temperature, which was normal, and then she had some pain killers. She went to bed for half an hour. After she had rested she was a brighter, she came downstairs, ate all her dinner and was full of chat.

She read her messages on Facebook and settled down to watch football. After the football had finished we went to see nanny before coming home and watching Soccer Saturday. In the afternoon the steroids kicked in and Mel was in good spirits, constantly talking and we took a few pictures of her in her new headwear.... and one of me too . . . . in her new headwear!!

Sunday 30th December

Today is pretty much like yesterday although Mel's cough isn't getting better. I went for a bike ride with Becky this morning and whilst out had a call from Julie to say Mel had dry skin on her hands which looked sore. I had to get some cream from Morrisons. Even with something as simple as sore or dry hands we have to be careful they don't induce infection.

Mel had some university friends visit in the afternoon and as with all communication and visits from friends, they lift her no end. She phoned her Nan and then rang her friend Rachel. Julie and I both said today that we don't seem to get any time together at the moment. It's the way it has to be unfortunately. We're sleeping on a mattress on the floor and by the time we've sorted out our bed, sorted out Mel for the night and sorted out the cats, we're that knackered we don't have time to sit up and talk, so we just get comfy and sleep for as long as possible.

Whilst Mel is feeling better (albeit steroid induced) we want to try and get her out the house. Tomorrow we're planning (dangerous word that is... planning), to take her to the shops in Derby. We've got a wheelchair and depending on how busy it is, we'll take her a ride round. It gives her something to look forward to and talk about instead of just staring at the four walls day after day.

If nothing else, this cancer has taught us that we never know what's round the corner and that's not being negative, it's fact. We don't know when she'll be able to go to the shopping centre or visit Birmingham again so it's important that we do these things whilst we can. We don't intend to put her in danger of infection, she's not neutropenic (this is when her blood counts are low and she's most at risk from infection. With this chemo it's day 10 to 14) so, it's a case of being sensible, taking care and at the same time doing something as near to "normal" as possible.

Monday 31st December

This morning we went to Derby's new shopping centre. We took the wheelchair and Mel had a great time. I wheeled her round and she enjoyed shopping in the sales. Mel bought a new hat which she has since lived in and she bought two new tops. After an hour or so we headed home. She was tired and hungry, but she'd had a good time and done something "normal".

Prior to going to Derby I went and booked the car in for a service and also went to see Ben Robinson, the Chairman of Burton Albion. In the past we'd been given tickets for a couple of games. Unfortunately both times, Mel was ill and we never managed to get there. I asked Ben if we could just come down to a game at short notice. He agreed and said all we had to do was turn up at the ground and ask for him and he'd sort us out. A nice gesture that was much appreciated. We may go to the game tomorrow.

I suppose at this time of year you should look back on the past 12 months and take stock. Phew, where would I start?

The house move in January..... The early trips to National Trust properties as we enjoyed our Christmas present (Membership to the Trust). They were early year highs. Another high was mine and Mel's trip to Liverpool to watch the Champions League Final in The Blob. We'd been there two years earlier and had to go back. We were recognised in the street and mobbed in the bar as fans remembered us. Two years ago I'd written a book about our trip to Liverpool and the infamous Blob. This time they lost, but we had a great time. Mel always says the Champions League Final day in 2005 was the best day of her life. I could have spent a million pounds on her and she couldn't have had a better time.

May came and went, June arrived and so probably did the illness that now dominates our life. The rest of the year has been one hospital trip, one diagnosis and one consultation after another. Since August we've had more downs than ups. My attitude to life has changed completely.

2007 has been a nightmare. 2008 will either be the best or worst year of our lives.

CHAPTER SEVENTEEN

New Year, Same Old Issues

New Year's Day

Today is January 1st, the start of a new year. We're glad that both Christmas and New Year are out of the way and we can get back to concentrating on getting Mel's lymphoma sorted out.

In addition to the ten steroids, Mel had to take extra tablets today, so we sorted out her breakfast and Julie sat with her whilst she took them. Her cough seemed worse today and sounded different. It was loose on her chest, but deep. She had a couple of coughing fits in the morning, but it petered out as the day progressed. She came downstairs about ten ish complaining of being hot, so we took her temperature. It was 36.8. Panic over.

I took Mel to see Burton Albion play Stafford Rangers today. It was strange. Mel got emotional shortly after we'd arrived. Being confined to a wheelchair made her realise how this illness has hold of her. We were treated well, Albion won 2-1 but we both said we shan't return until we can do so without the wheels.

Wednesday 2nd January

We lay down on the mattress at half past eleven. Prior to that Mel was on the 'Life' site. This chat site is invaluable. When Mel goes and chats to her new found friends on there, she always comes back more positive than when she went on. She talks to us all the time, and whilst we do our best, no-one can truly understand what she's going through unless they've been through (or are going through) it themselves.

Mel noticed last night that her ankles were swelling up; it's a side effect of the chemo, but one she's not experienced before. We contacted the hospital and they assured us it was normal, but to keep an eye on it. The cough has disappeared for the day and apart from being full of wind and tired she's not too bad. The wind is not the nicest of perfumes and is occasionally loud. Becky says it vibrates the sofa.

This evening she asked if we could go for a drive again. She chatted about the 'Life' site and about how she felt and at one point she went faint and nearly passed out. It's not easy trying to negotiate bends in the road whilst your daughter is on the verge of fainting but I managed it..... She said it was probably her blood counts dropping... I said she'd probably gassed herself!

Thursday 3rd January

Today we went to see the Benefits Advisor who is affiliated to the hospital at Burton. I just wanted to check we were applying for everything we could. We were.

Mel had a couple of friends visit this afternoon. When we got home she talked to us about how she was feeling in general. Listening to her confirms just how amazing she is.

She did say she woke up the other night with a feeling of overwhelming anger where she just wanted to hit out at something, at the injustice and unfairness of it all. I have to admit it's something I want to do myself... Often!

Friday 4th January

Mel was a bit down today. She wasn't impressed that Becky sneaked into her room and helped herself to a chocolate finger at 7am this morning. The hospital visit took longer than anticipated. Since taking the steroids she's become bloated. Her ankles, stomach and hands are worst affected and her face too. The doctor said it was due to water and salt retention caused by the steroids and that it should go down in the next few days. We have to measure her stomach everyday over the weekend to check it's not expanding. Her hair is very thin now. The GEM P causes substantial hair thinning as oppose to hair loss, but as Mel's hair was already very thin, it's taken more of it away. We were given a present to take home. A container for Mel to do a 24 hour urine collection. She has to do this from 7am on Tuesday until 7am Wednesday and I have to take it over to Nottingham on Wednesday morning so I really will be taking the piss!!

At the hospital her Hickman line couldn't be used to draw off the blood so they had to inject her arm. The nurse flushed the line and the saline went through ok which was a relief. The nurse said it happens sometimes. The chemo was administered, the line flushed and we left the hospital. We got home at about ten to three and I had time for a drink before setting off for the Income Support Tribunal at Derby.

As I sat in the tribunal office, I explain the problems we had had in gaining financial support for Mel. The chairperson of the tribunal was shocked and extremely sympathetic but explained that if I wanted to change the law I would have to start with my MP (great). As expected the decision of the Income Support people stood. The chairperson was almost in tears as she told. She said she didn't want to give me the decision but she was bound by the law. Consequently, we're in the same position. No Income Support, No decision on Disablement Living Allowance and no chance of Incapacity Benefit until she's been incapacitated for six months (March).

I now have to decide whether to carry on the fight or give in. I wonder if Mel's Human Rights have been violated by her not being provided for. Maybe I could sue the government for a breach of her Human Rights? I want to do something, if not for Mel then for others in her situation, but I don't know if I have the energy or strength at the moment. Maybe now isn't the time to make a decision.

Saturday 5th January

At half past seven last night, I looked across at Mel, she was fidgety and hadn't spoken for about twenty minutes. I asked her if she was ok and tears welled up in her eyes. She said she wanted to go and lie down. I sat on the bed and we talked about things in general. After a while she cheered up. I think the reason she was down was that the steroids were on their way out, whilst the chemo was on its way in. Like I've said before, it's rare that she's down for long.

Just before ten o'clock we said goodnight and as I looked at her lying there I had a reality check. I get reality checks every now and then.

A lot of the time we take her condition for granted. It's become the norm. Mel walking upstairs and being out of breath is now the norm, whereas this time last year, Mel running upstairs and me telling her not to make too much noise was the norm. Her hair has been thin for so long now, we forget it's not the way it normally is. Last night I sat on the bed, looked at her and could have burst into tears. How does she cope with it? How does she keep so strong? This illness stretches out in front of her with no end in sight, but she keeps battling on. I'm so proud of her, I'm so proud of Becky and Julie too. Becky for the way she is helping, not just with blood tests, but general day to day tasks and Julie for the all the help she's giving to Mel of a practical nature, all this and coping with her dad passing away, she is amazing. I want Mel to be her old self again; I want us all be our old selves again. I know that's a long way off. I hate the unfairness of it all. Last night I kept asking the question....Why Mel, why us...why anybody?

We'd not been in bed long when we heard Mel coughing. Julie nipped upstairs, checked her and we took her temperature. It was over 37.5 degrees. Julie came downstairs and I set my alarm for an hour later. This set the pattern for the remainder of the night as we monitored her temperature every hour or so. At three o'clock in the morning it hit 37.8 degrees. If it hits thirty eight then we have to ring the hospital and chances are we'd be called in. We were on standby but thankfully the swollen ankles, tummy and face had started to go down and at half eight this morning her temperature dipped below 37 degrees and it was panic over. We were totally knackered after a sleepless night.

When she awoke this morning Mel was bright and breezy again, probably due in no small measure due to her university friends visiting later today. Becky and I went on a bike ride to Woolworth in order to get her a bag of creams from the Roses and Quality Street pick n mix section. As I've mentioned before she has cravings and pick n mix creams are the latest... along with cheese on toast...and sausage rolls...and of course chicken!

Mel's friends from university came to visit this afternoon and it perked her up no end. Julie and I walked to the local supermarket to stock up on a few essentials. We're trying to be careful in what we buy, money is tight, but at the same time we've got to eat and live.

Sunday 6th January

We were all tired last night, Julie fell asleep on the sofa at about half past eight, Becky and I watched Notting Hill and Mel went to bed about half ten. I went upstairs to take Mel a drink and then on the way down I slipped and slid down the remaining steps on my back and into the clothes drier. As a consequence I have two sore elbows, a sore hand and a pain in my back. Julie's main concern was that the clothes drier was not broken whilst Becky couldn't do anything for laughing. Mel just asked us to be quiet as she couldn't get to sleep!

She hasn't been too bad today. She thinks that something is happening with the chemo as her breathing is a lot better; she even took her own tea plate into the kitchen. Can you believe that? How crazy does it sound? A sign of improvement is carrying her plate from the lounge to the kitchen.... All of about a dozen steps! But that's how we measure things.

Monday 7th January

After taking Becky and Sarah to Derby to do some "pre-return to uni" shopping, I went to my MP's office. I booked an appointment with her for next Monday, the 14th.

In the afternoon I had to go back over to Derby to pick Becky and Sarah up. Mel came with me. She seems well today. No coughing, she did have a headache but we took her temperature and it was well below the "panic" level of thirty eight degrees. When we came back from Derby Mel, Sarah and Becky sat in the living room chatting.

I looked through the patio doors into the room at the three of them all laughing and joking and it was one of those moments when just for a minute or two, you could almost believe there was nothing wrong.

Pat Holland rang from Burton Queen's Hospital to enquire how Mel was feeling and how she was getting on with the new treatment. We chatted for the best part of an hour and Pat revealed how she'd been in touch with the cancer support people at the hospital and she has applied for a grant for Mel from the hospital cancer support fund. Like the MacMillan fund (www.macmillan.org.uk), it's a charitable grant and whilst we're grateful, we shouldn't have to rely on charity. Anyway, that's all been said before and hopefully next week I'll take the first steps into changing things, if not for Melissa then for other students in similar positions.

Tuesday 8th January
I took Mel to the hospital this morning and she walked from the car park into the hospital and after her appointment with the psychologist she walked back to the car. She was a little breathless on the inward journey but fine on the way back. It's the longest she's walked in weeks and a sign that the chemo is doing something. The coughing stopped. It would be fantastic to get some positive news when we next see the consultant. We're wary because other chemo has started to work, but then stopped, We're taking nothing for granted, we're just enjoying her feeling so much better.

Today is the wee collection day. Mel started at half seven this morning and has to collect it all day.

After visiting the psychologist we came home, got changed and then went to Julie's dad's funeral. The funeral went ok, there were a few tears before and during and some laughter afterwards, especially when Julie's mum got the psychologist and gynaecologist mixed up! She asked Mel how she'd got on at the latter!

My mum and dad were due to visit tomorrow as was one of Mel's uni friends. However, my dad has an infection and Mel's friend has a sore throat, so needless to say they're not coming. Mel is currently neutropenic and for the next couple of days, very prone to infection. We have to be careful.

Wednesday 9th January
The sample was taken to Nottingham this morning. The final drop, dripped at about quarter past five and we set off. We had a bit of a problem last night, Mel had filled the container they gave her and was set to do more. I got an empty Coke bottle (2ltr), filled it with hot water, shook the water out, re-filled it about four times, finally with cold water, shook it dry and took it upstairs and it became sample container number two.

We'd just got back from our trip when the phone rang. It was Nottingham hospital. They can't accept piddle in Coke bottles. It would have been nice if they'd told us when they gave us the container... also, when we took the sample in, they had to take a blood sample from Mel.

Anyway, the upshot of it all was that the pee taken in the last 24 hours was now defunct and a new sample had to be taken. This was the cue for me to drive over to Burton Hospital to get two new containers and for Mel to start the collection all over again.

This morning Mel told me she had got herself washed and dressed all on her own and even managed to pick her laptop up from under the coffee table. She's even hoping to go a walk to Jackson's (shop round the corner) later. It's great to see and a sure sign that this treatment is doing something. There is no word on whether Becky is a match for bone marrow. We shall check that out on Friday. The walk to Jackson's went ok, although when she got back home she was out of breath. Although it's light years away from how things should be, it is a welcome improvement.

Thursday 10th January

After a hectic morning which involved driving Becky to town, an appointment at the doctors and a continuation of Mel's 24 hour sample collection, we set off for Nottingham at about one o'clock. Prior to leaving we had a call from Pauline, the district nurse to see if there was anything we needed. Pauline also enquired after our benefit issues and pledged support if needed. At Nottingham, Mel had blood taken. They were impressed with the sample she presented. Whilst there we asked a few questions that needed clearing up. Firstly, what time did we have to ring to enquire about a bed for Mel on Friday morning? Answer, nine o'clock. Secondly, what if there isn't a bed available. Answer, there will be. Apparently Dr. Haynes insists that the final part of the chemo has to be done tomorrow.

Finally, I asked the question about Becky being a match for Mel's Bone Marrow. Becky wasn't a match and a donor will have to be found off the donor register.

The chances of them finding a donor are very good. Mel had blood taken whilst she was there. On her Hickman Line, there are two tubes coming off it. The red line and the blue line. Normally the blue line is good, the red not so good. Today, they tried the red... nothing. They then fed some saline through it to flush it and bingo... the blood shot into the tube like a bullet from a gun. We were all relieved, in particular Mel who, prior to going to the hospital had been checking her veins to see if they were on form.

When we got home we told Becky she wasn't a match and she was philosophical about it all. She was disappointed, but realistic enough to know that at one in four, the chances were slim. About half an hour later I took Becky and Mel to see their grandma and they spent half an hour chatting to her and they had a cup of tea. When I picked them up, Mel complained of feeling a bit shivery. Prior to having a bath she took her temperature and it was 37.2 degrees. An hour later, at quarter past six it had risen to 37.8. It began to get worrying. Mel's face was extremely hot and she was shivery. We decided to take it again at quarter past seven. The rule is if it hits 38 degrees we have to call the hospital. At quarter past seven we took Mel's temperature again....

This time it hit 38.3 so I immediately phoned the City Hospital at Nottingham for advice. Whilst Julie packed Mel's bag for an overnight stay on the ward, I gave details to the hospital of Mel's symptoms.

The lady on the other end of the phone told me she would relay the information and get back to us. Within five minutes we received a call from the hospital. They told us to give Mel a couple of paracetamol and monitor her temperature for a few hours. We checked it at half past eight and it had gone down to 37.5. Mel felt slightly better, the shivers had ceased and her headache was going off. By half past nine it was down further to 37 degrees and the situation was under control. We'll keep checking her throughout the night and see what tomorrow brings!

Friday 11th January

We checked Mel's temperature a couple of times throughout the night and both times it was below the "worry" level. We rang the hospital just after 9am. They told us they'd ring us back after the doctor had done his ward round. They called back at about half past ten. Remember I said yesterday about the "there not being a bed is not an option".... apparently, it was. There wasn't a bed available today for Mel to have her treatment but they wanted us to go over to have Mel's blood checked and so they could check her over after last night's rise in temperature. So, at 11am we set off and drove through the pouring rain to Nottingham City Hospital.

We waited for about fifteen minutes in the reception before going into the main area to have blood taken. Whilst they sorted Mel out we mentioned to the nurse the advice from the Ward the previous evening about giving Mel paracetemol when we called about her temperature rise. The nurse was not happy. They should not have told us to give her paracetemol and they should have told us to come into the hospital. Apparently, the reason she shouldn't have paracetamol is due to her blood counts and that it can affect the results. The nurse immediately told the sister and the ward was told in no uncertain terms that it wasn't to happen again. To be fair Julie was worried about it, I just thought, well, they're the doctors, they should know! Next time we'll know to challenge them if they say anything.

After all that the Stem Cell Nurse came to see us to explain what the plans were for Mel over the next week or so. It turns out Mel is a bit of a guinea pig! In terms of her current chemo they can afford to leave it a couple of days, but certainly no longer, so there will be a bed available for her on Monday. In terms of the stem cell transplant they have to wait until the counts are up to a certain level. Normally, through previous cases, they can roughly anticipate when this will be, but collecting Stem Cells whilst using GEM P hasn't been done at Nottingham before so Dr. Haynes has been busily trying to find out at which point (roughly) they can expect to be taken. He rang the Royal Marsden in London for clues but couldn't get an answer. It later transpired that it was on the afternoon of the big fire there. They've also tried other hospitals to see if they have any ideas as to when the cells can be harvested, but they've drawn a blank so it's a case of suck it and see. It means that we will be making the seventy mile round trip to the hospital at least a couple of times next week, probably more.

Today Mel received a cheque from the MacMillan Cancer Care Fund. It is to help with expenses and a welcome addition to the finances. As I said last week, it says so much about this country when you have to rely on charity for financial support. The government financial support is nowhere to be seen! Thank you MacMillan (www.macmillan.org.uk) .

Saturday 12th January

No more scares overnight as the temperature returned to normal, we watched TV until midnight before going to bed. Mel couldn't sleep and sat up on her computer until about 2am. She was setting up her own blog on the internet, like me, she's found it helps to write things down.

Melissa's friend, Hammad came to see her today and it lifted her spirits so much. He stopped till mid afternoon and like all her uni friends, Mel enjoyed his company. Some of Mel's friends from Uni are signing up for the Bone Marrow Register, as is Becky. So, although Becky isn't a match for Mel, there may be someone else out there that can be helped. Mel's condition continues to be bright and these are moments to enjoy. We know that before things are put right, they may get worse, so it is important that times like this are made the most of.

So, for the time being, we're enjoying the happy bits, and at the same time we're getting her on her feet and making her do important tasks . . . . Like making tea!

Sunday 13th January

There's not a great deal to report today. I got up at eight, woke Becky up, loaded up the car and took her back to University. Becky and I chatted on the way up there about Mel, we both agreed that she's certainly feeling a lot better. That's the thing with this current treatment, there are definite signs of improvement in her, but all we can say at the moment is that she's feeling better, rather than getting better. The fact she is feeling better means the chemo is doing something, hopefully enough to stabilise things so the stem cells can be taken. I'm feeling positive at the moment. My optimism does take a battering at times, particularly with so much having not gone to plan over the last five months, but I'm confident we're taking the first steps to sorting her out.

CHAPTER EIGHTEEN
DVD's, PSP's, ECG's, PET's and MP's

Monday 14th January

At half past eight this morning I was sat in the office of Janet Dean, my MP. We were discussing the lack of financial support, for students in particular, when they are faced with a life threatening/long term illness. Janet Dean agreed that the situation was disgraceful. The upshot of the meeting was that she is arranging for myself and her to meet with James Plaskitt, the MP responsible for Work and Pensions. That meeting should occur in the next three to four weeks. Although it seems a long time, I'm not that bothered. As I explained to Janet Dean, it's no longer about Melissa, it's about the principle and making sure that other families do not have to endure what we have.

Whilst I had been meeting my MP, Julie had rung the hospital to check on the bed situation. Mel wasn't too good this morning, she had the headache that has plagued her since yesterday afternoon, but more worrying, she was starting to cough again. It was over 72 hours since she should have had the treatment and after such a positive couple of weeks we were concerned that the symptoms of Mel's lymphoma were returning. I mentioned the coughing and other signs were also there, not as prevalent as before the treatment, but they were returning all the same. I knew it, Julie knew it, and so did Mel.

Julie spoke to Faith and explained the situation. We received a call back to say a bed would definitely be made available and we should hear something around lunchtime. All the waiting isn't good for Mel and we are now left wondering if not having the treatment on Friday has caused this worsening in her condition.

Lunchtime came and went. Finally, after having enough of waiting and also getting concerned about the time it was taking I rang Faith again. She went to speak to the Ward and came back and told me there was a bed available and that we should set off immediately. We arrived at Nottingham just after four o'clock and so continued the waiting game. We were eventually seen by one of the senior sisters at about seven o'clock, three hours after we'd got there. After answering a ton of questions we were told that due to Mel's high heart rate they would need to do an ECG. She explained the doctor would be along shortly to examine Mel and to sign the prescription for the anti-sickness drug she needed to be taken with the chemo. Nine o'clock came and went and there was no sign of the doctor. I went looking for him. He arrived fifteen minutes later and asked more questions, many that had been asked previously (why do they do that I wonder?) and then went off to prescribe the drugs. At this point, Julie and I left the hospital... it was quarter to ten. We arrived home at eleven and flopped. I texted Mel to see how she was and she texted back to say they'd just started the final part of the chemo.

Today was a long day and one that has drained us both. We should be used to setbacks, but after the improvement of recent weeks, this is harder to take. Tomorrow promises to be another long day at the hospital....

Tuesday 15th January

I had a few texts from Mel throughout the night, requesting pyjamas, chocolate fingers and of course cheese. I also took her a couple of DVDs and the PSP. Becky bought us a big "Squishi" cushion from Durham at the weekend and that went with us too. I don't know what it is about this hospital, but they've invested in wooden seats. They look very modern and state of the art, but a couple of hours on one of them and you've no feeling left in your buttocks.

I woke up this morning with a blinding headache. If this is the sort of headache Mel is experiencing then God knows how she copes with it. We arrived at the hospital just after quarter to eleven. We were visited by Mel's consultant Dr. Haynes, he was accompanied by Faith and another female doctor who we'd not seen before. He asked about Mel's general condition and she told him about the return of the symptoms and how she was feeling in general. He then explained about the possible outcomes of the latest treatment. . . .

1. The treatment works brilliantly and the tumour has been reduced to such an extent that stem cells can be taken, a stem cell transplant performed and ultimately a bone marrow transplant can be done once a donor is found.

2. The treatment works partially. With the scenario there are two different possibilities. Firstly, it could be that the tumour has been reduced sufficiently to collect stem cells and this will be done in order to stabilise the tumour via a stem cell transplant, until a donor is found. The other possibility is that the tumour was reduced but has grown back too quickly and stem cells cannot be taken. If this were the case then Mel would have a treatment called Mini Beam, which on a power scale of one to ten registers at about nine and a half, but doesn't damage the bone marrow to the point where a stem cell transplant is needed. The aim of this is again to stabilise in readiness for a bone marrow transplant.

3. The treatment has had no effect at all. If this were the case then the doctor stated today he would move towards radiotherapy. Again this would be to try and stabilise until the bone marrow transplant can be done. They are reluctant to use radiotherapy in someone of Melissa's age due to the possibility of cancers returning in later years. However, as the doctor explained if this was the road they were forced to go take, their priority is getting her right now and letting the future take care of itself.

The consultant did say that option one was highly unlikely and he'd hope that option three could be ruled out too. They also talked of another round of GEM P if this current one has done some damage to the tumour.

We spent the day in the side room with Mel, we watched Green Street and High School Musical (two films so far apart its untrue). It helped pass the time as the fluids were fed through her Hickman Line. After the final drop had left the drip and she'd been given her supply of tablets we left the ward . . . it was 9:47pm. The drive home wasn't the best as some roads were partially flooded and the rain was pouring down.

Our next planned trip to Nottingham is on Friday for a blood count, line dressing, flush and also an x-ray. Dr. Haynes said today that Mel should have one done. It's one of those things that you want to know about, but only if it's good news! Mel went to bed, so glad to be in a big bed, with no strange hospital noises and best of all.... waking up in the morning to a day of mum's care and dad's cooking!

Wednesday 16th January

We got up at half past nine, sorted out Mel's breakfast and tablets and then went into town. Whilst Julie was in town (secretly getting my birthday present . . ha ha .... they think I don't know!), I called into work to see colleagues and update them. Whilst in the office talking to colleagues my mobile rang, it was Mel. The hospital had been in touch to say that her red cell count was low. It was registering seven whilst the norm is fourteen. The upshot being that at 9am on Thursday morning, they need her back in Nottingham City Hospital to do a blood transfusion. We'll be there about six hours.

With Mel's blood count being low, it could also explain how she was feeling at the weekend. We thought it was the symptoms returning, but maybe, it wasn't that. It's feasible it could be the low blood count combined also with the anxiety of going to hospital. Again, time will tell and maybe the x ray will confirm or deny our thoughts and theories. It's just another example of how this illness plays with your mind and emotions.

Thursday 17th January

We split ourselves in two today. Julie stopped with Mel at the hospital whilst I returned home after dropping them off to sort out the new car. We arranged to pick it up today due to us thinking we hadn't got to take Mel to the hospital, but plans have a habit of changing. We set off for our thirty two mile trip to Nottingham at 8am and got there about ten to ten. The traffic was horrendous.

Mel's day had been spent giving and receiving blood, though it's fair to say she received a lot more than she gave. She also had the x-ray taken of the tumour but we don't know any results. Her line was flushed and cleaned and her "G" injection given. She took her laptop computer with her today and though she didn't have an internet connection, it did help to pass a lot of the time. Mel also talked to Julie about the possibilities of the treatment not working and she said that if that was the case then she would just have to accept it and make the most of things.. She was adamant she did not want to become depressed and wanted to enjoy whatever time she had left. It's another example of how amazing our daughter is.

Whilst at the hospital, Julie struck up a conversation with a lady from Cambridge whose husband had lymphoma in his abdomen. He was in his late forties. He'd had R CHOP that had worked for so long (like Melissa) and then another course of chemo that again did nothing, but instead of trying something different, they gave up on him and just offered palliative care. They gave him some valium and eight weeks to live. His wife defied their prognosis and scoured the country for a hospital that would give him a fighting chance and they ended up at Nottingham. He needs a bone marrow transplant (Dr. Haynes told them if he'd got to him sooner he could probably have done a stem cell transplant) but his chances of cure are a lot better than if he'd stayed in the Fens. He's had mini-beam and is feeling better than he did when he came in. How terrible that where you live in the country determines your level of treatment!!

We heard from Becky this morning. She got a first in her essay at university, which is brilliant.

We don't have to go back now until Tuesday, so we have a few "hospital free" days.

Friday 18th January

We were sat at home last night when at 9:30 Mel suddenly started feeling unwell and dizzy. Her heart was racing and her hands were clammy. Her temperature was normal, but due to the pace of her heart we rang Nottingham to seek advice. They said they'd check with the doctor and call us back. No sooner had we put the phone down than Mel's condition deteriorated. She was having trouble breathing and we agreed the only option was to ring 999. Within five minutes an ambulance arrived.

A normal person's heart beats at between 80 – 100 per minute.. Due to Mel's Lymphoma hers normally beats around the 120 mark. The paramedics checked her and it was fluctuating between 170 and 280. They immediately decided to admit her. Julie went in the ambulance and I drove to A & E. We arrived there just after 20 past ten and were shown into a side room. We waited until the nurses had done tests and then were allowed to sit with her. The doctor tried to get her to blow into a syringe to lower her heart rate, which was now fluctuating between 155 - 190. It didn't work. They then decided to give her a drug which would reduce the rate, but with this came another problem. They couldn't use her Hickman Line through fear of infection, so she had to have a cannula fitted. With this news her heart rate reached 230. I tried to calm her down by rubbing her back and talking to her.

We reverted to the old plan when cannulas are fitted. She looks at me, I talk about something stupid, the doctor says "sharp scratch" and in it goes. It worked first time and despite the tears she was proud of herself. As she sat there with tears streaming down her face she looked across at me and said "I can't do this anymore, I don't know how much more I can take".... That is more heartbreaking than anything else. All we can say is to keep going and keep fighting. Of course, Mel knows this and she does, but at times I wonder how much more crap they can throw our way.

After having the canula fitted Mel was taken into resus to have the drug administered. The drug worked and her heart rate dropped to around 130. We were left alone for a while and when the A & E doctor returned some time later he said he wanted to keep Mel in overnight. Not the answer we wanted. Unfortunately, they had no beds on the wards so they put her in a side bay and let her rest. Julie and I settled her down and left the hospital at 3am. I hate leaving her on her own in hospital; it feels like I'm deserting her.

We got home, crashed out and I was awakened at 5am with a text from Mel saying her temperature was raised and they were going to do a chest x-ray. Julie and I got up at 7:30am and returned to the hospital by eight. We checked in on Mel and she was asleep so we went up to the Chemo unit to see her Burton consultants. We spoke to Debbie and Pat and explained the situation, Julie then went to see Mel whilst I phoned Faith at Nottingham to explain the night's events. Faith said they may possibly do an Echo on her heart as it's possible the rapid beat could be due to damage from previous chemo. For now though they didn't need to see her at Nottingham and she told us to enjoy the weekend!

Mel was a lot brighter and was busy telling us how she had to talk the nurse through using her Hickman Line during the night.

Dr. Ahmed & Dr. Zai, two of Mel's former consultants arrived on A & E and examined her and decided she could come home. Dr. Ahmed is brilliant, he's the sort of person who, when he enters the room, commands respect. He told Melissa and Julie to go home, relax and if she had to go back in over the weekend, tell whoever was in charge of A & E to ring him at home. . . . Whatever the time or day! Like I say, full respect! Mel had one more ECG and we came home. She had a bath, slept for a while and then devoured a cheese and potato pie!

Whilst she was sleeping I rang the DLA people. We'd had another letter saying they were processing our claim and if there's any problem to ring them. No financial support since August..... I think that's a problem! When I rang previously I was told quite categorically that claims took eight weeks. After speaking to the DLA representatives today, I find it's changed to twelve weeks so we've to wait another month. . . although when I sighed heavily he did try to reassure me by saying it might not be twelve weeks, it could be only ten. They are priceless

The nannies visited in the afternoon and Mel made the best of efforts to be sociable but she was way too tired and went back to bed about four o'clock. Whilst she was here Julie's mum did our ironing. She irons to gold medal standard, not only is she fastest ironer I've ever seen, but she does it all properly too. She even irons flannels and underpants. Just after four o'clock I drove my mum home and on the way back I cried. I think it was emotion overload from the last forty eight hours.

Saturday 19th January
With all that happened on Thursday night/Friday I forgot to mention the new bed arrived yesterday. It's awesome and last night we had the best night's sleep we've had in ages. Of course that could be because we were knackered from the previous night and we'd have slept on anything, but I like to think the new bed played its part. Instead of lugging the mattress downstairs, all we had to do was move the coffee table and wheel the bed in from the conservatory.

Mel slept well last night and continued to alternate between rest and sleep all day. Carol and the girls popped round this afternoon and that brought Mel downstairs, but other than that she's been upstairs and following Dr. Ahmed's orders. She said she felt totally washed out and had no energy, but as I explained to her, Monday we were waiting for a phone call to go into hospital until we actually went in at four o'clock. That night she was attached to a drip all night so got little sleep. Tuesday was the same as we didn't get home till quarter to eleven. Thursday we got up at 7am, were at hospital until 6pm and then back in A & E from 10pm till the following morning. Julie and I are knackered so God only knows how tired Mel must be. All that and chemo too!

The worry of what happened on Thursday and of it happening again is on her mind. We've tried to reassure her. There's been no repeat of the fast heart rate since Thursday and I'm led more and more to believe it was a reaction to the blood transfusion.

I received a letter this morning from Janet Dean MP, it was a just a copy of the letter she'd sent to James Plaskitt at the Department of Work and Pensions to discuss us all meeting up. It's a sign things are moving.

It's my birthday today.

Sunday 20th January

It's been a quiet day as we all try to boost our energy levels after last week's turn of events. Mel has continued to recover and spent most of the day in bed.

Mel had a good night's sleep last night and when she woke for her tablets this morning she was telling me that she dreamt she had hair. Her hair it is growing back slightly and coming back a lot darker than it used to be. Whereas before Christmas her head looked like a badly shaved cat, it now looks like a dirty tennis ball.

Monday 21st January

We contacted the hospital at Nottingham first thing this morning and asked that someone talks to Mel in the morning and discuss last week's heart rate problems. Mel is scared about the events of last Thursday and just needs some reassurance. We all do.

This afternoon Mel and I sat down together and watched two episodes of The Bill. Football and The Bill are "our telly", we always watch them together. Today we were sat watching The Bill and they were doing a hospital scene and they were reading out a young girls sats.. When it came to heart rate, the girl's was 200..... Melissa piped up, "Bloody 'ell, my heart rate was 280, hers is only 200 and she's been shot in the neck!"

Tuesday 22nd January

This morning we woke up at 7am, left for Nottingham just after 8am and arrived at the City Hospital at about twenty past nine. We left there at six o'clock this evening! In between time we had the first bit of positive news in months. Mel had her blood taken and her white cell count was 22. The GCSF injections have done their job (Mel guessed as much as she has the accompanying aches and pains).

This meant they could take stem cells, so after a bit of waiting around she was hooked up to the machine and the stem cell harvest began. The aim was to collect around 2 million stem cells and they set about putting twelve litres of Mel's blood through the machine.

Whilst waiting for the blood results, we met up with Faith, the Lymphoma Clinical Nurse and discussed Mel's heart issues on Thursday. She had spoken with Mel's consultant, Dr. Haynes and they suggested she has a scan on Monday morning. This gets an all round picture of the heart and they'll be able to tell if the heart has been damaged (by the RCHOP Chemo).

The course of true treatment never runs smoothly and as usual there was a twist in the tale. As they began the harvest, Alison and Maxine, the two stem cell nurses soon realised that Mel's Hickman Line wasn't playing ball. She'd had blood taken out of it an hour or so earlier and it was fine, but when harvesting the stem cells it was painfully slow and rather than being hooked up for three to four hours, Mel would have been there for three to four days. Bearing in mind Mel's fear of needles, she showed incredible bravery by telling them to try through a needle in her arm. She explained to the nurses her fear of needles. The nurses were brilliant and said they'd try once and if it didn't work, they wouldn't try again. They put some numbing cream on her arm (something she'd not been offered before), tightened the tourniquet, warmed her arm with a heated blanket and decided the left arm was best to try. Maxine found the vein and the needle was put in place. Mel didn't feel a thing and the Stem Cell harvest began.

Normally the harvest is done over three to four hours . . . . Mel was hooked up for five and a half and the whole twelve litres was harvested. Whilst she was hooked up they provided her with a portable DVD player so as her blood wound its way through the machine and Mel's body she watched Pretty Woman.

At the end of the harvest the nurses explained that we should know tomorrow how many stem cells they'd collected and she will have to be hooked up again.

Wednesday 23rd January

At five o'clock this evening I was ready to swear, curse and condemn all who commit evil to eternal damnation and all manner of horrid things. I'd got it in for murderers, drug addicts, thieves, paedophiles, fraudsters, thugs, hoodies and chavs. I wanted to get in my car and drive it at a hundred miles an hour into a brick wall, not because I wanted to damage myself, but just to release some pent up anger. By half past five I was calm, my tears were of joy and I loved the world again.

After driving to Nottingham this morning Maxine and Alison had got the room ready and Mel settled down for four hours on the stem cell machine. Just before 11am we were given the news that yesterday's stem cell collection hadn't gone according to plan. They needed to collect two million cells. They collected just 500,000. Due to various counts, they were doubtful today's harvest would be any better and with this in mind, we were told it was unlikely a stem cell transplant could be done to keep the cancer at bay. Dr. Haynes had been informed. He decided to book Mel in for a PET scan. We all went quiet. How much more of this can we take?

The registrar came in to see Mel to write her prescription for the tablets she would need over the next few days and when she'd finished we took it up to the pharmacy which is the other side of the hospital. I handed over the prescription and got asked the usual question, "Do you pay for prescriptions?", "No" I replied.

An older lady then came over and said that as the prescription was on a green form, I'd have to pay for the items on there. I argued that we don't pay, we've never paid for Melissa's tablets that are prescribed by the Haematology day care unit, but she was adamant. "Green Form, you have to pay, now if it's re-written on a yellow form, then we don't charge you", It was on a green form last time and I didn't pay, but that didn't matter. I wanted to say to her, "My daughter has cancer, she's just been given some negative news, I've driven an hour and a half to get here this morning and I did the same yesterday morning and you're pissing about over the colour of a fucking form". . . . I wanted to say that, but I opted for, "ok, I'll go and get it changed." I returned to the Haematology department, told the Nursing Sister what had happened, she took the green form off me, wrote HAEM DCU on the top of it and handed it back to me. I went back to the other side of the building, handed in my form with HAEM DCU written on it, a different girl took it off me and half an hour later I returned to pick up Mel's tablets. I feel like a rebel, I got a prescription and didn't pay for it and what's more it was on a green form! Balls to your yellow forms I say!!!!!

They sent another 12 litres of Mel's blood spiralling through the machine she was unhooked, her line cleaned up and she dashed to the loo.

Our journey home was in silence. Mel was crying at one point, Julie and I felt like crying too. It's not fair. Why Mel? Why us? I was so angry. We get a break, a bit of good news and then it's snatched away. My faith is being severely tested at the moment.

We arrived home, Mel went to bed, and Julie and I discussed the day's news and tried to be positive. It gets harder. We keep getting battered, Mel especially. I left a message on Faith's answer phone to see if there was any news on the PET scan date.

As I was driving Julie to the hairdressers the phone rang. It was Alison, the stem cell nurse. Following this morning's harvest, coupled with yesterday's they'd managed to collect just over the required two million stem cells. Thank you God, you're back in my good books! They'd collected just over one and a half million today, so added to the half million yesterday, we'd hit the target. There's a long way to go, the transplant has to work. A donor for bone marrow has to be found and the transplant completed, but after months of bad news, something has finally gone our way.

We went in there with the hope they could collect two million stem cells and they did. In the war against Lymphoma, we've just won a battle, it maybe only a small one, but it's a win all the same and any victory is one to be enjoyed, no matter how small, just ask any Derby County fans!

Thursday 24th January

We received a call from Faith this morning to say that Mel's PET scan has been arranged for Tuesday at 12.30. Dr. Haynes said it gives us an option we thought wasn't open to us. It means we'll be at hospital on Monday and Tuesday next week. Our appointment with Dr. Haynes is the following week, when we'll know the results of the PET scan and what the next stage of the plan is. But for today, we're taking a break from Hospitals!

Mel relaxed today, obviously pleased with yesterday's news she is looking forward to Becky coming home this weekend. The only concern on the horizon is that Mel is starting to get a little out of breath. Obviously, in the past, the lymphoma has returned soon after treatment has ended. If it does return over the next few days then we'll phone the hospital to get some steroids to tide her over until we go and see the consultant.

Friday 25th January

Julie and I have said that when we have these eventful days at hospital, it takes a couple of days to recover. It drains you physically and emotionally. Julie worked out our finances this morning and thanks to MacMillan's (www.macmillan.org. uk) donation we should be ok until the end of March. There is no word from the DLA about Mel's claim. Still no financial support from our caring government since August 20th!

Mel's had a restful day. Her cough seems to be getting worse and she wondered whether the suffocating feeling is coming back. It will be interesting to see how her condition progresses over the weekend.

Mel received a lovely email from her friend Vince yesterday and today she received another email out of the blue that brightened her day. It was from Dan Robinson, a goalkeeper who played for Burton Albion for four years at the time I was their photographer. He now lives in New Zealand and plays his football there and he sent Mel a message of support. I think it must win the award for "The message that's travelled the furthest distance" and Mel can lay claim to having had messages of support from all over the world!

Saturday 26th January

When we last saw Dr. Haynes he stated at one point in the conversation that he would be interested to see how long the tumour takes to start growing again after the GEM P chemotherapy had finished. We can tell him. Less than two weeks. Mel had been sweating in the night. The suffocating feeling she gets with her lymphoma was back and most obvious of all, the coughing returned. By yesterday evening she was in discomfort and it was plain to her and us, the tumour has started to grow again.

Mel wrote on her Facebook status last night that she was scared. We all are.

It's horrible to watch and I know I've said it a thousand times before, but she doesn't deserve this. I woke up several times in the night and I could hear her coughing and all we can do is go upstairs and see her, to see if there's anything we can do, but nine times out of ten there's nothing. We just have to sit and listen.

147

I received a letter from James Plaskitt via my MP today which basically said that Mel had to either use her student loan or give up university. They're all heart.

Good old Mr. Plaskitt should have been here all morning to listen to Mel coughing, he should have been in the room when she was in distress because the symptoms of Lymphoma were returning. At one o'clock I rang the hospital at Nottingham to see if they could prescribe some steroids for Mel to take away the symptoms that are causing her pain. An hour later they returned the call. They wanted Mel to go over to Nottingham so they could check her out.

We drove over to Nottingham and were seen by Dr. Sandor whom Mel knows from the Day Care Centre. She examined her, and told her she didn't think she'd need to stop in, but she just wanted to speak with the on-call consultant, Dr. MacMillan. When she returned she told us that they wanted Mel to stop in overnight and have a CT scan as they were concerned about her worsening condition.

Becky and I drove back to Burton to pick up some things for her, DVD player, DVD's and a few other essentials to try and make life in there as pleasant as possible. Mel had a cannula put in and her CT scan done whilst we were away. Doctor Sandor returned and ushered us into a side room. She explained that they'd compared the CT scan with the PET scan from October and the tumour has grown again. She went on to say that they intended to give Mel some steroids and they would be keeping her in until at least Tuesday. The Echogram would go ahead as planned on Monday.

It wasn't the news we wanted to hear. Yet again Mel was taking an emotional and physical battering. We went back to the ward and sat with her. The tears flowed and for once we all joined in. Mel cried as she said, "Why me." "I can't take much more" Heartbreaking isn't the word. I've never experienced anything more distressing than sitting watching her cry in pain. She was hurting so much and so were we. We finally dragged ourselves away from the hospital at quarter to ten and drove home wondering what will happen next. Becky has decided to put off going back to Uni tomorrow as she wants to be with us when we meet with Dr. Haynes. It's going to be another week of emotions.

Sunday 27th January

We arrived at the hospital just after nine o'clock and immediately could see an improvement in Mel's condition. The steroids had well and truly kicked in, she was chatty, the breathing was considerably better and the suffocating feeling had gone. The consultant, Dr. MacMillan, came mid morning and explained that he would discuss the weekend's events with Dr. Haynes on Monday morning, but he thought they would continue with the plan of High Dose Chemo and Stem Cell transplant. No start date was given, but we think it will be soon. The steroids (20 at a time) can only be given for four days, so after that they will need to do something pretty quickly to try and null the growth of the tumour. The PET scan has been cancelled for Tuesday as there is no need for it. The CT scan gave them all the information they need.

In the afternoon I put Mel in a wheelchair and took her a tour of the hospital, stopping at the vending machine to buy her some Maltesers. I discovered a great game to play with Mel in the wheelchair. In the hospital there are two sets of green tiles that run across the width of the corridor. The two lines are about ten yards apart and the object is to push Mel from one line to the other with at least one set of wheels landing on the green tiles. I came close twice although the first time she leant to the left and nearly ended up in the vending machine. It was great fun and although Mel was cursing us at one point, I know she enjoyed it and it's definitely a game for the future!

We left the hospital at twenty past nine this evening, 12 hours after we'd arrived. It was another long day, but Mel needs us and we need to be with her.

Monday 28th January

Today was horrible. As the day wore on Mel became more and more subdued and it culminated in an outpouring of tears around eight o'clock this evening.

We were visited by Faith this afternoon and she confirmed they are going down the radiotherapy route. Due to the tumour growing at such a fast rate, they feel the best option is to give her radiotherapy to try and reduce the size of the tumour before they go ahead with the stem cell transplant. The long term aim is of course to cure via Bone Marrow, but they hope they'll be able to keep the tumour at bay whilst a bone marrow donor is found.

As I mentioned before, Mel was very down and there was little conversation throughout the day. This morning she went for an Echocardiogram which was ordered following her heart rate problems last week. The results were ok. Her Hickman Line gave up the ghost today too. Our plan was to leave earlier today to give us more time at home, but as we sat watching TV Mel became upset and through her tears told us how she was fed up with there being no good news, fed up that all she had to look forward to was day after day in hospital, she was fed up of needles, of tablets, of cannulas, of her Hickman Line not working. She was fed up of not being able to breathe properly. She can't remember what it's like to breathe properly. Can you imagine that? Who can blame her for feeling so low? Part of her outburst of emotion was steroid related. The nature of that tablet beast is that when you're high you're very high, but when you're low you are at rock bottom.

With so much bad news over the last five months, she says it is hard to see anything actually working. I can't argue with her. How can we tell her to be positive when week after week the news is bad? I can't give her guarantees. I can't say the next lot of treatment will work better than the last. If I did she would know I was lying. The evening ended with me holding her hand and telling her to keep going, however hard it may seem, because by the law of averages we're due a break and I'd rather get that break at the end of the journey and it be the cure than at the beginning and then things go wrong afterwards. It's so hard for us to be positive, but we keep going. We're all tired.

Mel has friends visiting on Wednesday and Thursday and possibly the Nannies on Friday. A few familiar faces will help. Tomorrow she has her PET scan; they've decided that with the Radiotherapy treatment going ahead the PET Scan will give them an idea of where to target the cancer.

We realised this afternoon that the last meal we had was at midday on Saturday.

Tuesday 29th January

I'm knackered, probably the most tired I've felt since August.   Last night I slept for about four hours. I was tired when I left the hospital, even tired when I sat on the bed, but as a million thoughts swam around my head I couldn't sleep so I sat watching TV until the early hours.   I feel down today, lack of energy, unhealthy and generally just shitty.

We arrived at the hospital and had only been there a few minutes when Dr. MacMillan entered the room. He told us the outcome of this morning's PET scan will determine which route they go down.   Radiotherapy or Chemotherapy.   There is a chance that the tumour has covered the lung and if that's the case then they won't go for Radiotherapy as it will be too dangerous. She will need her lungs in as good a working order as possible for the bone marrow treatment, should they get to that stage.   The alternative is High Dose Chemotherapy followed by the Stem Cell transplant and at least three weeks in hospital.

Mel ate two ham cobs, a bag of cheese and onion crisps, and had a box of Maltesers and a Double Decker on the side ready to finish off. Oh, and a yogurt and a packet of chocolate biscuits too. As you can see, her steroid induced appetite is alive and kicking.   The rest of the day was spent idling round the room, I managed to grab ten minutes sleep on the floor behind Mel's bed. Mel was chatty this evening and talked about how she'd love to come home, if only for a few days between treatments, just to be able to watch some football and have a good session on the internet. She was calm this evening and spoke of messages and planned visits from friends. Her cheeks were red, her breathing slightly laboured, but she was a lot better than of late. Her "belly injection" was done by a student nurse, watched by Kaz, a very chirpy male nurse who is as happy and cheerful at the end of his shift as he is at the beginning; the needle was inserted and after a few minutes the pain subsided and Mel went back to drinking her tea.

When we arrived home this evening just after nine o'clock there was a letter from one of the senior people where I work. It basically said not to worry about work, concentrate on supporting the family and how they all hoped Melissa got well. The support from work does mean a lot and helps us through these tough times.

Wednesday 30th January

I have managed to sort out the Internet for Mel on her laptop. I went into The Carphone Warehouse and they gave us a good deal on a dongle. It basically means that Mel has three hours a day online to keep up with her Facebook, chat to friends on the Lifesite and talk to people on MSN. As well as that, she can keep up to date with the footy. If nothing else, it will help to relieve the boredom.

Mel had more steroids today, but that's it for now. Her friend from university, Gemma, visited. Messages and visits help her spirits no end.

The only major concern is that her Hickman Line has stopped working. They're trying to get blood out of it everyday but it's not playing. They may even have to take the current one out and insert a new one.

The doctors and nurses here at Nottingham have been fantastic. I've said it before, from day one back in August we have few complaints about the service and the treatment.

We've only had cause to complain about one nurse, and that was back in Burton, and it wasn't her nursing skills that were in question, just her people skills. Also, one of the staff at Derby blew hot and cold, but contact with her was minimal so it didn't cause a problem. Here in Nottingham, they've been superb and Mel is confident with them. Today she's being looked after by a student nurse, who is keen to please and tries very hard, but she doesn't have to, she's a natural. She is being tutored by Kaz, the nurse I mentioned yesterday, whose personality could switch on the lights in a dark room. They all have their own ways, but all are professional and caring and do a fantastic job. The only problem is, there aren't enough of them. But that's a slight on the Government and not on the hospital.

Tomorrow, we should see Dr. Haynes and things should start to happen. I always start to get nervous when we're due a meeting with the consultant. I don't think that they will be able to leave Mel without treatment for too long as the symptoms return so fast they can't afford to delay.

Becky went back to University today.

There's no word on Disablement Living Allowance. We did receive a letter from the Incapacity Benefit people. The good news is that Mel will get £63.41p a month . . . . The not so good news is that she has to wait until March 3rd to receive it!

THROUGH MELISSA'S EYES (Part Seven)

"Well i am still in hospital but due to dad buying me a cool wireless internet gadget i can get internet for hours a day, like proper internet i mean on my laptop so will prob use it in the evenings and maybe mornings.

Well its pretty crappy in here, mainly due to boredom but you all know the medical stuff. Wont know any more till tomorrow when we see Dr. Haynes. Its either gonna be radiotherapy then stem cell transplant or just stright to stem cell transplant. Either way i doubt ill be coming home anytime soon so dont expect too much!

Apart from that i dont have much to say today. Thanks for all the messages, i'm reading them all even though i cant reply to them all. I can also get on msn but im limited in energy and stuff so i may not go on too much.

Thats about it for now, i may update my blog as well on blogspot so feel free to read. Link is in posted items and as my listed website. Hope you are all ok.

Mel xx"

Thursday 31st January

We arrived at the hospital at quarter to eleven and had missed Dr. Haynes by a matter of minutes. As we walked through the door into the ward we were spoken to by Faith. The news wasn't good. The results of the PET scan showed that Mel's lymphoma has spread and is now under her heart and in parts of her abdomen. It has also made an appearance in the left side of her chest whereas previously it was confined to the right. They cannot do the radiotherapy treatment as the cancer has spread and they are trying to go down the BEAM route. With this treatment though they are not using the 'B and 'A part of the chemo, just the 'E' and the 'M, so is a modified BEAM.'. On a scale of 1 to 10 it is about an 8 and a half. The doctor isn't confident of it working, but as Mel is young and options are running low, he says it is worth a try. Following this treatment Mel will have the stem cell transplant and will be in hospital for about three weeks.

I mentioned yesterday that Mel's Hickman Line had stopped working. In order to give her the chemo, this has to work, so they've decided to take the current line out and insert a new one. Mel said at dinner time she didn't want to lose her line as she'd grown attached to it!

Yesterday I got the impression that there was bad news ahead. I've always considered myself a good judge of character and characteristics. When the nurse on the ward told us that Dr. Haynes was coming to "talk" to us, as opposed to "see" us, I suspected all was not well. About ten minutes after we'd been spoken to by Faith, Becky rang and I explained to her the news we'd had. I hate to have to keep on giving her bad news all the time. Becky was upset. Julie spoke to Becky this afternoon and Becky is stopping at University until next week. I'm glad, because the next week will concentrate on the treatment side of things and there would be little or nothing for her to do here. Ultimately though the choice is hers and if she does decide to come home, we'd understand.

Last night we checked our finances and we have spent more than we normally would. It is a bit of a worry, the main problem being petrol. We are hoping to get another grant from the Macmillan Fund (www.macmillan.org.uk) to help us along. At present we're filling up the tank, on average, every four days and it's £45 a fill up. Normally we budget £50 for the whole month.

The help from the Government is conspicuous by its absence! We did speak to the DLA people this morning; they left a message on our answerphone yesterday requiring more information. We called them back but the person we needed to speak to wasn't there so we have to ring back tomorrow. Apparently they are close to a decision. About bloody time!

This afternoon, Dr. Haynes came to see us all and went over what he'd explained to Melissa this morning. We sat there in silence taking it all in. As suspected, in terms of a cure, this is it. Either today or tomorrow she'll have her new Hickman Line fitted, and then they'll be straight onto the chemotherapy. The consultant explained that there are three possible outcomes. Firstly, the treatment works and it gives a durable response and a donor can be found and the bone marrow treatment goes ahead as planned. However, he did say that as the tumour had been resistant to previous chemo treatment, the likelihood of this working wasn't high. The second option is that the treatment works better, maybe it holds off for four to six weeks and then returns. Thirdly, we get the same response as before. What was a 20 - 30% chance of cure is now lower, but we keep battling on. We've stopped being positive, positivity has been replaced with realism. Dr. Haynes explained that they'd explored every avenue available and he'd even been talking to Switzerland this morning enquiring about new drugs. There isn't anything at the moment though that would benefit Mel in any way. We have to keep being strong.

I sat with Mel this afternoon and she talked openly about things, we chatted about the treatment not working. She talked about how she's dealing with the illness and said that reading other people's stories often helped. She said that if the next lot of treatment didn't work and we moved on to palliative care we would face that when we came to it. We both agreed that it's easy to say it, but doing it may not be so easy. She's worried about her friends and upsetting them with the latest news. Her main concern this evening was that I spoke with her friend Claire because she was worried how she'd react.

Mel was concerned about her own reaction to the news, she hadn't cried. She wanted to, but was somehow stopping herself. She wondered if the steroids were affecting her mood. We were told this evening that Mel's new Hickman Line will be fitted tomorrow, probably in the morning and we imagine the chemo will start soon after. It's been a tough day, but we keep going and though we have no magic wand, we will be there for Melissa and Becky all the way, doing the best we can.

We left the hospital and drove home, making the usual calls to family, before visiting Julie's mum and telling her the latest awful news.

CHAPTER NINETEEN
The Stem Cell Transplant

Friday 1st February

Mel's old Hickman Line was taken out, and a new one inserted. The old one had ceased to work due to the tumour pressing on the line. They were concerned that if they put another in her chest, the same could happen, so after consultation with Dr. Haynes they opted for putting the new line in her groin, a femeral line. It sounds horrible, but is effective. More amazingly, Mel had this fitted without any sedation. They were going to give her some, but never got round to it. By the time they realised she'd had none, she just wanted them to get on with it.

Later in the afternoon, Mel had gone to the bathroom and whilst there she felt unwell. She became dizzy, her hands were clammy and she experienced excruciating pain in her back. Julie called for help and Mel was helped into her bed and the pain subsided. The ward doctor's diagnosis was that the lymphoma was pressing on a nerve and as Mel had been sitting all day, moving had caused the pain.

Earlier in the day, I had cried. Josh Groban's song "You're Still You" came on the radio and tears followed. I try to save them till I'm alone. I'm a dad, it's my job. I went to pick Julie's mum up and I drove her over to hospital. It certainly did her good to see Mel and we all chatted for a couple of hours before making the drive home. During the day I'd driven over 150 miles.

Saturday 2nd February

Just before midnight last night I received a text from Mel. Her back pain had returned and she was waiting for the nurses/

doctors to prescribe Oramorph to relieve things. Concerned for her, I sent a text saying "Let me know when they bring the drugs." I suddenly thought about what I'd written and so added "Shit, if the police intercept this text I'll be sharing a cell with Kevin Webster." I got a "lol" reply and that text coupled with a couple of others kept the moment light hearted until the aforementioned "drugs" arrived. We texted our goodnights and went to sleep.

Mel is currently taking Oramorph, a strong oral painkiller. Prior to texting me, Mel had been looked after by Kaz, whom myself and Becky refer to as "Sunshine, Lollipops and Rainbows" because of his cheery, disposition. He told Mel's appointed nurse Jenny that he was her favourite, of course, Mel couldn't possibly comment. He put her back pain etc down to internet overload. They're only jealous because Mel has internet and they don't!! The banter with the nurses helps Mel and again is another example of the brilliant care that we are receiving at Nottingham.

When we arrived this morning Mel was asleep. She woke up and was in pain with her back. Julie went to see Mel's nurse and asked to see the doctor. The chemotherapy won't be starting until Monday, so she needs something to ward off the pain until then. The tumour grows so fast that by Monday her breathing would be awful and the pain would increase. I disappeared back to Burton to pick my mum up and whilst I was away the doctor came and took up Julie's suggestion that Mel be prescribed a smaller dose of steroids to ease the symptoms. Julie thinks she's got all the credentials now to be an extra on Holby City. She loves using the word tachycardia and tries to include it in her conversation on a daily basis. As for me, I struggle constantly to remember what day it is. I am also finding that there are so many things buzzing around in my head that I lose my train of thought easily. I can be talking about something and all of a sudden I completely forget what I'm talking about. Mel would call it chemo brain.

Mel's new line was used for the first time today and it worked! Result!

The rest of my day was spent driving between Nottingham and Burton, firstly to fetch my mother for a visit and then later this afternoon I took her back and came back to Nottingham with Carol, Julie's sister. Mel was tired this afternoon but made the effort to talk to us all. All my mum could say on the way home was "amazing". She was talking about the way Mel was dealing with everything and I can't argue with that. When Carol and I arrived back at hospital, Mel was asleep, but she gradually woke up and was chatty for the rest of the evening.

The change in Mel's condition since Thursday shows how quickly this cancer takes hold. On Thursday she was walking up the corridor and getting to the toilet under her own steam. Today, she struggles to get out of bed due to severe back pain and she needs a wheelchair to get to the toilet. She's trying to go on the commode by her bed, but she can't pee with people listening, she needs to have solitudal pees. Julie is the toilet lady and accompanies Mel when nature calls. The latest problem we have to think about is how to bath Mel without getting her Hickman Line wet when she comes home. I suggested tucking her line inside a pair of rubber pants. They dismissed this idea as being silly. I thought it was inventive and showed initiative. The other suggestion was a chair that Mel could sit in, in the bath and she could bathe and keep her line out of the water.

Today we received news from the Disability Living Allowance people; Mel has finally been awarded DLA. It's not a great amount, but it's something. We're thankful for the money; our criticism is that it takes too long to process. Mel was diagnosed on August 20th. She shouldn't have to wait until 2nd February to get some financial support.

As the evening wore on, her back pain eased. As we left the hospital this evening I saw Hannah and Kaz, two of the nurses who looked after Mel last night and I thanked them for their help and kindness the previous evening. They do a fantastic job and deserve all our thanks.

Sunday 3rd February

I woke up this morning, checked my phone and there was a message from Mel. I'm not sure what time she texted me, but I must have fallen asleep as soon as I went to bed. Mel was telling me she'd watched Match of the Day and wanted us to bring a book and some tissues into hospital in the morning. She ended the text by apologising if she'd woken me and said Nite.

We arrived at the hospital at about half eleven and when we went on to the ward Mel was talking to Becky on the phone. It was good to hear Mel and Bex chatting as I know it helps Becky when she's away. Mel was talkative today; the back pain had subsided with a combination of painkillers and steroids. The nausea had gone too. She polished off her dinner of Roast Beef, Mash Potatoes, Roast Potatoes and veg and then an hour later had a couple of ham cobs, some mini sausages and of course, the customary slices of cheese.. She sits on her bed and from left to right there is a box of Maltesers, some hand cream and headphones, a box of tissues, Apple & Pear squash, two ham cobs, four slices of cheese, four mini party sausages, some cheese and onion crisps and a packet of McVities Chocolate Biscuits. Don't you just love Steroids!

Her hair is growing back. Mel's friends visited in the afternoon and before they came she got changed into her England shirt. She talked about an inspiring story she'd read the previous evening of a couple of young children who had a form of cancer. One has since passed away, but despite the sadness of the story Mel spoke of how she found positivity from the sadness. The couple had made the most of the time they had remaining and if Mel's journey should teach us anything, whatever the outcome of her illness, it should be that you make the most of every single day. It makes you realise what is important.

People keep asking Julie and I, how we're coping with it all. We just do. Anyone would in our situation.. Sometimes it's easy, other times not so but we love both our girls and we'd do anything we could for them. I wish I could do more. The alternative is to run away and we couldn't do that. Like I keep saying, we get through the bad days, enjoy the good days and live one day at a time.

Mel phoned her friend Rachel this evening and explained everything to her. Rachel always says she doesn't believe the blog even though Mel writes it. She has to hear Mel say what's happening for it all to sink in. It is important to have friends to talk to. Sometimes to talk at, they don't have to say anything, just listen.

Tomorrow, the chemo starts and who knows how Mel will react to it, but for now she's eating well, talking and looking a lot better than she did yesterday. This evening she plans to check out her nurses on Facebook . . . but don't tell them :).

THROUGH MELISSA'S EYES (Part Eight)

"Hey everyone

Well a pretty uneventful day really in terms of medical stuff. Woke up at 6am to the usual obs; blood pressure, sats and temperature and also had bloods taken, through my new line I might add lol! All in working order. Then I dozed for a bit, surfed the internet via my phone and spoke to Becky on the phone just after elevenish. It was good talking to Bex and she seems good at the moment, apart from a nose bleed! Thats me and Bex last Sunday when I first came into hospital (Mel was referring to a photograph). *We watched the FA cup game in the Day Room!*

Mum and dad arrived then and I had a rather nice - by - hospital - standards beef roast dinner which I ate all of! Steroids eh! The on-call doctor was pleased with me and was glad to see the steroids had had an easing effect. The nurse I had today was nice enough again, a male guy I haven't had before, not very chatty but then to be honest I haven't really needed anything doing today!

161

I can't stop itching though which is annoying! It's a symptom of the lymphoma but it's just so irritating! Itchy arms and legs and back! The weirdness of this disease is just bizarre! Stitches and wounds from both lines are all itching too which is a good sign as it shows they must be healing up. My back pain has been kept at bay today, slight twinges but nothing significant and I've not had painkillers since 7am which is a record in the last 2 days! I was on them every hour! The steroids have eased my breathing and although I'm still pretty much bedridden I can climb out of bed easier and be wheeled to the toilet at least! I'm still on and off oxygen to ease things and I can still feel swelling in my face but it's nowhere near as bad as I felt yesterday and the day before. My leg is less sore from the line as well which is helping movement.

Then this afternoon I had some friends from uni visit, thanks to Bex, Mark, Andy, Nat Sarah and Steph who all came, I really appreciated it and I liked the chocolates, cake and juice!! So thanks again, it really does help seeing familiar faces and I can't say enough how much I enjoyed seeing you all there! And for making the effort to come! It really does show how great everyone at Aston has been throughout all of this. Please feel free to visit again whenever, I can't stress enough how much I enjoy seeing people.

I spoke to Rachel on the phone after that for about an hour or so and it was great to catch up, even if the news isn't the greatest to tell I find it better being open and honest with people and I think it was good for us to talk about it all and what happens now. It's better to be realistic as hard as it may be to face. I think I'm coping ok with everything at the moment which is maybe helping everyone else, I dunno if that sounds bigheaded! But I mean like I'm not shutting myself away into a depression and I'm being quite hopeful and taking each day at a time and not focusing too much on the what ifs and the future so it makes it easier to be normal and focus on getting through each day. I'm being realistic but I still have to have the hope that the unrealistic will happen if that makes sense! Maybe my tumour will suddenly decide to respond for the amount of time I need, u never know! But at the same time I have to be realistic so I'm not let down dramatically if it does go wrong again. Its about balance. And maybe if I'm like that and get that right it helps other people deal with it a bit more easily as well, I dunno if I'm explaining this very well! Lol. Anyway the gist of that was it was good to chat to Rachel! And I missed the weekend in Reading but I was there in spirit guys!! It sounds like you had a good time anyways so that's cool!

After that mum and dad came back, I spoke to nan on the phone. I can tell a change in nan now, I can't put my finger on it but she seems to finally be living in the real world with this illness and realising how serious it is and I think it worries her (well obviously) but she is still treating me normally and is still hopeful which is good and is what I need but I can tell she is beginning to accept the truth and everything now which is good also I think. The problem is she doesn't have anyone at home now to talk too now my granddad is gone so it's harder for her to get constant reassurance and I think she needs that from us more now. But I spoke to her and I think she appreciates it and was glad to hear that I was doing better today.

After tea I watched dancing on ice which I don't think is as good as in previous years actually but its something to keep an eye on! I think Suzanne, Gareth Gates and Chris from Hollyoaks are the best and that girl who used to be in Coronation Street too isn't bad. Glad Aggie went though, she was really crap to be fair!

I also phoned Hammad tonight as I had promised to today as he got back from skiing and obviously had only just found out the weeks events! We concluded in future when he leaves the country or goes on holiday he should pre-warn the hospitals I'll *be in as something is bound to go wrong! But we chatted for a good hour, glad to hear skiing was good and obviously we chatted about what had happened this week. Bit of a shock to come back from holiday too but Hammad is always easy to chat too and says the right things so it was good again, like Rachel, to get everything out and be honest. Like he said I'm trying to keep things as normal as possible and keep the problems physical rather than letting them completely take over mentally and he seemed to think I was doing well with that so I'll take his word for it and as a compliment! One day at a time and not letting it take over in a depressive way is the way forward. Obviously I have my sad moments and my depressing moments but at the moment they are rare and I am actually quite surprised at myself at how I'm managing to deal. I keep expecting me to like have a moment where it all just hits me and I end up in tears but it just hasn't happened yet! I plan to just enjoy the days when I can do stuff and get through the days when I'm weaker. I'll make the most of what I can do each day. Reality will hit me soon enough and I'll have a down day I know I will but I'm ok at the min and trying to keep it that way! Steroids help!*

There is an organisation called the Willows Foundation and it's an organisation that arranges special days for young people with life threatening illnesses, so like they'll pay for you to go to a West End Show or something or a football game. Anyway I've decided to apply for a special day and I should qualify no problem as I match all the criteria. My original idea was to have a day at Anfield watching a league match there but I don't think that's gonna be realistic and with match days only being on certain days etc and the travelling required I just don't see it happening. Plus that is something I could pay for myself and organise in the future if it is possible.

So I have decided to apply for a social afternoon with my friends and family, say between 20-30 people, I would hire out a hall in

Burton (I have somewhere in mind) and there would be a meal and some catering put on and I would be able to invite family and friends and have a kind of mini party I guess! It's something I haven't been able to do, like go out and socialise properly with everyone together and it would be a chance for all my close friends from uni and home and my family as well to enjoy a day together and just generally have a good time. I wouldn't have it as an alcoholic thing, like I would have wine or something with dinner but the idea wouldn't be to come and get pissed as that's not what it would be about. Plus I can't drink and I'm selfish! I would apply for them to pay for the price of the hall, the food and the travelling expenses of anyone coming from far away such as people from uni, obviously I don't know how much money I'll get but it should cover most people's costs. It would be done at a weekend and I would give people plenty of notice. Obviously I can't invite everyone as much as I would love too but I'll sort that out nearer the time about who can/ couldn't come etc. But yeh that's my plan for that. I'm gonna send the form off in the next week or so. Hopefully it should all work out and it gives me something to look forward too as well!

Aside from that I've done nothing else today. Think Chemo should start tomorrow or Tuesday latest I would I think so I guess we'll find out everything in the next few days. I don't know much about the regime at all really in terms of how long I'm connected to the drip and stuff. I'll ask tomorrow. Guess I'm slightly nervous about it cos its strong stuff and I dunno how ill I'm gonna feel but to be honest as long as it starts to make my symptoms disappear I'll cope with the side effects cos I know they are temporary! Hate this whole not being able to breathe properly malarkey! My belly injections continue as well and they still sting but I think I'm getting used to it! The nurses all have different ways of giving them, some put them in slowly which hurts more, others like jab them in like a dart which sounds more painful but actually isn't!! Just had some lovely oramorph to ensure the back pain stays away overnight! Hate the stuff but it does the trick!

Messages and visits are still appreciated as are texts which I have had plenty of so thanks again! Watched Match of the Day tonight without knowing the scores, shocked by Villa score! That's the only thing I don't have here....sky sports! But I can cope without! I'm settled here now and realise this is home for the next 3-4 weeks and I know I couldn't be at home right now so that's fine! Anyway that's me done for tonight. I finish the evening as I started the day, with obs and a blood sugar test!

Night Night xxxxx"

Monday 4th February

Mel keeps itching a lot. When she itches, I say something stupid like, oh it must be the sheets or your pyjamas. It isn't. It's a symptom of the Lymphoma. Throughout this illness, Mel has known when she should be in hospital and when she should be at home. At the moment she knows she's in the right place. She told us yesterday that if they decided to postpone her treatment for a few days and offer her the chance to come home, she wouldn't because she feels and knows she's in the best place at the moment. When we arrived this morning, she was on oxygen and her face was slightly swollen, her appetite is good and she was chatty.

Nurses came and went during the morning; the consensus of opinion seemed to be that Mel would have her chemo later in the afternoon. Dr. Sandor arrived and told her that after checking her bloods, her counts were low so they were going to give her a transfusion. Mel's nurse for the day is Melissa, an American girl, accompanied by soon to be qualified Hannah. They brought Mel about eight or nine tablets. These were the pre-chemo drugs that help to control sickness and other side effects that may cause discomfort. She swallowed those and then Julie helped her get washed and changed.

Faith came to see us and brought Melissa a form for the Willows Foundation. This is an organisation that arranges "special days" for people who have suffered or are suffering life threatening illnesses. Mel has decided she wants a dinner party for her closest friends and family. She thought it would be nice to get everyone together. It's typical of Mel that "her day" is as much a gift for her family and friends as it is for her. We talked to Faith about counselling for Mel.

Last month, Mel wrote her story for the Aston University Newspaper, I've seen the finished article today. It's an edited version of what's happened but so brave of her to relate it all in detail. There are pictures of her before and after treatment and the article is something she should be proud of.

Mel's dressings were all changed by "soon to be qualified, Hannah" and she referred one of the wounds, the biopsy, to the Tissue Viability Team who are experts in wounds and the healing of wounds. The biopsy was done in late August and five months down the line, it's not healed.

The line was midway through being flushed when Melissa (nurse) came in to tell us that there would be no chemo today. Apparently, Dr. Haynes had to speak to the PCT (Primary Care Trust) at Burton, which we presume is to ok the funding for the treatment. Mel had her blood transfusion, but that was it for today. Dr. Haynes came to see us just after four o'clock. He was having trouble with the PCT, who didn't seem to grasp the urgency of the situation. He'd ask them for the funding; they'd said that they have a meeting at the end of February when they discuss such matters. Why is it that whenever you deal with "Trusts" or "Management Committees" common sense seems to fly out of the window.

Dr. Haynes explained to me that they needed to do get the chemo started no later than tomorrow (Tuesday) as the stem cells couldn't be re-introduced over the weekend. Therefore it was imperative that they started tomorrow at the latest. If the PCT hadn't got back to him by tomorrow, he said they would go ahead anyway and, as he put it, "worry about the funding" later. It's our first experience of the effect funding has on treatment and although in this case, it's going to be ok, it is frightening when cold hard cash can determine whether or not a loved one gets the treatment they need and deserve.

The steroids are doing their job, but they will only work for so long. The back pain was making a return this afternoon and Mel asked for some painkillers to ease the pain. Faith, the Lymphoma clinical nurse then came back to see us and sat down to explain Mel's forthcoming treatment. The chemo is given over four days; there is then a day's rest, before the stem cells are re-introduced into Mel's system. Drugs are given to counteract side effects with ice lollies the order of the day for the final part of the treatment. She has to suck on them half an hour before and after the treatment as this chemo can make her mouth extremely sore and the ice lollies help stop this. Mel will stay on her current ward for the chemo, but when the stem cell transplant is given she will have to go to a different ward. Faith told us that when the stem cells are re-introduced the smell is like either tinned sweetcorn or tomato soup. Apparently, Mel can smell it at first, but not for long. After that it's just her visitors that can smell it.

She told us that they will do a PET scan after two or three weeks instead of the usual twelve weeks because Mel's tumour is so aggressive. I sat there listening to Faith explain how it will all work and I can't see anything going wrong. She made everything seem so clear cut that you can't believe it will not work. That's not the reality though and although the odds are against us, they're not insurmountable. We have hope, but we also are realistic. Mel continues to be amazing in the way she is coping. The cancer may be winning in the physical sense, but mentally Mel is whipping its ass ten times over.

THROUGH MELISSA'S EYES (Part Nine)

"Well its half 2 in the morning and I'm still awake. Steroids really not aiding sleep these days but I sleep better in the mornings anyway.

*Well I know I said I was meant to start chemo today but I didn't!
I missed breakfast cos I was fast asleep but I wasn't bothered.
Mum and dad got here about 11ish. I had my dinner which I
devoured and had a wash.*

*I had all my dressings changed on my biopsy, old hickman line
site and new hickman line site and everything is ok. This new
line looks neater than my old one. Its still a tad sore and it's a bit
swollen but that is normal. They are getting someone to come
look at the biopsy one cos its scabbing over and they want
something on it to lift the scab off and allow it to finally heal! Its
been there since August! Hannah the student nurse sorted it all
out anyhow, she's really nice and chats to us a lot throughout
the day which is good. She's a student too so we've got stuff
in common!*

*Anyway after that I was connected up to the flush ready for the
chemo but then it transpired that actually it wouldn't be going
ahead today. They have to get the funding for it through Burton
Health Authority and they were saying they had a meeting to
discuss such matters at the end of the month...err yeh that's
good for me, I need it NOW! Anyway Dr. Haynes is on the case
and is sorting it for tomorrow. He said if they don't get a decision
by tomorrow they will just go ahead anyway and worry about
funding later. Fact is, I need the treatment soon! It's scary that
funding can affect treatment though, but I'm sure Dr. Haynes will
get it done, well I know he will! I had a blood transfusion today as
my counts were a bit low and so they thought it might help and
may also ease my breathlessness a bit. So that started around
7ish and finished about 1 this morning. No issues as yet with it!*

*They also need to rush the chemo because they can't put stem
cells back in over a weekend and the chemo takes 4 days
followed by a one day rest day before stem cells are put back
in so they may have to infuse it a little quicker or maybe they
still start Wednesday so the stem cell day will fall on Monday. I*

guess we'll know tomorrow but I think they would prefer to go ahead tomorrow if possible.

Faith, my lymphoma nurse came in to talk to us about the actual process now for the next 3-4 weeks. Once I start my high dose chemo it will take 4 days. I am having the E and M drugs from the normal full BEAM chemo regime. The E is for Etoposide and the M is for Melphalan. Etoposide is given days 1-4 for 2 hours a day so I'm not connected all day or anything. Faith said I should tolerate it ok and they can give me some good anti sickness drugs that usually work well. The Melphalan is given over a short amount of time too, cant remember the exact time but I'll be connected to the drip on that day (day 4) for 24 hours because I have to have a lot of fluids with it, like bag after bag! So I'll be constantly going to the loo and they monitor your kidney function really closely. This is the harsher of the two drugs and a sore mouth is a common problem so they advise you to suck on ice half an hour before and after the treatment is given to help prevent this and they will give you mouthwashes etc. It can also cause diarrhea (lovely!) but again they can give you stuff for this.

So after day 4 I have a day of rest with no chemotherapy or anything. Then on day 6 the stem cells will be returned. I will most likely be transferred upstairs to the transplant ward for this part as that's what is usually done. I will be in a side room probably but not in isolation and can still have visitors though if you are ill or have an infection or anything its best to stay away during this time.

So the chemo by day 4 will have destroyed my remaining stem cells and so I need my old ones that were collected a few weeks ago back in me!!

When the stem cells go in Faith said some people experience a funny taste in their mouth, which is either like tinned sweet corn or tomato soup! Apparently it will be short lived though but any visitors that come will be able to smell it for a few days after! I'm hoping for tomato soup!

So the stem cells being put back in will help recover my blood and my system. It is at this point I will probably feel quite rough as they don't work straight away. However Faith said that once they do start to work they do so pretty quick and within 24 hours you can notice a big difference in wellbeing. After that it is a case of waiting for my counts to come back up. They will be low for a week or so and that's when I'm most prone to infection and at risk. Once they are at a suitable level I will be able to return home. I don't know how ill I will feel or how long it will take for the chemo to take my symptoms down etc. It's very individual and the amount of time I'm here for really will just depend on how I react to it all. So no I have no idea when I'll be home! They will probably do a scan a few weeks afterwards to see where we are with things.

Donor search has been initiated in case we get to that stage but it will take ages to find one or could do so I will just tell you as and if/when we ever get to that stage.
So that's my next few weeks basically! And that's all the medical news for today.

***

Aside from that Faith has offered me a counselling service so I can speak to someone outside of my family and friends for support and they will come visit me in hospital or at home. I did have a psychologist but with no longer being in Burton its harder to see her. And I think I need someone outside of everything who I can just chat too. I really like Faith, she's so easy to talk to and explains everything very well, she's sorting out the Willows Foundation stuff out too.

I'm still feeling ok in myself, same as yesterday really. Taking it as it comes, I'm not getting depressed, I can't. I'm finding it easier to be normal and in control. I'm being me.

One thing I do want to say and I hope I don't offend anyone cos I know I always say 'oh say what u think and I'm never offended' and I do still mean that and I don't want you to stop messaging me in fear of offending me cos it doesn't offend me as such but it makes me wonder if people are taking in what I'm saying. The reality of the situation that I am in. Maybe people just don't know how to react and thats totally understandable. Basically a few people keep saying to me 'oh its ok you'll get through this no problems' and 'I'm sure you'll be ok and youll be better soon, its just taking you longer' and things along those lines.

Well actually no you don't know that and that's not realistic, I understand why people say it, to make me feel better, give me hope and everything and like I've said, I'm being hopeful that this treatment will get me to bone marrow transplant stage which is my CHANCE of a cure but it ISN'T likely now. At one time I didn't consider not getting the chance of BMT, I just assumed I would, naively probably! And it was explained that I may not get there, I just chose not to hear that part. But my attitude has changed now.

The odds are against us, dramatically, the cure rate is LOW, lower than before. Lower than that 30% I quoted at Christmas. I don't have any specific stats now, I don't need them because its my statistic that matters but I do know that. I'm not stupid. I'm not being negative I'm being factual. My cancer is spreading and its aggressive, its never responded for more than 2 weeks before and to get to a BMT I need it to respond for AT LEAST 12 weeks! Really it needs to be longer and it needs to reduce in size alot. It could happen yeh, I'm not denying it and I wish more than anyone that it will but chances are it WON'T. The reality is that I'm looking at 4-6 weeks of holding it, feeling better and then maybe we move on to controlling it. I know I prob sound like I've resigned myself to this but I have to take the facts and the reality. I talked to Faith about it tonight and she explained there were things they could do to make my breathing more comfortable should we get to that stage so my quality of life would be improved and like I wouldn't have to live with severe breathing difficulties. I could still do stuff, they could potentially control it for some time depending on what options were available. Although it would eventually beat me I could have a while to enjoy myself and live a normalish life!

This doesn't scare me, it reassures me, I would rather have the knowledge that if I can't get a cure I can have a quality of life and make the most of however long I have. I know I'm being a bit blunt here but this is how I feel. I pray everyday my tumor will respond and I'll be in that cure statistic, of course I want nothing more!! I want a long, healthy life!!

But I also realize reality and if I start facing that now then I think I'll cope better in the future and make the most of what I do have. If anything this has made me realize the time we have here is so precious and you should just make the most of it! I am soooo glad I made the most of my 2 years at uni recently! It's made me realize the importance of it. So yeh I just wanted to point out this, I don't know if I should write this stuff really, maybe its too much for people to take in and stuff, but this is my blog and I want some sort of record of everything so I'm putting everything into, no matter how much it might be hard to read. I have so many thoughts, some of them have to spill out onto paper! and everyone darts around the issue I think sometimes. My family dont, we are very honest but I'm finding it harder to deal with people who don't seem to understand the reality of things.

People keep saying I'm amazing for coping how I do and they would just crumble. You wouldn't, when faced with this you find *a way of dealing! You have too! I'm not amazing, I'm faced with a situation and I'm getting on with it, I'm taking control of it and dealing with it how I want, if I wanna feel crap, I will. If I wanna have a positive day I will. But it's me who decides it. I do need help, its not easy and that's why I chat to people a lot and am so honest because it helps me. If I bottled it up I wud go crazy! I have a lot of thoughts so writing them down helps me clear my head.*

But please don't feel sorry for me or pity me, I'm not. I'm getting on with it. My life for the next 3 weeks or so is in this hospital so I get on with it, I enjoy what small pleasures I can, like being able to use the net, have visitors, chat to the nurses. It's my life right now. I'm not trying to be all superior and 'im coping so well with this' but I just cant be doing with sitting here living in daydream world where everything is going to be fine and lovely. No, I'm hopeful but I'm REALISTIC! And I think everyone else should be too. As hard and as harsh as that may sound.

Ok rant over and I'm sorry if I like offended everyone! Please don't stop sending me messages though. If u don't know what to say say that! Say your finding it hard to deal with if you are, say you agree with me, say you think I'm being unfair by being this honest, say what u think but please be realistic and don't try and tell me everything will be hunky dory and I'm gonna be fine, you can tell me you hope I'll be ok but not that I WILL be because u don't know! And it makes me angry when people say it because I think 'No your not the doctor, stop living in lala land and come back to reality!' Hope for me, pray for me but don't live in the dark.

Anyway this blog is probably too long for people to read now anyway, I'm surprised people do read on for this long. It just gives me something to write late at night when I'm awake! My nurse today was called Melissa, girl from America, lovely she was too! And Hannah the student nurse has already laid claim to taking my stitch out my new line on Friday so she can practice! Lol bless her, I trust her though! Plus cos of where it is I want someone I trust and who is a woman! I have to be a bit exposed when they are doing the dressing etc! I have people coming to visit on wed and thurs and fri so that should be good and mum and dad will be here tomorrow. I do so appreciate them coming everyday, I don't know how they do it! And how they cope with my constant demands like 'can I have a ham cob?' and 'I need a cup of tea!' Bex is back on Saturday too so some good freaking out with the line is due!

In terms of symptoms and how I am, my breathing is laboured, I can't walk to the toilet unless pushed in a chair and it's hard getting into the chair from the bed. I'm on oxygen overnight and for some periods in the day. My swelling feeling is reduced but flares up randomly during the day. The back pain comes in odd twinges but nothing compared to how bad it was the other night. The line is a bit sore but nothing major. The itching is not as bad as yesterday thankfully! My chest feels generally tight but my cough is being kept at bay. I'm comfortable enough, the steroids do all this and we know they won't last forever but they are doing a job at the moment. If I stopped taking steroids and had no treatment for about 24 hours my symptoms would be worsen very quickly. That's the speed at how it grows.

Essentially that's it for today and we will see what tomorrow brings...I am a bit nervous about the chemo starting but lets just get on with I say and Faith has explained all what to expect. Dr. Haynes should be round in the morning so I will see him then although I don't expect him to say anything new. So that's the news from Bed 1, Bay 4 on Toghill Ward in Nottingham City Hospital!

Sorry for being all like angry and stuff. Just have to say what I think. I need to take some more photos cos I have like none to add to this tonight! I'll put an old one up.

night xx"

Tuesday 5th February

Try as you might to live "One day at a Time", sometimes your mind does wander to the future and whereas twelve months ago it was an interesting place full of opportunities, it's now a very scary place that we tend not to go to. Originally, I called this blog "One Day at a Time" because that was the only way I thought we could get through this. It still is. My advice to anyone in this situation would be to try and do it this way. This lymphoma can throw up so many challenges, so many obstacles that planning goes out of the window. The other thing you have to do is to put your complete and utter faith in those that are caring for you, the doctors, the nurses and consultants. I always remember Dr. Ahmed at Burton saying in the early days that there will be times when things happen very quickly and there will be other times when it seems nothing happens for ages but, although it seems that way there is usually a lot happening behind the scenes and you have to take into account the bigger picture. You have to be patient and that is something that Melissa has learnt to do, but she's learnt to do it, mainly through trusting those specialists around her.

I would never call ourselves expert, but you do become knowledgeable and you should never be frightened to impart that knowledge to the doctors and nurses. At the weekend we knew Mel had issues with her back pain and her breathing. Julie suggested steroids to the doctors and they took her up on it. It may be they'd have done that anyway, but I think they appreciate we know Melissa's illness well having lived with it for the best part of six months.

Dr. Haynes went to see Mel earlier this morning to confirm that the chemo would go ahead today and he returned on his ward round at about eleven o'clock to re-iterate the same to myself and Julie. The funding hadn't been authorised by the PCT at Burton, but they were going ahead anyway. Dr. Haynes also told Mel that she'd be moving to a new ward to have her stem cell transplant. She'll be back in a single room when she's there.

The Tissue Viability nurse came to see Mel and the scab that looked ripe for picking was expertly picked. For the first time since August Mel's biopsy wound looks like a proper scar. It was a good spot by Hannah and proof if it were needed she's going to make a great nurse

Mel said on her blog last night that she wonders how we manage. To be honest, she makes it a lot easier, than it could be. We worry more when we're not at the hospital. The evenings are difficult. We need to leave to get home and unwind, but at the same time we hate leaving her alone. Like Mel, sometimes we are so realistic that I'm sure people think that we're being negative, but it's not negativity. It's reality. It goes without saying that we hope and pray that things work out, but we have to be able to deal with the fact that chances are they won't. We can't bury our heads in the sand.

After lunch I took Mel for a ride in the wheelchair, we went to get a magazine for her from the WRVS shop on the other side of the hospital. We'd only gone a short distance when she became extremely tired and fell asleep. We got to the shop, got the magazine, a cup of tea for mum and we returned. Mel was slumped asleep in the wheelchair and I looked like I was stealing her from the hospital. I kept expecting security to come and tap me on the shoulder for stealing their patient.

We got back to the ward and a nurse came in to tell us Mel's room on Fletcher ward was ready and she could move anytime. We seized the moment and transported all our stuff upstairs.

The treatment was explained. Mel gets a bag of chemo that takes two hours to go through. She has this for the next four days. She then has a break for two days with the final part of the chemo, the 'M' bit going through on Monday. Prior to that Mel has fluids to help her flush out her system. The first part of the chemo shouldn't be too bad, the usual side effects are there, but medication can usually take care of these. Mel's cells should be returned to her body a week today (Tuesday). It's after this that she will probably feel at her worst, when her counts are at their lowest.

~ *One Day At A Time* ~

Today is mine and Julie's 25th wedding anniversary.

Wednesday 6th February

We arrived at the hospital at about quarter to eleven .Mel was much the same as yesterday. Breathing not brilliant and Oramorph keeping the back pain at bay. The first thing Mel said when we arrived (actually, she said it before we arrived via text) was that the toast was first class this morning. Freshly made, as toast should be.

Mel got changed and then had dinner. The good news for Julie and I is that we've found somewhere to eat. I discovered it yesterday, a pub called The Fiveways. We went there today and had a nice meal and nicely priced too. So, in future, if we want a cooked meal, that's where we'll be heading. We've already said we'll take Becky there on Saturday to feed her up.

One of Mel's former teachers, Miss Hollingworth, visited her this afternoon and then Ray and Nikki (Brother in law and sister in law) dropped in to say hello. Claire was due to visit, but unfortunately she'd developed a sniffle and a bit of a sore throat overnight so we had to put her off. As I said yesterday, the rules here are so much tighter than Toghill Ward and for good reason. Hopefully, Claire's sniffles will be short lived and she'll be back to see Mel next week.

The second lot of chemo was administered this afternoon. So far there have been no side effects, the tablets are doing their job, but as with the I V E one minute you feel fine and the next woooosh, it hits you. Dr. Haynes said yesterday that Mel should tolerate this first lot ok. Mel starts a 24 hour weeathon tomorrow. They collect it, stick it in a container and analyse it. It's to check her kidneys are functioning ok before the final part of the chemo on Sunday/Monday.

We left the hospital around eightish as usual with Mel just about to watch England v Switzerland.

Thursday 7th February

Mel was tired when we got to the hospital. She gradually

woke up and then had a wash, got changed into fresh pyjamas and ate her dinner. Mel currently has three food related cravings, McVities Chocolate Biscuits (Plain), Maltesers and Mini Chocolate Muffins.

Dr. Haynes came to check on her general symptoms, see how she was and to explain that he'd spoken to the PCT. He'd got the decision on the funding. Mel's treatment will be funded by the PCT and Dr. Haynes' salary is safe for another month. How stupid that someone with his experience and knowledge should have to justify how they spend money on treatment. He explained that over the next few days, nothing much will change, the chemo will go in, followed by the fluids and then the stem cells will follow. After that we just wait and see. He explained that he would expect a noticeable change in symptoms within a week, which is the norm, but this time, it is the length of time for which the tumour shrinks and the symptoms stay away that is more important and that is what they will be closely monitoring.

Mel's friend Sooty came to visit her. Julie and I went for a whilst Mel and Sooty chatted away. We got back to Mel's room and were met by a lady from an organisation called CLICSargent (www.clicsargent.org.uk/Home). They offer support to young people with cancer including counselling, financial support and in some cases holidays for carers and patients. Mel will be put in touch with a Youth Worker called Rachel and her support will progress from there. CLICSargent offer support to young people up to the age of 24.

Mel's has the internet sorted now. We've learnt that this ward has internet connection for patients via the hospital's wireless connection. I'm in the process of sorting out a radio for her in order that she can follow the football on a Saturday afternoon.

The third lot of chemo was administered this afternoon. She started the 24 hour weeathon this morning. Mel's chest felt tight this afternoon, but she'd done a lot of talking and had had a busy day. She had her Clexane injection at six o'clock this evening, this is to keep her blood thinned and so avoid clotting.

She's never liked these injections, the actual needle isn't so bad, but as the stuff goes through her body it stings. Mel uses an ice cube to help disperse the stuff and make the stinging go quicker.

We've noticed that there seem to be two styles of injecting. There are the nurses whom we call "the artists" and those who we call "the dart players." The artists tend to put the needle in slowly, taking their time and displaying their art. The dart players on the other hand stab the needle straight into the belly as though double top depended on it. Once in, the technique is again divided into two. There is the "gentle squeeze" and the "trigger". With the gentle squeeze, the Clexane is squeezed gently out of the syringe into the belly. With the trigger, it's like a bullet from a gun and a lot faster. Mel says the best technique is the dart player combined with the gentle squeeze.

Friday 8th February

I managed to get Mel a radio today, it will enable her to keep up to date with the footy scores etc. I picked up Julie's mum and her sister Carol at five o'clock and drove back to Nottingham. We went up to the ward and saw Mel and Julie. Dr. McMillan had been in to see her earlier in the day again, just to check on her in the absence of Dr. Haynes. He said that the final part of the chemo that Mel has on Monday is the magic ingredient and that if this stuff's going to work, it's that bit that will do the trick.

Kaz from the Toghill Ward came to visit Mel this evening. This afternoon I had a call from one of the District Nurses called Pauline. She was ringing to see how Mel was so I updated her with all the latest news. They do a brilliant job and ours are particularly good. It was they who suggested the way to treat Mel's biopsy wound and thanks to them, although it took a long time to heal, it would have been longer without their intervention. They're going to call again in a couple of weeks to see how things are progressing.

We chatted to Mel for a while and left the hospital just after eight o'clock and drove over to Derby to pick Becky up. We drove home and whilst driving managed to get the nanny to wash, dry and iron a load of sheets and clothes. Now she's on her own she likes to keep busy and kept on at us to send her stuff to wash, dry and iron. We kept saying we hadn't anything, but she insisted so we've sent all our washing round there. I think we may have to dirty some stuff just to give her something to do. It's very good of her, although I have to say I'm having trouble getting used to having ironed underpants.

Saturday 9th February

With spending so much time at hospital, little jobs that I used to put off can be put off even longer, but you can't compromise when it comes to toilet seats. The old one needed replacing, so this morning at nine o'clock I was fixing a toilet seat. Whilst Julie and Becky got ready I nipped the bag of washing round to Julie's mum. We'd done her proud overnight and had managed to manufacture a big black bin bag full of clothes and sheets. She now has twenty four hours to turn the washing around. It's a tough challenge, but if anyone can do it, the nanny can.

Mel was in good spirits. We chatted for an hour or so and then Julie, Becky and I went for some lunch at The Fiveways. We set up Mel's new radio and she spent the afternoon drifting in and out of sleep whilst listening to the football scores.

Mel gets a break from the chemo today. She was much the same as yesterday in terms of how she felt. Tomorrow she starts her intensive fluid intake before the final and strongest part of this chemo begins on Monday. That's when we expect her to become lethargic and very tired. According to Dr. McMillan, the stuff she's had so far won't have done much, it's when it's combined with the Monday chemo that things will start to take effect. She's very poorly at the moment, but continues to deal with everything remarkably. She walks to the en suite toilet and back, but is breathless. Her back pain comes and goes, as does the suffocating feeling that accompanies this lymphoma. She's on high dose steroids and has the Clexane injections.

This evening, Kaz and Hannah came to see Mel, whilst this morning Jenny popped in to say hello. They are all nurses on the Toghill Ward and it's so nice that they keep calling in to say hi and check on how Mel is doing.

On the way home we phoned the Nanny and were delighted to hear she'd passed the washing and ironing test. It's all done and ready to pick up in the morning

Sunday 10th February

I woke up at three this morning and instantly knew I'd got problems. My throat was dry and when I coughed it hurt. My joints ached. I'd got a cold. Nothing major, not man flu or anything like that, but a bloody, nobbing, twatting, effing cold. I could chance it and go to hospital, it wasn't a major cold, but I knew that if one of Mel's friends had phoned up giving the symptoms I had, I'd have told them to stay away. I drove over to Nottingham with Julie and Becky and returned home, alone. I hate not being at hospital and to be honest, it makes me appreciate how Becky feels when she is away. You can make enquiries about how Mel is, but it's not the same as being there. One of the few things I can do through all this is to be there for Mel. At the moment I can't even do that. It makes me feel useless.

I know the importance of this treatment and how the next few weeks are going to be critical. I try not to think about it. But I do. Whatever the outcome, none of our lives will ever be the same again. It will stay with us for ever. Today was a sunny day, Julie and I should have been out walking in the countryside. Melissa and Becky should have been at university watching the football in the uni bars and planning their Easter visits home. I can't imagine when we'll next go out in the countryside. I remembered when we all used to go out, riding our bikes over Cannock Chase and Becky going over her handlebars and landing belly flat in the stream. I would give anything to go back to how it used to be. Mel watching today's Liverpool game at Uni and then ringing me to talk about it. Then she'd speak to

Julie and spend even longer talking about uni stuff. Whatever she's done in life, she's always had this amazing enthusiasm, she's still got it, though now she's enthusiastic in knowing all about the lymphoma and not only does she seem to want to know for herself, but also to help others. I'm sure it's helping her through this tough time.

I hate this new normal. We shouldn't have to spend all our days in hospital. Melissa shouldn't either. Most times I can cope with it ok, but today, when I'm alone, with no-one to talk to, nothing to do and nowhere to go, it hits me. This horrible nasty life that we've accepted as normal. It's wrong and it's not fair. My emotions are going through the mill today. I have to switch them off.

I was driving back to Burton this evening for the second time and a young woman pulled up behind me in her car, she was probably about mid twenties. There she was, smoking away. Puffing away, inhaling as much as she could and then blowing her smoke out of her open car window. . . then we'd drive off and at the next set of lights, sure enough, she'd pull up behind me again and have a couple of drags, puff smoke out the window and drive on. Her choice to poison her body, but she's ok. She's not stuck in a hospital bed; she's not the one who can't get to the bathroom without needing oxygen. I wouldn't wish Mel's disease on her, I wouldn't wish it on anyone, but like I say, it's not fair.

Mel starts the final part of her treatment tomorrow. She starts off with fluids, has the chemo, then more fluids. On Tuesday, her Stem Cells should be returned to her body and we wait. Whilst waiting for Julie to come down from the ward I rang Mel and spoke to her for about five minutes. She says her symptoms are pretty much the same, although her voice is a bit different. We were told by Dr. Haynes previously that when that happens it's a sign that the tumour is pressing. Hopefully, tomorrow's treatment, as nasty as it is, will alleviate some of that pressure and give her the relief and respite she deserves.

Monday 11th February

My cold is worse than yesterday, I ache more and it's in my throat too. I want it to go so I can go to the hospital and sit with Julie and Mel. On Saturday Julie and I received a cheque from my place of work. It was from the Welfare Fund to help with travel costs etc. Melissa also received a cheque from the Angie Whitehurst Charity Fund. This is a charitable cause within my work's organisation that help staff who are suffering or who have family who are suffering illnesses etc. I've stated it before, my place of work have been fantastic.

We don't know what to expect from this final part of the chemotherapy today. This is supposed to be the stuff that makes everything happen. It's hard to imagine it making anything happen. Amongst other things, the side effects include a very sore mouth and of course the regulation sickness. The cure for sickness will be the same as usual, whilst the antidote for the sore mouth is ice. Either in the form of ice cubes or ice lollies, Mel has to suck on them to numb the mouth and that in turn should stop the soreness. Medical science. . . don't you just love it!

Mel shed a few tears last night. We've all shed tears along the way. I try to keep mine till I'm on my own. This cold is so annoying. It's hard on both Julie and myself when we're not there to support each other. I'm continuing to take the tablets, drink fluids and later this afternoon I'll have a bath and try to steam it out. The trouble is there's no cheating. If there's any sign of the cold then I can't go, it's too dangerous, not only for Mel, but for other patients. The germs can be passed on through touch as well as through breathing, so even putting on a mouth mask on doesn't help.

During the night Melissa was really ill. She was sick and had diarrhoea. It was bad. Julie said when she got to hospital, the sight that greeted her was horrible. The doctors said it may be a bug she's picked up, or it could be the effects of the first lot of chemo. Either way, it's hit her badly. They're going ahead with the chemo treatment today, because they have to. They're

184

also filling her up with antibiotics and more anti-sickness drugs. They've also taken some of the stuff she passed to analyse to see if it is a bug. She is weak and tired at the moment and for the first time in six months I've not spoken to her. I love her so much and want to be able to help. I feel useless. I think it's going to be a couple of days yet before I shake this cold off.

Julie says her throat feels tight and she's worried that she's coming down with a cold. I suppose it has to happen doesn't it. Nothing is ever simple anymore, nothing ever goes to plan. We live in a perpetual state of "If it can go wrong, it will and if it can't go wrong, we'll find a way for it to go wrong"

All that is happening to us at the moment does put immense strain on my faith. I have to keep thinking back to the card I carry in my wallet with the "Footprints in the Sand" poem written on it.

There seems to be only one set of footprints in my life at the moment. . .

Tuesday 12th February

My aches and pains continue to hang around. Mel's stem cells are being re-introduced today, her counts will be at zero and I don't want there to be any chance of her picking up whatever it is I've got, for her it really could be fatal. I would hope by Thursday I will be able to return to hospital and stay there, but as with everything else, it's one day at a time.

We were up at seven and out of the house by eight this morning so Julie could get over to the hospital early. I drove back home and Julie stayed with Mel. Mel had stopped being sick but was very weak. All visitors have been stopped for the time being as she recovers from this latest bout of chemotherapy.

Dr. Haynes came to see her this morning and was satisfied with the progress she was making. The sickness and runs and other side effects were all expected and he wasn't surprised. He said that for the next 5 - 7 days she will be like she is at present. Mel also asked him what the term "lung involvement" meant as he'd used it when describing the tumour during the last PET scan. He explained that it meant the tumour was pressing on the lung and also involved lung tissue, which it always had.. He said he hadn't held back on the dosage of the "E" part of the chemo, which he could have done.

At about half past three my phone rang. It was Julie. She'd been sick and needed to be picked up from hospital. I quickly rang Julie's sister and asked her if she could come with me to the hospital as Mel needed some more ice lollies and both Julie and I couldn't go onto the ward. I went and picked Carol up and drove over to Nottingham. When we arrived, Julie was feeling a little better but Carol took the lollies up to the ward. She returned twenty minutes later and we got in the car and drove home. After dropping Carol off, Julie was ill again. She's washed out. I'm the same. We're throwing all we have into hospital visits and we've been neglecting ourselves. We need to keep up the hospital visits, but take time out to have meals and the occasional fresh air break. It's not easy to do both, but have to get the balance right. Otherwise we'll be no good to anyone. I suppose it's what people mean when they say . . . "Look after yourself."

The stem cells were returned to Mel's body. They took an hour to go through and she was monitored every five minutes throughout. They did find a bug in her stem cells and this was counteracted by antibiotics. She had someone with her throughout the transplant. Her heart rate also went up, this was monitored and she was given further steroids. . These were steroids on top of the steroids she had this morning. I spoke to her this evening and it was nice to hear her voice. We had a quick chat. She told me about the transplant and how she was feeling.

Wednesday 13th February
This cold is beginning to piss me off. I'm needed at the hospital and I want to be by Mel's side, but I also know giving Mel this bug could have serious consequences. It's going to be

the weekend before I'm fit enough to go and see her. Julie is feeling weak, but has been at hospital all day.

On the way over to pick Julie up this evening, I bought Mel a cuddly Monkey. It was to remind her of me! She had a nice card and a box of Thorntons from the Guild at Aston Uni today. It came just at the right time as she was feeling low. Throughout all of this Mel has coped amazingly well, but the last couple of days, the reality of the situation seems to have been at the forefront of her mind. We've got hope, but the odds are against us. We'll keep going, do our best and try to make the most of each day. Some days will be easier than others, some days will be unbelievably hard, but we'll keep going for long as we have to.

Julie says Mel has been better today. The fluids have stopped now and the swelling on her face has gone down. She's very tired and only wants either Julie, myself or Becky to visit. This evening she had to have her GCSF injections as well as the Clexane ones.

Becky and I spoke on the phone last night for nearly an hour. We talked about Mel's condition and Julie and my respective illnesses.

We now wait for Mel's counts to rise over the next seven to ten days.

Melissa and Becky in the park at Ashbourne

Early days at Paulet School

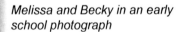

Melissa and Becky in an early school photograph

188

Mel and Me have a stand off during a water fight

Mel and Julie out walking

In the sea at Barmouth

189

*Mel selling tickets for the Young Enterprise Stars in their Eyes event
Picture courtesy of the Burton Mail*

*A family picture during a day out at
Hunstanton*

*New Year's Eve 2004 and a little tipsy after a
night out with Claire*

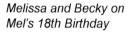

*Melissa and Becky on
Mel's 18th Birthday*

Melissa and Abbie

*Me and Mel at a wedding
in August 2006*

*From left to right,
Becky, Mel and cousins,
Georgina, Hannah and
Sarah*

Sophie and Mel. Sophie was the
first person Mel met at uni

Rachel, Clayton, Melissa, Dave
and Laura pose for the cameras
before a night out

Mel in the middle of some of
her closest university friends

Christmas at university

Another night out with friends at university

Mel and her friend Sooty

Cheers, just a quick drink before we go out

Ice skating in Birmingham

After exams in the second year of uni

May 2007....in Liverpool before the Champions League final

Smiling through the hair loss

*Mel and Becky,
Christmas 2007*

*The last ever family photograph, April 26th 2008, watching Liverpool at
Birmingham City*

CHAPTER TWENTY

To Hell and Back

Thursday 14th February

Overnight Julie's bug got the better of her, I spent the early and latter part sneezing and coughing. Consequently neither of us could attend the hospital to see Mel today so it was left to my mum to take in the supplies and check she was ok and her friend Sooty to keep her company this afternoon. Sooty is really good and I know his visits are appreciated by Mel. They're also appreciated by Julie and I and we can't thank him enough.

Mel is tired and didn't sleep last night. We exchanged a series of texts which finished about half past midnight. Mel had a visit from the psychologist today and she's seeing her again on Monday. I think this is important at the moment; it's good to talk to people who are not too close. Mel had the Clexane and the GCSF injections again this evening. I wonder if there is a limit to how many injections your belly can take. My mum told me Mel's bruises were impressive, particularly the ex line one. Alison, Mel's stem cell nurse, visited her yesterday.

As things stand at present it looks like Julie will be able to visit tomorrow. The bug she had seems to have gone as fast as it came. Becky will be there too, but I will be missing. My cold has come out, I've sneezed and coughed more today than I have all week. I want to be visiting, not sat at home on my own waiting. I want to be there for her.

We had a letter this morning from the Burton Hospitals Fund. They sent Mel a cheque to help with costs. I picked Becky up from the station this evening so she is home now until Sunday and Karen my sister is also visiting from Sunday so there are plenty of people around for Mel. I just wish I was one of them.

During the night, emotion got the better of Mel and she posted a message on the Webmagic forum . . .

"I am 20 years old and have NHL mediastinal diffuse large B cell type. I have had numerous treatments inc RCHOP, IVE, GEMP and am now undergoing a stem cell transplant. My stem cells were put back in 2 days ago. I am feeling really low as i know my disease is not very likely to respond to this treatment, it is being done as a holding process until i can nget a donor transplant but the doctors dont think i;ll get that far realistically. Most likely this transplant will get me some time and then they'll turn to controlling it. My mum and dad r both ill and cant visit me and im feeling low....i dont know what to do or how to deal with all this....i just want someone to talk too.......

Melissa xx"

When I read this message I cried my heart out. The response she got from people around the world was amazing and Julie and I can never thank those people enough. Words just cannot explain our gratitude for the support you are giving Melissa.

Friday 15th February
I think I've found a cure to replace the common sleeping tablet. It's two paracetamol, a Beecham powders, two teaspoons of Benyllin chesty cough syrup and a sniff of Vicks nasal spray. That's what I had before I went to bed and I slept well. Mel texted me in the early hours and I didn't even hear phone go off, despite it being next to me.

Mel's texts said she was feeling crap; I wasn't sure at first if this was a "sicky" crap or a "thinking" crap. Probably both as the latter usually accompany the former. She had an anti-sickness tablet and got slightly high in the night. Julie passed a late fitness test and I took her and Becky over to the hospital this morning.

I returned home and waited for the phone to ring. I had a text to say that Mel wasn't good, she was poorly with no energy. Her counts had dropped to nothing and she was weak and feeling sick. Dr. Haynes went to see her and commented on the fact that there seemed to be more air in her lungs than he'd expected, which is a good sign.

Julie and Becky spent most of the day just being there. Sitting in the room in silence. When Mel did wake up she used that energy to get angry and there was a return to kicking the end of the bed as she did on "cannula night". We tend to forget that for the last few weeks all she's seen are the four walls of varying hospital rooms. Julie says it did her good as after that she got up out of bed for a short while and sat in her chair.

In one of Julie's texts she also mentioned that Mel said she was missing me. It was nice to hear, but hard to deal with. My cough and cold won't go away. I went to the doctors today with Julie to get updated certificates for work.

This evening Mel was given a drug intravenously which I'm not going to give you the name of, but which leaves Mel whizzed. It's the same drug she had on cannula night and it sends her through the ceiling. Shortly after she'd had it, she told Julie that she had to "ring dad". She rang me whilst under the influence and we chatted, or rather she chatted for a good half hour. She told me she was missing me, we discussed football, how she was feeling and how good this drug was.

Saturday 16th February

I received a call from Mel at 2am. She'd had her drug and was a little high. We chatted for about twenty minutes before she dozed off. I can tell when the tablet is working as her response to questions get longer and longer. In the end I said, "I think your getting a bit sleepy now, shall we say goodnight" and about thirty seconds later she replied "Yes" and we said goodbye and went back to sleep.

During the call, Mel explained that she was suffering from stomach pain so they decided carry out an x ray. She was wheeled down to the x ray department and they checked her out. The results aren't known yet, but as a precaution they just wanted to check there wasn't anything there that was cause for concern.

I dropped Julie and Becky off at the hospital. I feel utterly useless. Mel is the same, tired, weak and poorly. The worse she's been. It's a Saturday, I hate Saturdays, we should be watching football, we should be going to football.

All I can do is drive to and from fucking Nottingham twice a day. Other than that I sit here alone, watching the clock, wondering what's happening, wishing I could be there. I'm not that ill, but I'm coughing and sneezing. All I want to do is sit in that room with Mel, hold her hand and be there for her.

I thought about going to church in the morning. . Punching a vicar might be just what I need!

THROUGH MELISSA'S EYES (Part Ten)

"I feel so weak and crappy, i dont know how i am amanging to write. Stop sending me message saying 'how r u today?' i cant answer and most of the time i feel like shit. Its what Facebook and this blog is for. I'm not saying dont text me but text me normal stuff or i' hope ur feeling better' - just dont ask! please. Thats it for today cos i feel sooo weak

Mel xx"

"Its now 245 am and im awake but slolwy drifting off. they give me this anti cikness drug that makes me high and then kncocks me out. Sorry to be so blunt earlier but when iget about 5 days a day sayin 'How r feeling today' i can't answer!! i feel toomuch like shit, if you wana know read this and facebook. Its why they are here. by all means wish me well and text me but please no silly questions. u can ask how i am in a facebook message everynow and again but not all the time. My dry mouth is my issue at the min as well as the diorrea which isnt really easing. i can barely eat or drink its just so dry.

Dr. Haynes came into and said everything was normal, my breaathing was better, counts have dropped faster than i thought though and i'm due 2 bags of blood tomorow. Alll my drugs are given throuhg my line and my drip as i cant swallow tablets at the min.

the drive for the xray dept was fun tnoihgt - they wanted to chekcn nothing wrong with my abdomen cos its been hurting alotMum cam 2day with becky and that was good. im leaving it here xxxxxx"

Sunday 17th February

Mel is washed out and has had a needle inserted in her arm with a box attached to it to drip feed her anti-sickness drugs on a permanent basis. She can't move without feeling sick and hasn't eaten much this week. Her mouth is dry and sore, though sucking the lollies help a little. Her counts are so low; she has no energy and spends most of the day drifting in and out of sleep. She called me last night in a drug induced state for a short natter and then this morning she texted me a couple of times. She just needs to get through these next few days.

My cold and cough continues to hang around. This morning I dropped Julie and Becky off at hospital and then drove to Newstead Abbey for a walk. It was lovely to get some fresh air, but I missed Julie, I wish she could have been there with me. We love walking. I got a call from Becky asking me to return to the hospital as my sister was there. Karen lives in Germany and is over with my two nieces for the week. She'd stopped off at the hospital to see Mel and for the girls to see Becky. Whilst Karen went onto the ward to see Mel, Becky and I looked after the girls.

I took Becky to the railway station at half one and she returned to uni. I drove back home. I don't feel as bad as I did yesterday. I didn't punch the vicar and apologies to any vicars who may be reading. I'm not a violent person.

I returned to the hospital in the evening to pick Julie up. Mel had slept most of the day, the copious amount of drugs she's taking leave her drifting in and out of sleep.

People keep saying they're praying for me. I know it's nice and they mean well, but God hasn't listened for the last six months, why should he start now.

Monday 18th February

Another day spent waiting for texts and calls to see how Mel is getting on. Truth is, she's not getting on at all. She was due to have platelets and blood this afternoon. Her mouth is very dry and bleeds and she has a rash. She is a physical and mental wreck. We have to keep telling ourselves that she will start to pick up. The doctors say they aren't dealing with anything they didn't expect. Mel drifts in and out of sleep throughout the day and at the moment doesn't want any visitors other than Julie, Becky and myself.

My own symptoms, trivial as they are, returned last night and I've spent the day in bed. The aches returned and I'm no nearer being fit than I was a week ago. I keep saying I'll be ok in a couple of days, but the couple of days come and go and I'm no nearer seeing Mel again. I sent her a text this evening to tell her that I love her and I'm thinking of her. My sister, Karen is picking Julie up from the hospital tonight and driving her tomorrow in the hope that maybe with a complete day's rest I can get rid of this cold.

Tuesday 19th February

Mel had another bad night last night. This chemotherapy is stronger than anything that's gone before. She's been to hell and back. She has no energy, her mouth is sore and she has diahorrea. She is talking about not wanting to have a Bone Marrow Transplant (if she gets that far) because she can't' bear to be this poorly again. I'm sure if she reached that stage she would go through it, but it's an indication of how bad she is. I sometimes think people don't realise what she has to deal with. Not only the illness from the chemo, but the psychological aspects of everything. She had the final part of the chemo over a week ago. She's been through all this and we don't know if the chemo will ultimately do what it is supposed to do and we won't know until her symptoms return or until the twelve weeks that it takes to sort out a bone marrow donor is completed. We just keep hoping. It's all we have left. It's torture.

A visit from Dr. Haynes and Faith this morning confirmed what Julie and I suspected, that despite the horrible side effects, Mel's general condition is what the doctors expected and they're happy with the way things are going. They forecast that in the next couple of days she should start to feel better as her counts begin to rise. Dr. Haynes also checked Mel's chest and was happy with what he was hearing. Faith stopped with Mel after the doctor had left and had a good chat with her. In the short time she has been awake today; she's been a bit brighter, but a million miles away from the Melissa we know and love. Most of the time she struggles to keep her eyes open and today she's been on morphine constantly. At one point she threatened to get an empty sick bowl and start pulling her hair out for entertainment value. She decided against it though. A sign that maybe, she's turned the corner and will soon start feeling better.

Wednesday 20th February

I saw Mel today, but it was only for five minutes. The only problem I seem to have now is a cough, so I lathered my hands with cleansing gel and went up to see her. Julie said she is feeling better and when I went in she was checking messages on her computer. She remembers very little of what has happened since Friday as she drifted in and out of a drug induced, chemo affected sleep. I wish I'd known, I'd have told her I was there all the time!

A simple task like washing wears her out at the moment. Her breathing seemed good and she was wearing one of her buffs. Her hair is coming out and she'll be bald before long. Mel uses wash and go . . . it's not the shampoo, it's just that she washes it and it goes!

Another day of improvement, long may they continue. I don't know why, but I've suddenly got a good feeling about this treatment. It may be because I don't want to believe that she's been through all this and won't get a positive result.

Not much else to report today, oh apart from the fact that I got a call from the Willows Foundation. They arrange special days/treats for young people with life-threatening illnesses. Mel sent her form last week. She wants a party with karaoke and a casino theme for family and close friends. Kirsty from The Willows is on the case and we just have to give them the green light and we're on. Apparently they can organise events at short notice too, which is handy.

Thursday 21st February

I went to see Mel this morning, but only for a short time. My cold continues to blow hot and cold whilst Julie is showing many of the same symptoms. We sorted Mel out and after a couple of hours we had to leave. My sister Karen went to visit later in the afternoon so she wasn't on her own

Mel continues to feel better, her main problem is swallowing. The chemo has effectively burnt the inside of her food pipe and gut and therefore swallowing is painful. She is slowly getting her appetite back, but has to eat stuff that is soft or she has to take tiny bites. She was taken off the drips this morning and is now taking her tablets orally. She's very weak but as the days go by she gets stronger. Her hair is falling out all over the place and her bruises, particularly the one from her old Hickman Line has to be seen to be believed.

The plan now is to get Mel off the drips and drinking enough fluids so that they don't have hook her up. Then it's a case of getting her in a fit enough state to allow her home.

THROUGH MELISSA'S EYES (Part Eleven)

"This shouldn't be too long but then again it is me and we know how I like to ramble on! Lol, I thought I would give you guys

some sort of update on here. The last 4 or 5 days have been probably the worst of my life if I'm honest. I don't remember too much about them, I've been pretty spaced out most of the time, I don't really even remember my aunty visiting on Sunday morning, sorry Karen!

I've been asleep for most of the days, too weak to move really from the bed, I haven't wanted to talk to anyone, my mouth has been so dry I haven't eaten anything properly, I had/have a bad pain when I swallow which is still bothering me but I have been told will ease. I also had really bad diarrhea but that, touch wood, seems to have slowed down now with some new medicine but for a while it was bad! Unless you have ever had this high dose chemo stuff you can't begin to imagine rough it makes you feel, bad man-flu – not a patch, it's awful, I can't put into words how ill its made me. How it still is making me cos I'm by no means better as I write this. Yes I am now capable of speech and staying alert for longer periods of time but I am still hooked up to fluids 24/7, can't swallow tablets really and am very very weak but I am showing small signs of improvement.

My hair is coming out again, like it had grown back but I'll be bald again by tomorrow or Friday I should think. Not that its an issue anymore anyway! I'm sorry for the blunt way I put across about texts the other day, its just that I was getting about 5 or 6 a day saying 'How r u feeling today' and I didn't have the strength to reply and the point of these blogs and facebook groups is for you to find that out! And also we don't know if the chemo is working yet, without scans its impossible to tell, yes there is more air moving in my lungs which we take as a positive sign but we don't know anything and we won't until I have a scan in a few weeks. Even then, it will probably have caused some kind of response but it's a case of waiting, if my symptoms come back in 4 weeks, it's worked for 4 weeks, if they come back in 3 months it's worked for 3 months....it really is a waiting game with no clear answers.

Other than that I've felt very low emotionally and it really has made me wonder if I would undergo a bone marrow transplant for the small chance of cure it could offer me, its a lot to put my body through. I mean you think I've put myself through this in the realistic frame of mind I'll get 2-3 weeks, potentially a bit more of feeling ok. Not a lot really is it?

A bone marrow transplant, yeah offers me a chance of a cure but that chance is still only 25-30% which isn't a lot so I'd be putting myself at a very big risk for a 20-30% chance of cure. I know you probably think it's selfish but part of me would just want them to control it at that stage and give me as long as possible with the best quality of life. I don't wanna spend the rest of my life in and out of hospital feeling like shit! But this is a long way off and I'd be asking lots of questions before I took a final decision. Besides chances of us getting this far is minimal anyway! The risk of GvHD (See glossary if you don't know about it) is also a risk factor, having donor bone marrow is a risk in itself, the risk to your organs, its not exactly a straight forward treatment!!!

My Willows foundation day is taking shape nicely now and soon I will reveal all the details and dates. It's basically going to be a big party but during the day not the night, for all my friends and family.

I think that's about it for now really, it was nice to see dad tonight briefly and hopefully in the next day or so he'll be back properly. I'm still not up for any other visitors but will let you know when I am.

Thanks guys
Mel xx"

Friday 22nd February

Why is God "cockin a deaf un"? You see, in the last two or three weeks there have been four or five prayers sent on our behalf, but despite those, all that has happened is that I'm even more miserable because I have a stinking cold that has resulted in me hardly being able to see Mel in the last two weeks, Julie has now come down with a cold that has meant for the second time in six months, neither of us has been able to visit. This in turn made Mel upset because we can't be there with her when she needs us. You will understand if at the moment I don't think God is on our side. Hopefully he'll come on as a second half substitute and win the game, but for now, he seems to be firmly on the sidelines whilst all crumbles around him.

With myself and Julie not being able to visit, we again called on my sister Karen who has been an absolute star and without whom we'd have struggled to get through this week. I also called on another star, in the form of Claire, one of Mel's oldest friends and she is going to see Mel later. As for Julie and I, we just sit here, her sniffing and me snotting, trying to will these colds to go away so we can get back to visiting and caring for our daughter.

We spoke to Mel a couple of times on the phone this morning and she is feeling a little better. Her throat is sore, but has eased a little and she managed to have a wash herself this morning and get changed into fresh pyjamas. Even her consultant, Dr. Haynes has a cold and she hasn't seen him today. Mel's counts are all coming up ok, but her platelets are struggling (they expected this) and they have given her some more today. She's very weak.

Whilst at home I have become increasingly annoyed with the advert on TV for BUPA about someone who has cancer and they come out with all these quotes, such as "She was given a nice comfortable room" which infers that on the NHS she would get a grubby room and her treatment would be inferior. I can say without a shadow of doubt that if we'd paid BUPA a million pounds, Melissa couldn't have had better treatment. She has received and continues to receive the best.

I am hoping to be able to resume visiting tomorrow (Saturday), whilst it will probably be another couple of days at least before Julie makes the trip to Nottingham. We're hoping that maybe by the middle to end of next week, Mel will be allowed home. For now, we have to get through today and hope that tomorrow I'll be back there. If not, Claire has volunteered to sit with Mel all day, so we are covered. Karen goes home to Germany tomorrow, probably glad of a rest, but like I say I don't think we'd have got through this week without her.

Karen is planning to do a trek of the Great Wall of China in October, raising money for the Lymphoma Association (www.lymphomas.org.uk) and the Nottingham Hospital. The Lymphoma Association (www.lymphomas.org.uk) have been a tremendous help to Mel during her illness and have put her in touch with some wonderful people who have helped so much and to whom we are eternally grateful. Nottingham City Hospital is where Mel has been having her treatment and again, she could not have wished for better. The funds raised go towards research and development of treatment for blood disorders, such as Lymphoma, Leukaemia and Myeloma.

Today is Julie's birthday. She would like to thank everyone who has sent her a card, but she is not opening them until she is feeling better. She doesn't feel much like celebrating today...

THROUGH MELISSA'S EYES (Part Twelve)

"I'm feeling pretty shitty if I'm honest. Physically I'm improving but emotionally im finding this very hard right now. Mum and dad r both too ill to visit again and I need them so much to be here, I just wanna cry all the time and I just don't know how im supposed to be coping to be honest. My aunty and friend are visiting and that has helped but there's nothing quite like having your mum and dad around supporting you.

My counts are on the up and they say I should be allowed home by the middle of next week which is great I know but

I just cant even seem to see that far ahead right now. I just feel so depressed and I don't know how to get myself out of it. I feel so weak and energyless its untrue and my swallowing is so painful at times. The diorrea is pretty much gone, not wanting to jinx anything and the side effects are easing but it's a slow process. I wasn't prepared for how shitty this whole thing makes you feel I swear. I don't think you can be. Its sooo sooo hard, the hardest thing ive ever done in my life and like I said…its made me consider my options with regards to a bone marrow transplant….its just so hard when you know that it's a slim chance of a cure as well.

To be honest theres not much else I can say so im gonna leave it there. Im so mad at the world right now that everyone is ill when I need them…I know they want to be here but its so frustrating – why aren't we ever due some luck???? Its NOT FAIR!!!!!!!!!!!! I WANT TO SCREAMMMMMMMMMMM!!! WHY ME????? WHY DID I HAVE TO GET STUPID FUCKIN CANCER!!!!!!!! I WAS FINE!!!!!!!!!!!!!! I WAS ENJOYING UNI AND NOW THIS!!!!!!!!!!!!!!!!!! NOW I MIGHT NEVER GO BK AND ITS NOT FAIR!! I'm sorry I had to rant.
Mel x"

Saturday 23rd February

My cold is on its way out so I've been at the hospital all day. Julie's cold is better, but not good enough for her to risk spending a day on the ward, so we had a role reversal of the last two weeks. I arrived about half ten and we chatted for a while until the registrar came in to see Mel. The good news was that her counts etc were up and her platelet counts had shot up from 13 to 58. This meant she didn't have to have the GCSF injections, however there had to be a down side and in this case it was the return of the Clexane injections.

The registrar had been instructed by the consultant Dr. McMillan to keep an eye on Mel over the weekend, the aim is to allow her to come home around the middle of next week. At the moment Mel is hospitalled out. She needs some of Dad's home cooking and be able to rest and recover in her own time. It's going to be a tough time, but I'm sure she will benefit from being at home. We'll have to visit the hospital a couple of times a week and at some point there'll be a PET scan, but I think the sooner we can get her home, the better.

After dinner she put her coat on, wrapped a blanket around her, sat in the wheelchair and we went to get some Jaffa cakes. We went outside for some fresh air, it was a bit breezy but good for Mel to get out of the room for twenty minutes or so. When we returned to the ward we were both knackered, it was the most exercise either of us had had in four weeks. She fell asleep on her bed and I zonked out in the chair. We were both asleep for the best part of an hour.

We woke up just before my sister and her two girls came for a final visit and then they returned to Germany. Mel and I listened to the remainder of the football. Whilst listening to the football commentary we chatted about which food she'd like when she gets home, what we're going to do and we discussed the Willows Party too. She needs to keep busy at the moment, it's important and that's why it's important that we visit. It's been horrible the last two weeks, being stuck at home. That is behind us now and we can look forward to visiting until we bring her home, hopefully by Wednesday. I left the hospital just after eight o'clock.

Sunday 24th February

Mel is ready to come home. If you check my blog over the last few months you'll see I've mentioned before that she knows when she needs to be in hospital and she knows when she needs to be at home. Right now, home is where her heart is and she's hoping (and so are we) that tomorrow (Monday) she'll be given the green light to leave the Fletcher ward and return to the Branston ward. She's been in hospital over four weeks and has been to hell and back. She's recovering well and now needs to come home to continue this stage of her recovery from the Stem Cell Transplant.

Julie and I spent the day at the hospital and were joined mid afternoon by Claire, who came to visit Mel for a couple of hours. Julie finally opened all her birthday cards and her presents and we spent the afternoon chatting and listening to the radio. After Claire had left we took Mel for a ride out in the wheelchair and went up to the restaurant for a coffee, her emotions have been on a roller coaster today, as have ours. She desperately wants to come home and her hopes were raised when the registrar reported that all counts etc were up and there was every chance they may allow her home tomorrow. Of course, the registrar can only report to the consultant, the final say will be his and that is what is stressing Melissa. She desperately wants to know she can come home. She hates the mornings and the evenings when we're not there, she wants to be at home in her own bed, waking up in her own time and eating home cooking. They are planning to take an x-ray tomorrow which may give them a small indication of how the chemotherapy has attacked the tumour. Mel's platelets were down slightly which meant that she didn't need to have her Clexane injection this evening. They are also winding down the amount of tablets she's taking.

We left the hospital at ten past eight. There were tears before we left. It's horrible. I wanted to pick her up and smuggle her out of the hospital, bring her back in the morning and hope that no one had noticed. She needs to be home now. This part of the illness is over. It's done. We need to move on and that means getting her home. We'll get back to the hospital in the morning and fingers crossed we'll have her home by the evening.

Monday 25th February

At twenty past six this evening we drove onto the drive, home at last after a day of waiting, waiting and more waiting at the hospital. Firstly we were waiting to see if Mel was going to be allowed home, then after they agreed that, we were waiting for an x-ray and finally we were waiting for the pharmacy people to sort out Mel's tablets. Hospital days are so long and for the three of us the day just dragged. Mel was stressed due to the "not knowing", but eventually we made it home. Julie put the accumulated hospital medicines away and I went to Tesco to do a shop. We'd nothing in the house at all as we'd spent the best part of the last month at the hospital.

It was four weeks and two days to the hour that we first went there. In that time her health has deteriorated to a level, the likes of which I wouldn't have believed possible. Her interest in most things have disappeared and will take time to return. She has no energy and even getting up the stairs at home is a major event. Getting home at the end of this stem cell transplant isn't a light at the tunnel, the tunnel is dark and we don't know what we'll hit next. It's great that she's home and I'm sure her recovery will be speedier and easier at home, but we're now playing another waiting game.

It can take patients two or three months to recover from stem cell transplants and that is when they go into hospital with relative health. Mel was ill before she went in so her recovery will be even harder. Before we left we spoke with the lymphoma specialist Faith and she arranged an appointment for Mel to see Dr. Haynes a week on Wednesday.

This evening Mel shed a few tears, she is struggling to adjust. She wants energy, she doesn't want to be sat doing nothing. At the moment she has little interest in anything. She is weary and has no motivation. As she gets stronger this should improve. Just after nine o'clock she decided to go upstairs to bed. Each step was a calculated effort, Julie holding her one side, me supporting her hips behind her. What should normally take a matter of a few seconds, took the best part of a minute, if not longer.

Tomorrow, it will be a home cooked dinner, a visit from the Nanny and we'll try to relax as much as possible. We all need to recharge our batteries.

Tuesday 26th February

Mel's first night at home wasn't full of deep and meaningful sleep, she drifted in and out in much the same way that she did in hospital, the main benefit was that it was a damn sight more comfy in the big double than in the hospital single. My mobile rang in the middle of the night as she wanted to go to the toilet and needed assistance. Julie went upstairs to help her. I didn't sleep that well as I was on edge waiting for the phone to ring. I didn't take a sleeping tablet last night as I feared it would knock me out and if she needed us I wouldn't hear her.

Mel has a distinct lack of interest in anything at the moment, it's almost a form of depression. Football, TV, even the internet is a monumental effort. She says she has no motivation to do anything, but I think that to be motivated, you need energy and as I stated earlier, at the moment she has none of that.

Whilst I was out this morning, Julie got Mel out of bed and helped her wash and change. They also had a tug at the remains of her hair and it all came out with relative ease. From a thick covering a week ago, she's now completely bald.

We were joined for dinner by Julie's mum. Julie's sister came to visit this afternoon. One positive element about Mel's state at the moment is that she does have a good appetite. As well as her usual cravings, she is eating a lot of ice cream. I think this soothes her throat.

Earlier in the day, Julie rang the Disablement Living Allowance people to let them know that Mel was out of hospital. If she is in hospital for longer than 28 consecutive days they stop her money until she comes out. Luckily, she was just under. The other job to be done today was to measure the bath. This information was needed by the District Nurses so they could order the seat for the bath so Mel could have a shower.

Pauline and Julie, the District Nurses are going to visit later in the week. They are absolute diamonds.

Wednesday 27th February

We arrived at the hospital this morning, Mel and Julie got out whilst I went to park the car. Mel walked into the unit, albeit very slowly, but she managed it and sat in the waiting room. I joined them and we were ushered into the room where Mel had her stem cell transplant. They tried to take blood out of her line, but neither the red line nor the blue line was working so they had to try and take it out of her arm. The nurse tried first but got nothing. Her veins are battered and bruised. Dr. Sandor was called for. She is Premier League when it comes to hitting veins. She got the blood and sent it off for analysis.

In the meantime we spoke to Dr. Sandor about the steroids and temazepam we needed. She has enough steroids to last her until Monday, but we're not due back at the hospital now until next Wednesday (a week today). So we needed more steroids and she also needed some temazepam to help her sleep at night. The doctor came back with the blood results and they were good. Dr. Sandor wrote the prescription out and I took it up to the satellite pharmacy to get it sorted. As I've had problems in the past with the pharmacy wanting to charge us I asked the doctor to confirm we wouldn't have to pay. She rang the pharmacy and confirmed I wouldn't have to pay for the prescription. I went up to the pharmacy, handed in the prescription and was told I'd have to pay for the temazapam as it wasn't part of her cancer treatment.

I wasn't happy but I was told by the pharmacist that the Pharmacy's Senior Management had met with the Haematologist's Senior Management and they'd sorted out payment for certain medicines. As I pointed out, it was obvious that her senior managers weren't very good because the message hadn't got through. I couldn't be bothered to argue. I made my point and left. They'll have to wait for the money. Obviously, a good night's sleep isn't part of her treatment, yet another example of our country's red tape.

We drove home, had lunch and Mel has spent the rest of the day in bed. Today she got upstairs and it only took her a minute. She's weak, but there are tiny signs of improvement.

Thursday 28th February

I had an email from Janet Dean's assistant today. A meeting with Mr. James Plaskitt MP, Minister for Department of Work and Pensions, has been set up for Thursday 6 March. I am unhappy as I have not been invited.

Mel is tired, she got up just before lunch time and Julie helped her get dressed. She took her tablets and then ate her dinner. During dinner she had a slight nose bleed, but nothing too serious, another nose bleed followed mid afternoon, but again it was only slight. Noted but nothing to worry about at the moment. She's a few seconds quicker up the stairs, but still needs help.

I replied to Janet Dean this evening, explaining my disappointment at not being able to meet with James Plaskitt MP regarding Mel's five month wait for financial support. I was offered the chance to write down some points for Mr Plaskitt to take on board, but as I explained, they do not convey the true emotion of what we have had to deal with.

I quoted the MacMillan Guide to Benefits which states the following....

"Income Support is a means tested benefit for people under 60 on a low income. It is intended to cover your basic living expenses. Income Support is for people who do not have to sign on for work, such as carers, loan parents or people with a serious illness or disability."

I explained that what the above quote doesn't tell you is that if you are a student, even though you qualify under the above, you won't receive a penny.

Mr Plaskitt and those responsible for handing out financial support for students with long term illnesses should have been with us over the last month. The system is heartless.

I can understand those who climb Parliamentary buildings for publicity. It works. Maybe if I climbed the Houses of Parliament, I'd get a meeting, people would take notice. The TV cameras and newspapers certainly would. They'd give me a meeting. Gordon Brown said today in PMQ's that decisions are made "down here" and not on the "rooftops". The trouble is, those on the rooftops aren't the only ones with their heads in the clouds.

All that should be needed are two letters sent by consultants at the hospital to the benefits agency to state the illness, the severity, the length of time for treatment and where the patient is being treated. Financial support should then be granted automatically. It's not difficult.

Friday 29th February

James Plaskitt replied to my letter today telling us what we can claim and what we should do. He completely misses the point in what we are trying to achieve. We know what we can claim. We applied for Disablement Living Allowance long before Mr. Plaskitt got involved. It wasn't following his advice, it was long before that. Typical politician, trying to make out they're actually having an effect and doing something. There then began a series of emails between myself and Janet Dean's office as I tried to put across my reasons for pursuing the injustice of Melissa having to wait for five months for financial support because she is a student.

I've decided that if I get no joy from the Minister then I have three options. Go public and give my story to the media. Wait until just before the next General Election and then give my story to the media or just forget the whole thing, walk away and concede to the old adage . . ."You can't fight City Hall."

Mel continues to get a little stronger each day. She shed a few tears this evening, due in the main to boredom and her lack of interest in anything. The future is scary for her, not knowing what will happen and what is round the corner. Visitors are coming tomorrow, I just hope they don't expect her to be the life and soul and full of chat. She is weak and everything is an effort for her.

Now we are back at home, this is our daily routine. Julie and I get up, shower, dress and pop in to see Mel, ask how she is and see what she wants for dinner. We go downstairs, pack away the fold up bed, move it into the conservatory and put the coffee table back in its rightful place. Julie then goes upstairs and sorts Mel out with morning tablets etc. I go to Tesco to get the supplies for dinner and tea. I come home, put the shopping away and about half eleven or so, Julie will go upstairs and help Mel to wash and dress and bring her downstairs. Whilst she is doing that, I'll be cooking the dinner. We potter about in the afternoon, getting Mel drinks, snacks, chatting with her etc, at about quarter past four I'll put the oven on to warm up for Mel's tea. Her appetite is very good and she's eating two cooked meals a day. So, between quarter past four and quarter past five, it's food preparation time. After tea, Julie will wash up and if we haven't had a hot meal with Mel, we'll then do our own light tea. The evenings are spent watching TV before it's bedtime. Julie goes upstairs with Mel to get her ready for bed and make sure she has her night-time tablets. Before she goes we move the coffee table and its contents to the other side of the room. Whilst Julie is upstairs with Mel I go into the conservatory to get the fold up bed. I wheel that into the lounge, open it up and make it. After settling Mel down, which can take up to an hour or more, we come downstairs and have a drink before getting into bed and going to sleep.

Sounds easy when you write it down!

THROUGH MELISSA'S EYES (Part Thirteen)

"Well I haven't updated for a while because I've just been way too tired and disinterested in everything. I still am. I'm home now but am still very very weak and tired. Yet I don't sleep well at night. I don't have any motivation to do anything and typing this is an effort in itself. I am up for visitors now but bear in mind if you come I'm not gonna be all chatty and talkative, I'm very very weak and barely have the energy to get out of bed in the morning. Having a wash is huge effort and getting upstairs is extremely difficult.

I have an appetite but I can't taste much as my taste is all buggered up. The food has to have a lot of flavour for me to even begin to taste it. I feel pretty low emotionally, I just have no interest in anything and talking to people is an effort at times. I feel a little stronger each day but it's a very slow process.

Unless you have been through this treatment you can't even begin to imagine how it makes you feel. My legs are so weak, just pulling myself up from the sofa to get to the dinner table is an effort. Its gonna take me a long time to recover from this and I mean psychologically as well as physically.

To be honest there's not much else I can say. This blog will be updated as much as I can but I don't always feel like doing it at the min. I guess in time I will update more.

Thanks for all your messages of support and I do read them all, even if I don't reply.

Thanks again

Mel xx"

The day after . . .

"Theres not too much to say really today. It's been pretty uneventful. I feel the same, low, crappy and disinterested in everything. I just wanna feel normal again, I don't want to be worrying about getting up the stairs to go the toilet. I want to be able to sleep properly at night and not think about in the morning having a wash is such a huge effort. I want to be able to do something that interests me in the daytime. I went out in the car today but that was an effort and I slept when I got back. I was totally unprepared for all of this transplant malakry. It was sprung on me so quick, I knew I'd feel ill but not as ill as I have done.

I want to be able to have the energy to talk to people but I just don't. I have a vague interest in football but even that is limited.

My taste is so buggered, everything has to be piping hot and flavoured up for me. I want visitors but I hope you don't expect too much from me, I just don't have the energy to be all chatty and talkative at the moment.

I cried this afternoon, I just don't see an end to all this and that's hard for me at the moment, I want to be able to do stuff but I just don't have the motivation. Its like in the day, what do you do? There's only so much time you can spend on facebook, I cant concentrate on books properly and dvds just don't interest me. Everything I had had has been taken away and sometimes I just want it all to be over. I don't know how much more I can deal with. At the moment I cant even contemplate having a bone marrow transplant, I don't know if I could put myself through it for the minimal odds of it even working. But maybe my attitude will change with time I don't know. I feel like I just wanna sleep all the time because then I don't have to think about things and I can relax but if I sleep too much in the day I worry I wont sleep at night. It's a vicious circle.

To be honest I cant say anything else, theres noone that can understand how I'm feeling right now to be honest and as much as I try and explain things that's not going to change. I just wish I felt more positive. Its just a waiting game now and I cant tell if the chemo has worked, all I know is my breathing is improved, which is great sign yeh but for how long? Its anyones guess.

I guess I just have to try and believe it will get better, well it has too cos it cant get much worse.

Mel xx"

CHAPTER TWENTY ONE

Winning Battles

Saturday 1st March

I didn't sleep last night, the wind and rain battering down and rattling the gate made it almost impossible. Mel woke up in the middle of the night and wanted Jaffa Cakes and afterwards felt a bit sick. I think in the end I managed about two hours.

After lunch we had a visit from the District Nurse Pauline. She stayed for nearly an hour and for the first time I noticed a change in Mel. She was very chatty to Pauline and there was a chirpiness about her. It continued throughout the afternoon and into the evening. Pauline said she would sort out the bath chair so Mel can have a shower. Because of the position of her Hickman line she can't have a bath and she's too weak to stand in the shower. This minor problem can be solved with the aid of a bath chair.

After Pauline had left we watched a bit of football and then Mel had a load of friends visit from University. It was the best we've seen her in a long time and it was so good to hear her chatting with her friends about normal things. There was some hospital talk, but not a great deal, the rest of the time they chatted as normal. I can't say how much I appreciate her friends visiting. It means so much, not only to Mel, but to Julie and I too. The visit from her friends didn't take its toll on Mel as much we thought it would. This evening she spent time on her computer. One of the issues since she left hospital has been her lack of interest in anything, but gradually she's showing signs of wanting to do things.

Despite the daily improvements she is weak. The stairs are mountainous and walking to the kitchen is a marathon. It will be interesting to see what the x-ray from last Monday reveals when we next see Dr. Haynes, but for now we'll enjoy our chatty bald Mooch.

Sunday 2nd March

It wouldn't be a normal weekend without a mercy dash to the hospital. I went to deliver the Mother's Day presents and cards this morning and after calling at my mum's I noticed I'd had a missed call on my phone. It was Julie. I rang her back and I thought I heard Mel laughing and half expected a request to pick something up from Morrisons. I then heard Julie say that Mel was in agony with pains in her leg and to get home as quickly as possible.

As I drove home, I was thinking blood clots. I got in the house and Mel was in tears and screaming in pain. The pain was in her right leg and I could tell it was excruciating. The hospital had said to get her to hospital as soon as possible. A choice then had to be made. Burton or Nottingham. I decided on Nottingham, If we went to Burton we'd have to explain everything to A & E and by the time we'd been seen it could be an hour or more. Whereas Nottingham knew Mel and if the roads were ok I could be there in three quarters of an hour. We set off, Julie and I in the front, Mel in agony in the back. I didn't drive at 100 miles per hour down the A38. Nor did my speed reach over 100mph on the A50 or M1, but we got to Nottingham hospital in just over half an hour.

We were taken to a side room and Shaz, one of the registrars put our mind at ease immediately. Her opinion was that basically, it was muscle fatigue. Due to her immobility she hadn't been using her leg muscles and when she does they get achy. We'd already given Mel codeine and paracetamol and that is what they told us to give her if it happened again. The scary thing for us was the fear of the unknown. The pain was like nothing she'd felt before and driving to the hospital with Mel screaming in the back of the car wasn't nice. A couple of hours earlier, I'd sat in my mum and dad's house telling them that we dealt with life one day at a time and whatever life threw at us, we dealt with it . . . today, if it were needed, was proof of that!

Monday 3rd March

I don't like Mondays. Monday signals the start of a new week and you wonder what is going to be hurled at you in the next seven days. The leg pain reared its ugly head again today. The paracetemol and codeine didn't help and the hospital suggested Oramorph. This is a stronger painkiller and in the past has worked on severe pain. We rang Pauline, the District Nurse, she in turn rang the doctor and he came round, saw Mel and prescribed the Oramorph. He also suggested the problem with the painful legs may be due to gout. Julie did her usual research on the Internet and it is likely that could be the cause of the pain. It's all to do with flushing out the broken up bits of the tumour properly and a drug called allopurinol which Mel was prescribed previously, but hasn't been this time. The object of allopurinol is to help prevent a build up of uric acid and flush the broken down bits of the tumour out through the kidneys and in doing so prevent gout. We shall put this theory forward to Dr. Haynes on Wednesday.

Other than the leg pain, Mel is weak, needing help coming down the stairs, but feeling ok. Her interest levels are rising which is a good sign. Becky rang this evening and she is continuing to flit between essays and socialising. She'll be home soon and I'm looking forward to us all being together at Easter.

I suppose the good thing about Monday is that it only lasts till Tuesday!

Tuesday 4th March

Mel has been active on Facebook today, setting up groups for fundraising and her Willows Party in April. Her breathing is fine, although she does have a rattly cough which is irritating her. Two of her friends visited today; firstly Gemma from Uni and then Claire came round for an hour. Mel was really chatty and talked about all she was doing and had done.

Pauline, phoned to check on Mel earlier and other than that it's been a quiet day. Since she had the "Force 10" chemo, Mel is struggling with taste, which is a shame because she's eating like a horse. She's on two cooked meals a day and she eats ice cream by the tub full. . . . I suppose we could feed her the cat's food, as long as we dressed it up nice and made it look like mince. Maybe add a bit of black pepper and a sprinkling of parsley. After all, it's a lot cheaper than mince and if she can't taste the difference, where's the harm!

She tried on one of her wigs today and is contemplating going to hospital in one of them tomorrow in order to shock the docs and nurses, who have yet to see her with proper (or improper) hair. I thought I saw a darkening of the scalp today so maybe the hair seeds we planted on her head are beginning to grow. We'll keep her head well watered and hopefully by April it will have a healthy covering.

Nothing much else to report, we wait now to see what tomorrow's visit to see Dr. Haynes brings. Mel will have her bloods done first and then following that we have our appointment with the good doctor. All things being equal, after our appointment with him we'll be taking Mel out to lunch at the pub, her first dining out experience in over six months.

Wednesday 5th March

How do we deal with good news? After speaking with Dr. Haynes this morning we got into the car and for a short time none of us knew what to say. After seven months of constant bad news, it was difficult to take in what we'd been told. We didn't believe it. We've become conditioned to appointments ending in disappointment.

I drove over to Nottingham Hospital, dropped off Mel and Julie at the entrance and they waited for me whilst I parked the car. Normally they go straight in, but with Mel having shown such a good improvement since she was last there, I wanted to be there when they saw her. I wanted to share the glory of her looking and feeling so much better. Everyone commented on how well she was looking and how good her wig looked. We went with Angela to have the line flushed and bloods taken. Neither of the lines worked. They were flushed and blood was taken via needle from the back of the hand. We walked through from the Day Centre to the Clinic and Mel got a "Wow, look at you" from Faith the Lymphoma nurse. It was the first time she'd seen her with hair and on top of that she was walking unaided. Mel's walk is strange at the moment. She's not used her legs for so long, it's almost like she's got to get used to walking again. It's difficult to explain, but it's more of a slow plod than a smooth walk, but she'll soon be zipping along.

We waited in the clinic for ten minutes before we were called into Dr. Haynes' office. He also showed surprise when we walked in. The way she looked, the way she was walking, the way she was breathing, it was all new to him. We sat down and he told us that the blood counts were brilliant. No need for transfusion or platelets. He referred to the x-ray that was taken before she was discharged and he put it up on screen. Alongside it he placed the one taken on the 17th January. The difference was marked. There was far more air in the latest one and the tumour has reduced significantly. It's a fair size, but there is a visible, significant improvement. He said overall he was pleased with the way things had gone and we were on target for the bone marrow transplant. The lists had been looked at and although no donors have been approached there are two potentials that are a match.

The next step is to take a PET scan. This will show the number of active cells and will hopefully give Dr. Haynes the chance to present a positive case to the PCT (Primary Care Trust). Everything has to be costed and justified and if the treatment continues to hold the disease and the PET Scan shows a reduction in active cells, the case for going ahead with the Bone Marrow Transplant will be presented to the PCT and the wheels will be put in motion. The cough that has appeared over the last few days was mentioned but Dr. Haynes said this may not be a bad thing. It could well be the lungs have been released from their crushed state and air is getting through them, causing the cough. The same too with the leg pain, he stated there are a number of things it could be (the GP's suggestion of gout not being one of them), but certain things concerning the leg pain would possibly show up on the PET Scan.

The results of that scan are critical in the quest to get to Bone Marrow Stage. We should get the PET scan appointment within the next seven to ten days. In terms of our next clinic appointment, Dr. Haynes asked Mel if she wanted one in a week or two weeks. She had a think and chose to see him next week. As she said afterwards, things can change and she'd rather have the appointment there if anything new should crop up. The doctor checked her breathing and was pleasantly surprised at the improvement. He finished the appointment by telling us, there is a long way to go, but we are at where he would have hoped to be at this stage. We're on target!

And that's the good news we had to deal with. We eventually found our tongues and went to the Fiveways pub for a meal. We planned what we would do over the coming days. Mel wants to go to Birmingham to see her old work colleagues and friends. We discussed a trip to the seaside when Becky was home for Easter and we talked about going back to the hospital at Burton to thank people there for their care in the early days. We got to Fiveways and Mel walked from the car to the pub, another minor achievement. It was Mel's first meal out in over six months and to celebrate we all had a pudding!

It would be easy to think after today's appointment that we've conquered it and that's it, Bone Marrow Transplant here we come, but it's not that simple. We're on target and that's all we are. We've another two to three months of this if we're to get to bone marrow stage and that is a long time. We know that today we've got a victory and we're enjoying that, but we still take each day at a time.

Thursday 6th March

Mel continues to have a good appetite but her taste buds are deserting her. After going to Tesco I went to the PCT loan department to pick up a bath stool for Mel. It's a really good place. Basically, anyone with a medical condition who needs certain equipment to help them with their daily lives can borrow it. The guy gave me four choices and I took two of them away to test them out. We'll just keep what we need and take the others back.

When I got home Mel was asleep. We were going to go into town this afternoon but she was too tired. We sat and had a chat. We feel under pressure after yesterday's news. We have to keep our feet on the ground. It's early days, we're only a quarter of the way through and so much can go wrong. Mel is feeling the pressure too. She feels that because the news was good, she should be doing more, but as we keep telling her, despite the good news she is ill. It's only three weeks since she had a stem cell transplant. Until last week she'd not been out of bed for a month. It's a slow process and the only way to do it is to take her time and do things at her own pace. Her leg pain is causing problems and last night she was in agony. Oromorph seems to do the trick, but she can't decide if that's because it takes the pain away or because it sends her to sleep and she doesn't feel the pain! Her cough which had appeared over the last few days seems to have gone away.

Friday 7th March

I had a letter today from James Plaskitt MP. It was addressed to Melissa and read as follows. . .

Dear Melissa,

I had a meeting today with your MP, Janet Dean. The first thing I want to do is to thank you, your parents and Janet for bringing your case to me and for asking that it receive my personal attention. I have been aware of other people who have had similar problems in trying to secure financial support through the course of an illness, and have had to withdraw for a while from full time education. Having thought carefully about your case, I do feel that I need to look again at the way our system works.

I am going to discuss this matter with the universities, with my colleagues in the Department of Innovation, Universities and Skills and with my officials here in the DWP. We must, working together, be able to find a way to make sure we can help someone in your position without, at the same time, creating a problem or unfairness for somebody else as a result. It is clear to me that we must be more supportive and considerate at those times when individual circumstances clearly demand it.

I am copying this letter to Janet, who I have promised to keep informed of progress. I am sure she will, in turn, keep you posted.

James Plaskitt MP
Parliamentary Under Secretary

HOW GOOD DOES THAT FEEL? THEY ARE LISTENING!

Mel received another letter in the post today. It was a parcel from New Zealand. Former Burton Albion goalkeeper Dan Robinson sent Mel a signed shirt from Waikito, the team he now plays for in NZ. It was a great surprise for Mel.

Mel spent the morning in bed due to the severe aching in her legs. She took pain killers and at half past eleven she got up, got dressed and we drove over to Birmingham. We took her to University to see friends and work colleagues and to give her the opportunity to have an Einees All Day Breakfast. . . something she's been dreaming of for the last six months!

Whilst Mel was at Uni, Julie and I went for a coffee. I felt strange being at the University. It was great that Mel was there, eating her all day breakfast, playing pool and visiting people, but at the same time it brought back memories. Memories like the first time we took Mel to University and she was met by the Aunties who helped her move in, the times I'd picked her up and dropped her off and listened to endless stories of all she had been up to. When we got home Mel's tears flowed as the emotion of the visit kicked in. This time last year she was out partying, enjoying her course and living life to the full. Now, everything is an effort, even talking to people takes it out of her and a normal life seems a million miles away. There is the thought that if this treatment holds the disease for twelve weeks she'll be feeling well. She then has to turn the clock back twelve weeks and go through all this horrible treatment again. Of course, the ends justify the means, but can you imagine, going to hell and back, feeling better and then having to go through it all again, only worse. The stress at the moment, for all of us, is worse than when she was in hospital. We didn't think that was possible!

I know this posting should probably be more positive, after all, we've had good news from the MP, and Mel's been to uni, but these pieces of good news are nearly always tinged with sadness. I suppose I could just write about the good things, but then that wouldn't be a true account. Yes, there are bits of good news, but the emotion of what we're going through shouldn't be discounted. It's very real and has to be dealt with on a daily basis. Hopefully, in time, the balance of power will shift, the good news will overtake and win the day. It may happen, but like Mel's normal life, it seems a million miles away. . .

Saturday 8th March

Mel woke at 8am this morning wanting pain killers for her aching legs that weren't aching, but were about to. She recognises when the pain is about to start, so takes the painkillers to prevent it. She went back to sleep after that. We got up just after ten, Julie made Mel's cheese on toast and I sorted out her ice cream. She ate those and then had a little box of mini Jaffa cakes to take with her tablets.

Whilst all this was going on she was very chatty. She was talking about the Bone Marrow Transplant, her aching legs, her stem cell transplant and pretty much everything else. It was a reminder of how she used to chat away on trips home. She's always had this amazing enthusiasm about everything she's done, be it school work, part time jobs, university life, she's always thrown herself into everything. She's even doing it with this disease. She wants to know as much about it and associated treatments. She reads other people's experiences on the Internet and it helps her to build pictures of what is happening to her and also to come to terms with each stage of the disease.

THROUGH MELISSA'S EYES (Part Fourteen)

"Just to let you know we went to clinic on Wednesday and saw Dr. Haynes. The news is positive. The xray i had last week shows a reduction in the tumour and my chest is definteley better than it was before the transplant. Its held it for 3 weeks so far which is the longest its ever held for and all the signs are positive. We are on target to get to the bone marrow transplant, if it can continue to hold it. I will have a PET scan within the next week or so to confirm all this and alot depends on that. They have 2 potential donors and once the PEt scan comes back, if the results are good from that then they will start to look at planning the donor transplant. It is good news but it also does not mean everything is all ok and i'm deffo gonna get the BMT. It means we are on target and so far everything is going to plan which is great but we need to take everything in perspective and in context. The PET scan results are essentially what is important but so far so good! I don't have any more chemo now, its a case of this last lot ive had holding it for as long as possible, until i'm ready for the BMT essentially.So yeh thats the news. So far so good!!

I'm not really updating at the minute cos to be quite frank i dont have the energy or motivation. I am slowly improving but its really slow and my energy levels and interest levels are pretty low right now. Having visitors really tires me out and sometimes its hard when they are here to make conversation so i apologise if you've been and i've not talked much. I went to birmingham on Friday and it was good but it was also very hard, a year ago i was involved in the elections, this year i found it a struggle to stand for a 5 minute game of pool.

Nothing really seems real to me at the minute, i feel like im living my life from the outside. I feel i should be interested in more but i'm not. I can sit and stare at the TV for an hour or without taking in anything thats on it but there's nothing else to do. Moving from the sofa is an effort, getting up is an effort, having a wash is an effort. Writing this is an effort.

And yeh we've had good news but its all got to be in context, this time next week my symptoms could be back though obv we try not to think like that. we are realistic in the fact that it could happen.

Also my side effects are still here, my aching legs arent going away, i can't taste food, my mouth is sooooo dry its untrue. Its really really hard and its gonna take months to recover. then should i recover i have to rewind 12 weeks and do it all again with the bone marrow transplant. an even more complex and dangerous procudure that involves the same side effects but probably worse. but then if i dont get to that stage it means the sct didnt work and we move to pallitive care which obv we dont want so im in a no win situation really. well i guess the bmt is the win situation but when ur going thru it it bloody well wont be.

i dont really know what else to say, except yeh im fed up! if u cant tell. i wish i felt more inclinced to do stuff but i really don't. i'm sick of being ill, im sick of having cancer, im sick of telling people how i feel and just cos im not smiling and happy im not ok, i probably am in terms of me being ok but me being ok isnt a normal persons being ok. I feel fat and bloated, i feel weak and tired and not like me. i dont feel like me anymore and thats what i cant stand. im sick of being ill. i dont like being bald anymore, i hate the fact that i have to force myself to want visitors, cos i know i should have them, i'm just not very chatty when they come and then i feel bad cos i feel like i should have made an effort.

and so yeh thats my rant for today. sorry its so negative but i just cant be arsed to gloss over the reality. This is shit. recovery is slow and im fed up.

i guess i should be grateful we got good news....its just sometimes its as hard to take that as the bad news.

mel xx

ps - i apologise for the spelling and grammar in this blog but i wrote it in blogspot n u cant spellcheck etc n im being lazy when i type."

Sunday 9th March

Mel's aching legs do not seem to be getting better and she is weak. She hasn't improved since Thursday. She is feeling down, though this is probably due to the aching legs. It is so hard for her and for us.

She felt hot too but we took her temperature and it was normal. She has no taste and her mouth is so dry it makes her feel sick. Tomorrow we are going to ring Faith at the hospital to explain about the continued aching legs. We think it may be something to do with her bone marrow, but need to be reassured. The other thing we've noticed is that she is shaking. When she's holding her knife and fork you can see her hands shaking, the same at other times too. She is bloated, her ankles and knees are more swollen than usual. All these symptoms may be normal, but they're worrying.

With all that in mind we're going to ring in the morning and ask if we can go into the hospital tomorrow to see one of the doctors in the day case centre. Hopefully, It will alleviate her fears and ours. She feels that there is something not quite right and needs reassurance. So do we!

Monday 10th March

We rang the hospital this morning and spoke to a doctor who was aware of Mel's symptoms. He gave us the option of going to Nottingham or waiting until Wednesday when we see Doctor Haynes. He wasn't unduly worried. He thinks the leg ache is to do with the bone marrow Mel is producing, whilst the bloating could be to do with the steroids. Mel decided to wait until Wednesday.

Becky went to give blood. Inspired by Mel's plight she thought she'd do her bit for the cause. When she arrived she wasn't allowed to donate as she is anaemic. We think she's brave. We expected her to keel over at the first sight of the needle!

Last night we sat on Mel's bed and had a chat to her. She feels down at the moment. I explained to her that it's not surprising. Even after last week when we got some good news, she has to put up with this leg ache and bloating. Nothing is ever simple. She should be feeling a lot better now, it's a week since she saw Dr. Haynes, but rather than going forward, she has gone backwards. Hopefully, when her leg ache goes (whenever that will be) and the bloating goes down, she'll feel better. There is also the emotional side of things concerning the disease itself, the bone marrow transplant and whether she'll she get that far. It's a lot or us all to deal with. I think that sometimes she expects too much of herself.

After tea we watched a film. Mel was tired and went to bed for an hour. I took her a drink upstairs. In the time it took me to get up and go to the toilet, Mel had managed about four steps up the stairs. She is so weak and I just wish there was something we could do to make her feel better.

Tuesday 11th March

First job this morning was to nip round to the local shop. We'd run out of bread and also needed some potatoes for Mel's dinner. When I got back I folded up the bed and went a drive over to Tamworth. There were two objectives in my journey. One was to catch up with some work colleagues; the second was to get some cheese. There is a fantastic cheese shop in Tamworth.

When I returned home Mel was still in bed and Julie was putting the finishing touches to dinner.

I made a cheese and potato pie for tea. The Nanny came round for her tea. We're going to watch the football this evening and then we'll send her home with a load of ironing to keep her busy. She has to earn her tea! We were watching football this evening and The Nanny was talking to Julie about ironing and how she found it very peratheutic" I don't know which was stranger, what she said or the fact that we knew what she meant!

And that's it. Another day done. Another day nearer BMT day. One more to chalk off the list!

Wednesday 12th March

The Leech theory of if something can go wrong it invariably will, strikes again. A routine trip to see Dr. Haynes has resulted in Mel being back in hospital. The constant leg pain that has been worrying us for the last week or so was diagnosed as a DVT. (Deep Vein Thrombosis) which in layman's terms is a blood clot. She was diagnosed this morning and by two o'clock Mel was back on Toghill Ward, strangely enough in her old bed.

Over the last day or so Mel's legs continued to ache with the right one in particular giving her constant pain. The doctor checked her over, her stomach and ankles remain bloated and when he looked at her legs, it was plain to see the right knee was swollen. It appeared like a lump the size of a tennis ball had formed on her knee. He said that was fluid retention caused by the blood clot and immediately set his assistant

Faith the task of finding Mel a bed. There were tears as yet again events seemed to be conspiring against her. We made a list of things we needed from Burton and I drove back home to collect, pausing before I set off to inform Becky of what had happened. Becky swore a lot!

Of course, this blood clot could have had very serious consequences had it been left. Dr. Haynes told us that they had to prevent the clot reaching the lung and he told us that once on the ward Mel would be given a drug intravenously over the next 48 hours which would break down the clot. Following that, Mel's Hickman Line would be removed. It is rare for the Hickman Line to cause DVTs but it can happen and to avoid any future risk they want it out of the way. That will be done on Friday, as will the PET scan. We won't know the results of that until Monday. That will reveal the progress of the stem cell transplant and associated chemo in its fight against the tumour. It should also show that the blood clot has been zapped. We expect Mel to be in hospital until early next week.

It's another example of how life changes for us at the moment in the blink of an eye. This morning we thought a quick trip to Nottingham would be followed by a carvery lunch at the pub. How stupid to think that anything could go without a hitch. One minute you're planning a meal out, the next you're in a hospital ward and your daughter is receiving life saving drugs.

Mel is feeling down about the whole situation, the strain on her emotions is unimaginable. She's in pain, she's tired and she doesn't want to be in hospital. It seems she takes one step forward and six back. She'll bounce back, we'll try to make sure she does, but each time she gets knocked down, it's harder for her to bounce back. She doesn't want us to leave her in the hospital at night. We don't want to leave her. We want her back home, eating our meals, sitting on our sofa and gradually feeling better everyday. . . . I'm sure I've wrote that sentence before . . . more than once!

Thursday 13th March

There was one piece of good news yesterday. Whilst Dr. Haynes was checking Mel over and after he'd diagnosed the blood clot, he did mention that her chest sounds clear. The PET scan is booked for tomorrow so we'll know more then. I currently have this feeling that it's going to be good news. It's not based on any medical or scientific fact, it's based on the theory that for Mel to have to go through all this, there has to be a good ending. For that reason, and that reason only, I think the scan will show a marked change in the tumour.

I couldn't sleep last night. I was worrying that the phone might ring and we'd have to hot foot it over to Nottingham in the middle of the night. At about half past three in the morning Mel and I had a textual conversation, discussing amongst other things, Everton's defeat in the EUFA cup, Derby's further decline at Chelsea and the most important thing of all, the food she wanted us to take to the hospital in the morning. The texts were heart-warming as they indicated a lift in spirits. It strange how you can tell someone's mood from the cut of their texts.

I went back to bed at about quarter past four and slept on and off till the alarm went off at quarter to eight. We left home just after nine, drove over to Nottingham and stopped off at the Mega Tesco store about a mile from the hospital. We grabbed loads of supplies, some which were requested and others that weren't. The lady at the checkout said to us "Enjoy the rest of your day". We resisted the temptation to pour a bottle of milk over her head.

Mel changed her blog yesterday. I read her first posting at quarter to four this morning and it's nice to see that she had enough interest to set it up. Like I say, you can't keep her down for long.

When we arrived at hospital Mel was asleep. She woke up and was chatty. The swelling on her face remained, also her thigh where the Hickman Line enters her leg was very swollen, but her knees and her ankle, although swollen, had reduced in size. The plan for today was to keep the Heparin going through her body. This is intended to dissolve any clots and thin the blood. The levels have to be just right as too thinning or not enough can be detrimental to Mel's health. They have managed to use her Hickman Line to feed this drug through. They feel that the line itself has caused the clot, but they can't take it out at the moment as they may disturb the clot and that could be dangerous. She has the PET scan tomorrow and once that's done, the consultants will look at it to check that any clots have dissolved. They will then remove her line.

This scan shows up active cancerous cells. If we're "on target", Dr. Haynes will be able to show that the Stem Cell transplant has done its job and he will then present the business case to the Primary Care Trust in Staffordshire, highlighting the fact that we're on course to Bone Marrow Transplant. As I said earlier, my gut feeling at the moment is that it will be good news. Surely, she can't be going through this trauma for it not to work.

We have promised her that the day after she gets out of hospital then we're off to the Carvery for a slap up lunch. Becky is invited too, although Mel blames Becky for her being in hospital. Every time Becky is due to come home, something happens and Mel ends up in the Toghill Ward. There could be a link!

Tomorrow (Friday) I am driving up to Durham to pick Becky up from University as believe it or not, it's nearly Easter. I will drop Julie off at the hospital and then drive up to Durham. I have promised to take Bex out for lunch . . . but only if she's done her packing by the time I get there! She keeps getting distracted apparently!

Julie and I went to the shop for a tea and a walk to stretch our legs and on our return Mel divided her time between being sick and sleeping. The sickness could have been due to the stronger pain killers or it could just be that she's eaten too much. The former seems more likely. The ward receptionist came in to tell us that transport had been booked for Mel tomorrow to go for her PET scan. Although the scan centre is within the hospital grounds, they are organising transport for her. They will take her round there on a stretcher. They're concerned that if we took her (as we did last time) then her leg may be moved more than they'd like it to be. Further proof to us of the seriousness of the situation. Just before seven o'clock Mel washed and changed again with Julie's help. It's so pityful to see her having to be washed and dressed by her mother at the age of twenty. If anyone asks you what true love is, it's that.

Last week all the signs were that we're on target, tomorrow we'll know whether our arrows are hitting the bullseye or going wide of the mark. Despite my feeling that we'll get a good result, the stress is unbearable.

Friday 14th March

Whilst I was tackling the traffic on the A1 and coming perilously close to running out of petrol, Dr. Haynes called in to see Mel and Julie. Mel had been for her PET scan earlier in the afternoon. He came into the room, gave one look at Mel, smiled and said "It looks good". He then asked Julie if she would like to have a look at the PET scan on the computer. The scan showed that the active lymphoma cells were greatly reduced. There is some active disease (under the arm and in the abdomen), but he was pleased with the result of the last treatment. He also said that there is an identified donor and he will now put a case to the PCT to persuade them to fund a bone marrow transplant. All in all, the picture is looking as good as we could have expected at this point. The time scale for the bone marrow transplant is approximately eight weeks. At last a scan result which made everyone smile, including the consultant. The scan didn't throw up anything conclusive about the DVT in Mel's leg, so they will continue with Heparin over the weekend and do a Doppler scan (bit like an ultrasound), on Monday and remove the Hickman line.

My day was spent driving up the A1 to Durham, wondering what news would be forthcoming from the hospital. After picking Becky up and taking her out for the promised lunch we set off for the Midlands. When we arrived back at hospital at around six o'clock Mel was in a considerable amount of pain. This was due to the DVT and the problems associated with it. Her mouth continues to cause her problems although we've found that ice lollies and Glacier Fruits help the problem.

One day at a time, but as days go, today was a good 'un!!

Saturday 15th March

Mel was awake when we got to hospital. Her legs were aching, though not as much as the previous day. Prior to going out for dinner Julie helped her get washed and changed before the nurse came to sort her bed out. During this time Dr. Sandor came to have a look at her. She confirmed that the scan was booked for Monday, the line should also be removed on Monday and she should be out of hospital by the middle of next week.

Mel is quiet...This was taken from her blog late last night...

"I'm still in pain in my leg though, they are keeping me on the anti clotting drugs over the weekend. I still feel low emotionally,i feel detached from everything, like nothing is real and i havent taken in that its good news. Although it is i can't help thinking 'omg ive gotta go through this all again' and i feel so crap at the moment its hard to see positives in things. I wish my leg pain would go, i may feel better then. My mouth is still unbearable and i hate being in hospital. I wish i felt better, i should do really given the news but i just dont see an end to hospitals and cancer and i can't get over that at the moment. I just want to sleep all the time so i don't have to think about it. its pretty shit but i guess i should try and start coping cos im really not right now. Sorry for all the negativity"

It's not negativity; I think she's dealing with the reality of the situation. This constant rollercoaster of a ride that Mel is experiencing is playing havoc with her emotions. There is so much she's got to take in, whilst at the same time dealing with the pain and swelling in her legs from the blood clot. Obviously, we're happy that things are on target, but we're not getting carried away and thinking the next few months will be a breeze. Far from it. There are still some tough times ahead, but on saying that, when we first came into Nottingham City Hospital, we'd have been happy just to be where we are now."

CHAPTER TWENTY TWO
Losing the War

Sunday 16th March

Before we left yesterday Mel had a good cry. The emotion of the last week poured out of her. The blood clot, the news on the scan, the weakness, the fear of future treatment, it all came out. We sat and talked for a while and finally left the hospital just before nine o'clock. She watched Match of the Day after we'd left and apart from being woken at 3am for a blood test, she slept well.

We arrived this morning at ten o'clock and Mel felt a lot better. Becky had come with us. We know we're in for a rollercoaster ride of emotions over the next few months, but we continue to deal with things as they happen and try not to worry before they do. We know certain things. We know Mel is going to get very ill again if she reaches Bone Marrow stage. We know she will be in hospital for around six weeks after the transplant. We know she's scared. She told us last night. We also know that no matter what, we'll be here for her.

The leg pain is a lot better than it was and she's all but stopped the pain killers. She does get the odd twinge, but nothing like before. It returned around tea time and she did have to reach for the pain killers, but it's on its way out. She continues to have the Heparin drug fed through her line and this will continue until Monday. She's having some E45 cream for her legs which have become sore. She says her mouth feels different. She has little or no taste, but it's not as dry. The swelling on her face has reduced and when we returned from lunch she was really chatty, telling us all about student elections at university.

Monday 17th March

Mel is brighter today. She wrote on her blog late last night and it's a wonder her fingers don't ache as much as her legs. She didn't get to sleep till about 2am. Her blog echoes pretty much what I said myself. The news is good, but we're keeping our feet on the ground. Mel is feeling down, but she's trying her hardest to claw her way back up. She will. I said yesterday, we're in for a rollercoaster ride of emotions over the next two or three months, but we're happy to be at the stage where she's on target for a Bone Marrow Transplant.

When we arrived this morning Mel was sat on the side of her bed. She'd just walked to the toilet. Another milestone. It's about 15 yards from her hospital bed. We helped her wash and change into fresh pyjamas and afterwards, Julie went for a cup of tea and I stopped and chatted to Mel. We talked about the previous evenings Match of the Day and also the copious amounts of TV that is gradually building up on Sky Plus. Something to keep us occupied in-between meals when she gets out of hospital.

There was no sign of the Doppler Scan or the Hickman Line being removed. Mel is still on the Heparin drip and has now been on it continuously for five days. She's had a few minor leg pain twinges, but nothing serious. The scan will show up any abnormalities in the flow of blood through Mel's body. Hopefully there won't be any and the line can be removed.

After dinner we returned to the ward and Mel was asleep. I could have nodded off too. I have to say though the chairs they have on Toghill were not designed with comfort in mind. The arm chairs are straight backed and you can't do anything in them other than sit bolt upright, whilst the other visitor's chairs are wooden with no buttock protection whatsoever. Eight minutes in one of those and you need a major buttock massage, never mind eight hours. Julie tried her hardest to sleep, as I did at one point, but it's impossible. The only way to nod off is to get up quickly and bang your head on the drug cabinet. Other than that, you close your eyes, but are conscious off all around you.

Just before 1:30 Dr. Sandor, the registrar came in to tell us that the scan would now be done on Tuesday as they were fully booked today. Providing there are no more clots and obstructions around the Hickman Line that would then be taken out. With that in mind, I expect it will be Wednesday (maybe even Thursday) now before Mel is let out.

We went for a coffee and returned to the ward at four o'clock and on the way up to the ward saw Jenny (from the day centre) and Dr. Haynes. We told them Mel seemed better today. Dr. Haynes should have been putting Mel's case forward to the Primary Care Trust today. He has to present her as a business case. He will tell them that as the Stem Cell Transplant has been so successful, they should continue and go ahead with the Bone Marrow Transplant and he will give them reasons for doing so.

Mel woke up when we returned to the ward, just in time for tea but soon nodded off again and slept well into the evening. Today, she's hardly been in pain, therefore she's been able to sleep more. When she did wake up she kept apologising for not being awake and talking to us. We would then tell her not to be so silly and to go back to sleep. This happened about half a dozen times throughout the day. By half past six this evening I'd lost all feeling in my buttocks, if there's such a thing as a buttockectomy, then I am in need of one!

THROUGH MELISSA'S EYES (Part Fifteen)

"Sorry I havent't been updating much, its been a rough couple of days and well weeks really. Its like I started to recover and feel better and then took 2 steps backwards with this whole blood clot business and I was low before I even came into hospital becasue of the pain and the swelling. I really did feel depressed and I'm not totally ok now but I feel a little better today and maybe I'm turning a corner - though I'm scared tomorrow I'll just plummet right back down again but I'm trying my hardest not to. I had no intersest in anything and I seriously didn't care

about anything, and I'm not totally back to caring and being intersted in doing a whole lot today but things have started to come back a little. The emotional side of this thing is so hard.

When I was told about my scan I just nodded, I didn;t take it in and I haven't even now though I'm starting to and I almost get excited and happy which probably sounds so strange to everyone, your sat there thinking 'what? almost happy' but you have to understand for 6 months now all I've had is bad news and for something to go right is almost unbelievable and I'm scared to let myself think it. When I was fist diagnosed not being cured wasn't an option but then it slowly became the reality and for the last coupla months I've prepared myself for the fact that I most likely won't get a cure and then even having to deal with the fact that getting to Bone Marrow Stage was unlikely but then in a matter of weeks its all turned around again and we are on target for the BMT and there is a chance I can get a cure and get a remission, something I had almost written off, not cos I was being negative but with the history of the disease and what the doctors had told us that was what we expected but now that has changed and I think I'm slowly starting to imagine again what it could be like after treatment, I could have a life again, maybe if the BMT works, and there's no gurantee it would but I'm more hopeful now than I've ever been (not wanting to jinx anything of course) I could go back to uni, I could have a normal life and I think I'd almost written off that and trying to get back to the idea of actually beating this thing has taken alot out of me. I was at the point where all I could see was treatments to control the disease but now the most unlikely has happened and I wasn't prepared for it but now I think I'm finally beggining to see that this could work and maybe I could get a remission. And I am pleased about the results, of course I am though I don't think I'll believe it until I see the actual scan! But I know I can lie down flat in bed, something I haven't done since August! I don't know if all that made sense but I don't think I can explain it any better.

In terms of the blood clot situation, I'm still in some pain though its less and I'm hoping it goes away soon! They are doing a Doppler scan tomorrow which is like an ultrasound type thing on my leg to see whats going on, it can tell blood flow or something and once the results of that are back they will go from there but the liklihood is my line will be removed and the Heperin (anti clotting drug I've been hooked up too since Wednesday) will be stopped and I should be allowed home, all being well and no unforseen problems occuring on Tuesday/Wednesday so that should be good. I just hope the pain has gone! At the moment I'm very weak, I've gone backwards about 2-3 weeks in terms of that as again I haven't been walking. I can't even walk to the toilet in here, I have to use the commode, how embarrasing is that? A 20 year old using a commode and having to have her mum help wash her. I hate the fact I have no independence - but that will slowly come back a bit over the next few weeks before it starts again with the BMT (fingers crossed we get there) and I won't have a line for a few weeks so at least I'll get a break from that. Although I will have to have my THIRD one put in for the BMT. I swear I have no luck.

My taste is all funny at the moment, I really can't taste anything, everything tastes like cardboard. Certain things I can just about taste and its very hard to explain unless you've experienced it. I had it with RCHOP and IVE but not as bad. I've got a good appetite which is unusual after an SCT but I think it was the steriods I was on. Also my mouth is really dry although that has improved today so I'm hoping its on its way out and its not just a one off day! I'm looking forward to getting home to dads cooking cos the hospital food is bland enough anyway so when you can't taste stuff its even worse!!! At least at home we can spice stuff up a bit and make it have flavour plus the food is miles better!! They are also taking blood from me about 3 times a day and cos the line is the issue with the clot they can't use it (not that it ever bled anyway very well) so my poor veins are well and truly battered and bruised! I was so low though to be honest the last few days when they came I almost just didn't feel the pain, thats how crap I felt. It was like 'yeh do it whatever i don't care' Now today - I felt the pain!! and It wasn't cos it was more painful in terms of the blood test it was just I think I cared more. Which is good! but less fun in terms of pain!

I get out of breath just getting in and out of bed at the moment but its purely down to lack of energy and weakness not the lymphoma which is nice to know!! Its kinda nice knowing something isn't pressing down on your lung! Apparently on the scan there is some lymphpoma still in the chest but only a tiny bit, a bit under the armpit and a tiny bit in the abdomen but considering it covered the whole of my lung and more of my abdomen etc its pretty good!! Apprently on the 'before SCT scan' i was pretty much glowing everywhere and now there's only a few bits which the Dr. expected, he didn't expect it to be totally clear because of the nature of my tumour but its the only treatment that has done anything and held it for this long.

The BMT will be in about 8-9 weeks and they have a donor identified and I think they are being approached once the Dr. sorts all the funding out and puts a case to the Primary Care Trust who decide if I'm worth a shot at a BMT but I will get it, Dr. Haynes is one of the countries best Lymphoma specialists and I very much doubt they'd disagree with him!!
I hope tomorrow I feel the same or better than I do today, I feel like I'm on the edge of a cliff and I could go one way or the other and I know which way I want to go but I have no control, anything could trigger me to fall even though I really don't want too. I'm not saying I feel totally right and better in myself but hopefully I'm slowly getting there.

I'm starting to get tired now so I'm gonna go.

Night night xx"

Tuesday 18th March

Once Mel is out of hospital Doctor Tansey, our GP is going to come and visit us. It's better this way as we have just one single point of contact and he is aware of our situation and knows us.

When we arrived at hospital Mel had gone for her Doppler Scan. Whilst she was away Dr. Haynes came to see her. He explained to us that he'd contacted the PCT, the donor was being chased up and that at the moment there wasn't much else to be done. It was a case of watching and waiting. Still on target. Still no guarantees. Just watching and waiting.

Mel is likely to be in hospital for another couple of days. He said it was important for her to stay in bed until they know the results of the scan and exactly what they're dealing with. Mel returned at about quarter to twelve. The person doing the scan had told her they'd located a blood clot at the end of the Hickman Line. Dr. Sandor returned just before two o'clock and explained it all. Due to the position of the line, it was possible for Dr. Sandor to remove it herself. Once removed the plan was to put a cannula in Mel's arm and feed the Heparin through that for 24 hours. She's to stay in bed apart from getting out to use the commode.

Just before four o'clock and with no sign of a doctor I went on a mission to find out if Mel was having her line removed. Dr. Sandor was trying to find out from the registrar about procedure when removing the line. It was something to do with it being close to a main vein. She came back to see us an hour or so later to tell us that the line would be taken out tomorrow as the radiologist hadn't got back to her. It wouldn't affect how long Mel would stay in hospital and by Friday, she should be home.

There were tears after tea. Mel was feeling down and said she had no energy, no life in her and she felt as though she'd lost her personality. It was hiding. We talked to her, explaining that whilst she is so weak and lacking energy, she won't feel good. But once they sort this blood clot out and she comes home we can have another bash at building her up, injecting life

245

into her and in time we'll find that personality that occasionally goes into hiding.

Wednesday 19th March

We arrived at hospital just after 10.30, having searched town for some talking books for Mel. Mel's mood was good when we arrived but it dipped just before lunch, probably due to the impending withdrawal of the Hickman Line. We know when she is getting stressed about things she becomes irritable and can't settle. She also had back and stomach pain, the back pain they think is due to her lack of mobility over the last week, whilst the stomach pain was attributed to the blood clot situation.

During lunchtime the nurses came in and stopped the Heparin. I'd asked the sister on the ward earlier about when they were planning to take the Hickman Line out and she said it would be sometime after lunch, but they had to switch off the pump that was feeding the Heparin through for at least an hour prior to the removal of the line. Julie and I took it in turns giving Mel back rubs to try and relax her whilst she waited to have her line removed.

As the procedure neared, Mel began to feel sick. All signs that she was getting nervous. Finally, Fiona the registrar came to take a blood test. Once the results of this were known, the removal of the line could begin. An hour came and went and at half past four another registrar came with a trolley of implements. He got everything ready. Julie and Becky had long since disappeared for a coffee. I sat next to Mel and held her hand. I put the TV on to give her something to take her mind away from the line removal. The doctor then disappeared and went to phone the laboratory for the blood test results. They'd lost them. Because it was three hours or more since the Heparin had stopped they didn't need to do a repeat test so he set about removing the line.

Firstly, he anaesthetised the area around the line entry. As he did so Mel squeezed my hand tightly and nearly broke three of my fingers. She said it didn't matter because if she broke them we were in the right place. After three local injections he began to pull the line out. You imagine that it's only a couple of inches into the leg but when he pulled it out it was like sucking spaghetti and seemed to go on for ever. By the time he'd got it out it was more than a foot long, no wonder it made Mel's eyes water!!!!!!

The registrar thinks Mel will be on Clexane injections to start with then she'll have Warfrin tablets. This should be for around six months. She also has to wear the tight fitting white stockings for the next 12 - 24 months. Again this is part of the treatment to prevent more clots forming. I also asked whether or not she could move about and the registrar said yes. The wound should heal well as he didn't have to dissect the area and there was no need for any stitches.

So, that's it, she's Hickman free for the first time since November. She will need another one when she gets to Bone Marrow Transplant stage, but they'll do that at the time. We've got through another trauma, the line is out, the clot will dissolve and hopefully, on Friday, we'll be bringing her home

It's been a tough day, but a satisfying one. We feel we've made progress and taken a big step towards getting her home. Mel perked up no end after the line removal I'm sure that tomorrow she'll be chomping at the bit to get out of hospital.

THROUGH MELISSA'S EYES (Part Sixteen)

"Just a quick entry I think. I had my Hickman Line removed today which is really good now its done though i was crapping myself beforehand! The last one realy hurt when it came out so I was well scared and I had to wait till half 4 before they came to do it! They also did a blood test to test my clotting or something and they did it in my arm like down by my wrist! so weird! and painful I may add though not unbearable or really bad.

Having the line removed was nowhere near as bad as i thought. The local aneasthetic stung like hell but that was the wost part! I had it done in my bed with my dad there with me and we put

247

deal or no deal on the TV to try and distract me!! Dad watched the Dr. pull it out - I didn't!! But now its out its so much better!! I can have proper baths and showers without having to worry about covering it up!! woohoo!! I will need another one for the BMT but i think they will just put that in at the time cos they don't want one in at the min cos of the potential complications they can cause.

The clot, they discovered from the ultrasound was around the line, literally circulating the line, they showed me on the machine though it just looked like black and white blurriness to me! Anyway the line was stopping it from being able to disperse and dissolve hence they have removed it. And the Heparin drug I've been on for 5 days is a blood thinning drug which assists the body in being able to dissolve it. It must have been alot bigger than it was cos my leg was swelled right up and now its gone right down and the pain is pretty much gone too now. So now my body naturally will disperse the clot with the assistance of the wonderful clexane injections. The heperin which i was having through my line has stopped now and I now have to have the wonderfully stinging injection once a day into my stomach! I've had these before and the injection is fine but they really sting after!! After so long I will go onto blood thinning tablets, this will last for about 3-6 months and I also have to wear tight fitting stockings for 1-2 years in bed at night to prevent against further clots. So its all good fun!! Hopefully they should be letting me go on Friday so only a coupla more days!

My taste is still all funny and my dry mouth varies, one day its ok, the next it drives me mad. My back is also really hurting cos i've been lying in the same position for so long and my stomach is sore too but apparently that cud be clot related just cos of where the veins went so that shud ease.

I feel okish in myself, it varies day to day to be honest, sometime during the day but I'll get there. I'm looking forward to some home cooking!!!

Think thats about it for now - nothing else to report! Thanks for all the messages in the guestbook!!

Mel xxxxxx"

Thursday 20th March

We had to pick up washing from the Nanny and some Easter cards from my mum and dad this morning. We left Burton about 9:45 and when we walked into Mel's room she was sat up in bed chatting to Lisa she seemed a lot better than she had in previous days. I had a feeling that they may let her home today and asked if she felt like she could go home. She said yes, but thought it would be tomorrow.

Just before 11am Dr. Sandor came into the room and explained she could go home once her medication had been sorted. Immediately after lunch, Mel wasn't feeling too good and was sick. It's the third time in a week she's been sick and although the hospital aren't concerned it's a mystery as to why it's happening. She says her mouth is really dry and that could be the reason she is being sick.

Dr. Haynes visited Mel five minutes before we returned from lunch. Sod's law that the consultant visits whilst we're away! He told her she wasn't to do much moving around and not to jump up and down if Liverpool score on Sunday against Manchester United. The body should dissolve the clot of its own accord but whilst it's there the danger is that it could get into the main vein and into the lung. In the unlikely event that happens the doctor assured her she'd know about it and we'd have to ring the hospital and come in straight away.

He explained that the search was still on for a donor. The ones they thought they'd identified weren't compatible. Once a new donor is found the process takes ten weeks and that is the critical aspect of Mel's disease. Despite the scan showing a positive result, it has to keep holding for ten weeks after in order for the transplant to take place. Dr. Haynes is pleased with results though and that's what we hold on to.

We got home about six o'clock. Mel fell asleep on the sofa and woke only for the District Nurse to do her Clexane injection.

Friday 21st March

We got to bed just after midnight last night. After just over a week of luxury in our own bed, we returned to the fold up bed in the living room. Whilst we're at home, as long as we've nothing to do in the morning, I don't set the alarm now. We wake up when we wake up. It means we sort of get the sleep we need.

I woke up a couple of times in the night and both times I'd gone to check Mel and she was sleeping soundly. As well as the worry over temperatures we now have the "blood clot" signs to keep an eye out for as well as the original Lymphoma too. It's not like we're watching her twenty four hours a day, but at the back of your mind you're aware of the possibilities. Other than that Mel's only other "out of the norm" issue was her back. She's getting bad back ache at the moment. She's taken codeine and Oramorph to control the pain.

It has been a quiet day, and as of quarter past seven, no dramas, hospital dashes or anything out of the ordinary.

Saturday 22nd March

If you don't count the backache, the stomach ache, the lack of energy, dry mouth, nausea and occasional coughing then Mel is fine! Nothing ever seems to be easy with Mel's particular strain of this disease. She hates being like she is, we hate seeing her like she is and seeing her in constant pain is a strain for us all. She woke at 3am this morning complaining of back ache, so we got up, sorted her out with some pain relief and also made up a hot water bottle.

The rest of the day was pretty much the same as yesterday. Tesco, Morrisons, dinner, football, tea, TV and then bed. Whilst at Morrisons I parked the car by the woods and stood staring into the trees remembering how the four of us used to walk our dog through there. Simple things. What I'd give to be able to walk through those woods again, with the four of us, talking, laughing and playing hide and seek. We'd look a bit stupid, two forty somethings, an eighteen year old and a twenty year old playing hide and seek, but who cares. A call was made to the hospital at midday to confirm it was ok for Mel to take Ibuprofen to help ease her pain. It was.

Cousin Sarah, Georgina and Carol visited and Mel, Sarah and Becky chatted for most of the afternoon. The Ibuprofen seemed to do some good and for a short while she had relief from the pain. I encouraged her to get up more often and she did this a few times. The idea is to try to help build up her leg muscles. But at the same time she can't do too much as the blood clot is an issue

Sunday 23rd March

Easter Sunday today, but no Easter Eggs for Mel, she's gone off chocolate . . . apart from After Eight mints.

At the moment, nothing much is changing. Julie and I have to pretend to be doctors when aches and pains surface. We have to make decisions and we always question those decisions. It's frightening at times, but we do it.

Since Mel came out of hospital on Thursday she hasn't improved. She hasn't got worse, but there's no improvement. It would be nice to see improvement, but she can only get upstairs on all fours, gets chest and back pain and whilst she's not depressed, she is down.

Julie and I didn't get up till after ten this morning, we didn't see the point. Mel was asleep, Becky was asleep. There was nothing to get up for. Mel admitted last night she's feeling irritable. We know she is. We understand why she is and it's horrible to watch and deal with.

Monday 24th March

As with yesterday and the day before, nothing has changed. Mel is no better. She has back ache, she was coughing in the night and had stomach pains when she woke up. The dilemma is, do we phone the hospital or not? It may be the stomach pains are down to hunger or it could be the blood clot working its way up. The back ache could be due to any number of things whilst the coughing is God knows what.

These aches and pains may just be the result of the high dose chemo (five weeks ago) or the blood clot. We're not doctors but we're expected to make these decisions. We don't know what to expect after a stem cell transplant. We don't know if this is normal. Happy Easter? It feels like we're being crucified at the moment!

The only difference from yesterday was that Julie and I got out for a half hour walk. We talked about how it was affecting us, how things were affecting Becky and of course how things were affecting Mel. It's so hard at times. As we walked around the golf course by the river we remembered twelve months ago. We'd moved house, the conservatory was being built and all was well with the world. How things change.

When we got home we had a chat with Mel about our own worries. We're concerned that she's becoming institutionalised. We want her to try and move around a bit more. She's looks like she's sinking at the moment and I tried to deliver a morale boosting chat. I said we'd take her to town tomorrow afternoon, maybe out for lunch later in the week. We need to get her out to take her mind off the situation as much as we can. The difficulty is that we have the doctor saying "Don't move around much", but at the same time Mel has to build herself up. We're doing what we think is right. That's all we can do.

My plan of leaving the alarm hasn't worked. I end up wasting too much of the day so I'm back to setting the alarm for eight o'clock.

After our chat, Mel was a lot happier. We have to say what we feel. She knows we have her best interests at heart and how much we love her but sometimes there needs to be honesty and tears.

Tuesday 25th March

I've said many times I take one day at a time because you never know what the day is going to throw at you. Today was a perfect example.

It started like any other. I woke up, made Julie a cup of tea and then folded the bed away.

Our plans for today were simple. In the morning I would go into work to hand in my latest sick note. After that I'd go home, make dinner and then in the afternoon we'd go into town taking Mel with us in the wheelchair. It was a chance for us to get her out in the fresh air and see some different scenery, not just the four walls of home. I started the dinner and asked Julie to get Mel up out of bed. Julie called from upstairs. Mel was in pain and in tears. She wanted to go to hospital. She'd had a bad night, her back and stomach were aching and she was breathless. She was coughing a lot. She needed to see a doctor.

I suspected they may keep her in, so as a precaution we packed her bag. We got to the hospital at about 3pm and saw one of the doctors. We had to walk about twenty yards from the waiting area to the treatment room. When we got there Mel was gasping as though she walked miles. As she'd not been moving around at home, I hadn't realised that her breathing/breathlessness had got so bad. We talked through things with the doctor, he consulted Dr. Haynes and it was agreed she should be admitted. An x-ray was taken, blood too and we were shown to Mel's room on Fletcher Ward. Once up there she was seen by the ward doctor who fitted a cannula (Dad's cue to hold her hand and keep her talking). Blood was all over the bed sheets and then not satisfied with the cannula, he wanted to do blood gases. A painful injection into the back of the wrist. Mel has had these before and they are painful, but this guy was good. He gave her a local anaesthetic, I held her hand, Julie went out the room and the doctor took the blood gases. We spent the rest of the evening in hospital, with Mel drifting in and out of sleep and pain. We drove home.

The x-ray showed that the tumour is reduced. I was relieved as my fear was that it was growing back from another area and thus causing the breathing difficulties. Mel had said the breathlessness was different from when her breathing was lymphoma affected, but I was scared it was attacking on a different front. Thankfully, as I said, it wasn't. The doctor's initial diagnosis is that it is an embolism. A CT scan tomorrow will confirm or deny this and they will treat her accordingly.

We've managed four days out of hospital.

Wednesday 26th March

Whilst Mel was sitting dozing in the day case centre yesterday, Jenny, one of the day case nurses was administering chemo to a guy. She was telling him about side effects, when he could drink alcohol, what alcohol he could drink etc. She asked him if he had a partner or if he lived alone to which he replied that he lived on his own. She then asked if he had any family and he told her that he only had a sister, he hadn't told her he had cancer as they weren't close and hadn't spoken for five years. Explaining that the side effects could sometimes be a bit frightening and appear suddenly she asked if he had a good group of friends who could look out for him. He hesitated and then just answered. . . "Not really, but I'll be alright." I thought it so sad that this guy was going to go through all this with limited, if any, support, other than that of the nurses and doctors at the hospital. I know that without the support of family and friends Mel wouldn't have coped half as well as she has.

The hospital phoned just before we left home to tell us Mel had been moved from Fletcher Ward back to Toghill. Mel was asleep. Dr. Sandor came to tell us that they suspect the problem is a PE (Pulmonary Embolism), but they are going to do a CT scan tomorrow (Thursday) to check that's all it is and they're not missing anything. The outreach team are also on standby should there be any problems. They are in effect the Intensive Care Unit and they're monitoring her closer than usual on the ward. If anything untoward happens and they're needed, they come to treat her on the ward. It's another sign that she's in the right place getting the best treatment.

She seemed bright in herself, I think she knows that something is wrong, but realises she's in the right place to have it sorted and that brings peace of mind. Both Julie and I commented yesterday on how brilliant the system is at Nottingham compared to other hospitals we'd been in. If there's a problem out of office hours at Burton you have to go to A & E, wait to be checked in, sit around for hours while they take blood and find out what's wrong with you, before they start treatment. When Mel had a problem such as this, we never managed to get sorted within three hours. At Nottingham though, she is taken either to day case or on to the ward and seen by people who know her and her disease. It's a far better and far more comforting system. We always felt that at Burton there should be an "out of hours" place to go to be seen more quickly instead of having the rigmarole of Accident and Emergency.

In terms of her condition, she remains on humidified oxygen. She has pain in her back and stomach and woke in the night with severe chest pains. This was dealt with by the nurses. Dr. Sandor came mid-afternoon to tell us they wanted Mel to take some more anti-biotics as they fear there may be an infection that is causing problems as well as the embolism. She explained that it could be just the embolism, it could be just the infection. . Or it could be both!

We think we should be more worried. We know this can be potentially life threatening, but so is the Lymphoma. I think that your reaction is the same whether it's one life threatening illness or ten.

Thursday 27th March

Mel is not good today. Her breathing is poor and deteriorated in the afternoon to such an extent they doubled her oxygen levels. To give you an idea, it took all her energy just to brush her teeth. Getting from the bed to the commode at the side of the bed is a major task. Her heart rate is fast and due to this a cardiologist has been asked to check her out. She was "Nil by Mouth" from half past eleven as she was due to have the CT scan at half past three in the afternoon.

I spoke to Dr. Sandor and she explained that the object of the scan is to determine whether or not there is a large or small blood clot (or no clot at all) and also if there's an underlying infection. Mel is on two lots of anti-biotics and the hope is that these will start working soon and she'll get better quickly. Both Julie and I agree that the scenario is very similar to when she had pneumonia. It's horrible to see her so ill again, so ill that it takes all her energy just to talk to us. So ill that she cant' walk the eight yards to the toilet. So ill that it takes everything out of her just to reach to the bedside table and lift a plastic cup of water. She is on fluids now as she wasn't drinking enough. These are fed through the cannula in her left arm. She's permanently on humidified oxygen and she's taking a lot of pain relief for the incessant pain in her back and chest and we're hoping that this scan will tell them what they need to know in order to get rid of whatever it is that is making her so ill. The outreach team are on standby. We feel helpless. We sit by her bed watching her sleep. Occasionally she wakes up for a sip of water or if the nurses come to do her obs, but other than that she has nothing to give.

When she moved into the bay Pam was her roomy, but Pam departed looking a picture of health for her seventy plus years and was replaced by Audrey. Audrey's husband and daughter are spending as much time at the hospital as we are. One room, two beds, two very ill people, both breathless, both in pain. One is over seventy. The other is twenty. Neither deserving of what they are having to endure.

Mel went for the scan and we were taken there by the fastest porter in the world. I'm sure there were sparks coming from the floor and at one point he took a corner on two wheels! The whole process from leaving the ward to returning took about an hour. Just after five o'clock Julie went for a cup of tea. She'd been gone two minutes when Dr. Sandor came in with the scan results. It's seems to be the way that if one of us steps out of the ward for a milli-second, a doctor or consultant will appear with an update.

Dr. Sandor explained that the good news was that there was no trace of a blood clot. However, there was trace of an infection and it is that that they have to sort out. The scan showed up something around the lung and it seems there's a lot of fluid. They are looking at putting a chest drain in Mel to get rid of the fluid, which in turn should aid her breathing. They will then rely on anti-biotics to get rid of the remainder of the problem. She also needs an ultrasound scan, which will be done tomorrow, to show how much of the infection is fluid. The presence of the infection explains the breathlessness and pain. Basically, her body is working twice as hard to fight it off. The good news is that out of the three possibilities, lymphoma, blood clot or infection, it's the best one to have. Serious enough to warrant keeping a very close eye on her, but better than the alternatives.

Apart from the tubes and masks that are attached to Mel, there is another sign that she's very poorly. I wore my Everton shirt to the hospital today and when she saw me she didn't say, "Dad, there's some shit on your shirt".

I wonder why when my daughter is so ill that I sit here writing this blog, but there's nothing else to do. We're by her bedside and we sit and wait. For nurses, doctors, scans, consultants, signs, results or news...We just sit and wait...

Friday 28th March

Before we left the hospital on Thursday night, we had a cannula episode. The people doing the CT scan knocked Mel's cannula. The dressing was soaked in blood and it clogged up the end of the line. That was taken out, and a new one inserted. They sent for one of the professional cannulisers and we told Mel that we'd stop with her until he'd finished and she was settled. At twenty to eight he arrived. I held Mel's hand and he attempted to insert the cannula. As he threaded it into one of the veins in her arm it looked like he'd succeeded but he hit a valve and the attempt had to be stopped. With Mel screaming in pain, he tried again. This time he was successful and slowly the fear in Mel's eyes abated. It was a traumatic end to the day, but as we said on the drive home, these episodes are becoming less and less traumatic for us. They're a part of life now although I'm sure Mel finds them as bad as ever.

Neither Julie nor I slept last night. We're both on edge and sleep isn't something that comes easy.

We walked onto the ward just after ten o'clock and as we walked down the corridor, the curtains around Mel's bed were drawn. I commented to Julie that she was probably on the commode. Nothing so simple. Her table was across her bed. She was sat up holding on to it. At the side of the bed was Dr. Sandor and she looked relieved when she saw us. She was about to attempt to drain some of the fluid from near Mel's lung. The idea being that if they managed to get some, they could get it analysed and hopefully identify the infection and treat it accordingly. The other benefit of this was that draining the fluid may also help Mel's breathing to become easier.

I stood at her bedside and held her oxygen mask in place with one hand and steadied her back with the other. Because she's in pain when she's sat bolt upright, I needed to hold her in position, so the doctor could administer the anaesthetic and then drain the fluid. Whilst I held her and talked to her, Dr. Sandor gave her the first injection of anaesthetic. Mel cried out in pain. We waited a few minutes. The second was given, followed by another short pause and then the third. All the time, Dr. Sandor was checking her obs. At one point her heart rate touched 175 and her blood pressure which is normally around the top nineties, dropped to 91. A few minutes later the doctor tested the area with the needle and Mel felt nothing. She began to drain the fluid, firstly for analysis and then to assist the breathing. She emptied the syringe into three separate pots and then the rest in a bed pan. All through the ordeal I talked to Mel and tried to keep her calm. The calmer her breathing the easier it would be for the doctor to get the fluid. In all she managed to get about 60ml of fluid, (it was a brown syrupy liquid) the site was covered with a plaster and she left, thanking me on the way for my assistance. Before she left she explained where the fluid had been lying. Over the lung itself are two layers of "tissue like" covering. The fluid had amassed in between the two. It puts pressure on the lung and the difficulty in breathing is increased. The idea of draining, apart from analysing the fluid, is that the pressure is released.

After the doctor had gone, Julie returned to the bay and washed and dressed Mel. The whole episode left Mel thoroughly exhausted. The sister on the ward came and changed her bed sheets, during which we had an interesting discussion on student nurses and hospital corners. Mel then slept for a couple of hours. Julie and I nipped over to Fiveways for our lunch and then settled back in our respective chairs to wait for Dr. Haynes or Dr. Sandor to bring us news of the analysis of the fluid. Mel woke up about half past one for her tablets.

Dr. Haynes, Mel's consultant, arrived with his entourage at about quarter past two. Mel's condition is down to an infection, a type of pneumonia. A course of strong anti-biotics is what is required and she will definitely be in hospital over the weekend and into next week. I would expect that over the next couple of days she'll begin to recover from the infection. It would be nice to think (again) that after this episode Mel could have a couple of months free of infection and other associated problems, but we're realistic enough to know that be it in five days, weeks or months, this could all re-occur and we'll be back here on Toghill, by her bed cursing the injustice of it all.

Yesterday, I spoke of the lady in the bed opposite Mel who was poorly. Unfortunately her condition worsened overnight and she passed away late this afternoon.

Finally, in terms of Mel's lymphoma, which at the moment seems like the forgotten illness, the signs remain good. It seems the high dose chemo/stem cell transplant she underwent seven weeks ago produced a durable response. We're on target and where Dr. Haynes would like us to be. A potential donor has again been identified, but as we know from previous experience, this does not mean they're an absolute match and the Bone Marrow Transplant will go ahead, but it's another sign that they're on the case and continuing the search!. Hopefully, we'll have more luck with this potential match. As yet the PCT has not responded to Dr. Haynes' request for funding, but that shouldn't be a problem. As our focus has been concentrated on, first the blood clot in the leg, and then the infection, we tend to forget about the lymphoma. When the blood clot situation was first diagnosed the tumour had been held for five weeks. It's now seven and that continues to bode well.

Saturday 29th March

Our emotions are being battered once more. After the talk with Dr. Haynes and Dr. Sandor yesterday we were pretty confident that Mel would soon begin to pick up and feel better. It doesn't seem to be the case.

We planned to leave the hospital yesterday (Friday) evening at around half past seven. We left at nine. The family of the lady who passed away in the bed opposite Mel left about an hour after she died, leaving her on the bed. The Healthcare Assistant came and washed her, wrapped her in a sheet, covered her in a blanket and left her on the bed. It was all done with great dignity and the Healthcare lady was brilliant. Another task that I didn't realise their job encompassed. The porters were called to come and fetch the deceased lady, but they didn't. Mel didn't fancy being left on her own in a room with a dead body. Although she couldn't see her, it was the thought of it so we said we'd stop with her. By nine o'clock there was no sign of the porters so with Mel drifting into a drug induced sleep and with her blessing we left her in the room with the body.

As we were getting into the car I had a horrible thought. Mel doesn't sleep with her glasses on and things look blurred.

What if whilst she was asleep, they moved the deceased lady out, then admitted another patient. Mel could wake in the middle of the night with curtains draw back, see a shadowy figure on the other side of the room and ... well . . you know where I'm coming from! We had to laugh. It may seem in bad taste, but sometimes you just have see the funny side of things amongst all this. If we didn't we'd never get through it.

I fully expected Mel to be feeling better today (Saturday). We arrived at the hospital just after half ten and she was fast asleep, looking as poorly as ever. We spoke to Dr. Sandor and she explained that Mel would be kept stable over the weekend and then have a chest drain inserted on Monday. This will be done with the help of Ultrasound. It will drain the fluid off the lung continuously. They are awaiting the results from the cytology department regarding the fluid taken from Mel yesterday. They are critical as they should tell them what they are dealing with. It seems that despite the fact that they know it's an infection, they're not sure what it is and what is causing it. In the meantime Mel just lies on her bed hardly moving, hardly able to breath and hardly speaking, eating or drinking anything.

We mentioned to her nurse that since she came in on Monday, she's not had a proper meal and is just nibbling on bits of apple. She is on a bag of fluid constantly. Julie washed and dressed her and Dr. Sandor returned to tell us that on top of everything else, Mel's blood test results showed she was anaemic. With that in mind they are going to give her a blood transfusion. This afternoon she had her tablets and within half an hour she was fast asleep. Before she fell asleep she wanted a drink of water and held out her had for it. There were no plastic cups so I went to the other end of the ward to fetch some. When I came back she was in the same position. Reaching out for the cup, but fast asleep. This is so hard to sit and watch.

On our way into the hospital we bumped into Lisa who Mel shared a room with last time round. She was admitted yesterday with low blood counts. She needs to be in hospital but looks so well. They moved Mel to another room after lunch. It's much more airy and a lot bigger than the other bays. There are only two beds in it, we're not sure yet what the name of Mel's new neighbour is, but we've seen her and said hello to her loads of times. They came to do her sats just after two o'clock and they were ok. Heart rate was 134, BP 97, although they were oxygen assisted. Just before four o'clock Julie and I went for a coffee and updated Becky.

When we returned, Mel was listening to the footy scores on my computer. As I sat in the chair by her bed, she kept calling out the scores and incidents to me. Despite the illness and how ill she feels, the spark appears now and then.

Mel's nurse for the day brought her Clexane injection and evening tablets. The blood arrived shortly after and the transfusion began. Dr. Sandor said this morning that after receiving this blood, Mel may feel a little better. The antibiotics appear to be doing little, but then again maybe they're stabilising her and without them she'd be even worse.

It's been a tough day, one of the toughest. Mel is sleeping a lot. Her breathing is as bad as I've ever seen it. As for Julie and I, well, we don't know what to think. We have to wait till Monday for things to start happening again. Weekends are so hard!

Sunday 30th March

Last night Mel had two bags of blood and they continued with painkillers and fluids. All they are doing is making her stable over the weekend. She slept well overnight and maybe that's why she has talked more today. I hope that over the next couple of days they'll be able to get to the root of this problem and start making her feel better. It's so frustrating at weekends. Nothing happens. Well, emergencies do. But whole departments close down and therefore things like results are put on hold. I presume Government funding is behind it. We didn't sleep again last night. An hour less sleep anyway, plus millions of thoughts racing round our heads, we were never going to sleep like babies.

Today is pretty much the same as yesterday. Mel was brighter in herself and chatted away. She ate a few tiny morsels of the roast beef dinner, but nothing much. She listened to the football this afternoon. We took a radio into the hospital but couldn't get a reception. We borrowed the nurse's radio but that was worse than our own. We tried listening on our respective computers and only mine would continuously connect so we ended up with Mel lying in bed and me sat at the side of her sharing a pair of headphones on a short wire!

I have noticed that Mel's started falling asleep in the middle of doing things (a bit like Everton's defence). She'll be cleaning her teeth or eating and she just dozes off. When we came back from dinner I walked into her room and she had fallen asleep eating her ice cream. Another example of how tired she is. It's strange though, she's brighter and more talkative, but in terms of the breathing, the pain etc, nothing has changed.

We've got through the weekend. I never used to like Mondays, but after spending a few weekends in hospital with Mel they've now got a certain appeal.

Monday 31st March

Mel's breathing and pain is the same. She's bloated too. The bloating is as a result of the fluids they are pumping into her system. It's a monumental effort to do the tiniest of tasks such as eating and brushing her teeth. We've no word from the cytology department and she was waiting for the chest drain to be inserted. Mel was seen by the registrar Maria, a German lady doctor whom we encountered in Derby all those months ago. We recognised her, she recognised Mel and it was quite the little reunion. She examined Mel and agreed with us that there was a lot of fluid build up in her body. She said that from her stomach to the top of her chest on the right hand side was full of fluid and once that was drained Mel's breathing would become easier. She said she would try to organise Mel's chest drain for the afternoon. It didn't happen. There wasn't time.

She will be put on the list for tomorrow (Tuesday). The fluids were stopped. I can understand them not knowing what is wrong with Mel at the moment. I can't understand why they seem do be taking their time in finding out.

A physiotherapist came to see Mel this afternoon and talked to her about breathing exercises and moving around once she gets her breath back. We feel we're in limbo. Nothing has happened. Mel's condition hasn't changed and we're waiting for things to be done, three days after they first said they needed doing.

We just sit here and wait. Worrying of course, because when you don't know what's happening, that's what you do. Tomorrow, Mel will have been in hospital a week and she's got worse without getting better. You sometimes expect a downturn in her condition just after she arrives whilst they sort out what the problem is, but we've been here a week. She's got worse and they've just stabilised her with no explanation of why she's feeling like she does and what they can do to sort it out. It's debatable whether the antibiotics have done anything. They may have stopped it getting worse, but they've not cured the problem.

There was a phone call to Burton Chemo Unit to cancel Mel's appointment with the psychologist tomorrow. In seven months she's seen her twice, maybe three times. Nottingham do not have this facility, so we have to book appointments through Holly who covers Derby and Burton. Every time Mel has a scheduled appointment with her something happens and she winds up in hospital and has to cancel. When you try to make another one it's normally about three weeks down the road which isn't very good. Debbie at Burton has said when Mel is ready she'll try and get her a new appointment quickly.

Mel was told today she qualifies for the extra menu. It's what you get for being a regular on the Haematology Wards. It's not Cordon Bleu, just a more varied choice. Tiredness took a hold again this evening and Mel fell asleep whilst holding her cheese sandwich! I can't remember her ever doing anything with food other than prepare it, pile it up on her plate and eat it!!

CHAPTER TWENTY THREE

Tears and Fears

Tuesday 1st April

I don't know where to start today. I don't know if I want to start.

Yesterday we decided to cancel Mel's Willows party. With her being so ill, there was no way she would be strong enough.

We arrived at hospital about 10.45 and Mel was on oxygen and fast asleep. She thought she was nil by mouth as they were going to insert the chest drain, but wasn't sure.

At about 11.30 Dr. Haynes, came in. Mel was drifting in and out of sleep as he told us the news we feared. The lymphoma has returned. The pathology results on the fluid taken last week revealed active lymphoma and that our one chance of a cure for Mel had gone. He explained that they'd thrown everything at the disease, but it had beaten them. There was nothing more they could do. Mel's care would now be palliative and ultimately terminal. Once out of hospital her care would be transferred back to Burton. The McMillan Nurses would provide support, as would the District Nurses. We were stunned. Julie and Becky cried. I tried not to. I don't want to cry. If I cry I admit defeat and not crying is my way of not being beaten by this horrible disease. He explained that the fluid would keep building so they needed to stop that. He went on to say that they would glue the two membranes covering the lung together and this will stop any fluid gathering there. As he finished speaking Mel woke, she hadn't heard the majority of what he'd said. Julie sat one side of Mel's bed, I sat the other and I broke the news to her that the lymphoma had returned. It was the hardest thing I've ever had to do.

A porter turned up to take Mel down to the radiology department to have her chest drain inserted. They got her onto the trolley bed and I went with her, holding her hand, talking to her and explaining more about what Dr. Haynes had said. The porter was a bit of a character who proceeded to tell Mel that once she'd had this chest drain done she'd be disco dancing in Nottingham. The tit!

After he'd gone I explained to Mel what the radiologists would be doing. They'd insert a chest drain to drain the fluid from her body. They drain it in 500ml stages with a break of an hour in between. The drain should be in for 24 -36 hours. Then they will send a powder (I'm sure the registrar said talcum, but she's German so I may have misheard her) down the line to seal the space between the two membranes to stop the build-up of fluid re-occurring. We also talked again about what Dr. Haynes had said. There were tears from Mel. I can't cry. My eyes sweat a little, but I can't cry.

We returned to the ward and they used a PatSlide to get Mel back onto her bed. It's a bit like a wide surf board that they slide between the bed and the trolley and then slide Mel over. Once she was settled, Mel had some dinner and we sat with her most of the afternoon and talked. She was dealing with it remarkably well. The odd tear, asking a lot questions and at one point she fell asleep in the middle of scratching her nose. She asked calmly if her care was now palliative or terminal. We discussed telling the family and friends. I offered to ring her closest friends, but with the exception of her oldest friend Claire, she wanted to ring them herself.

In terms of the treatment today, it's aided her breathing. She sat talking, albeit slowly, without oxygen for a good thirty minutes, only an hour and a half after having the drain in. I went out of the hospital, rang family and then returned to the ward. Mel had been chatting to Julie and Becky. She has some questions for Dr. Haynes tomorrow, as we all do. We want to know how long they think she'll have. Mel also wants to know .With Mel falling asleep as she spoke, I asked her if she'd

266

like me to ring her closest friends. She asked me if I would so I went and made the calls. It's not easy telling young people that one of their best friends is terminally ill.

When she comes home, we want things to be as normal as possible. I'll still diss Liverpool and tell her to pick her clothes up off the floor at home. I promised her that we'd answer her questions and tell her the truth. We've always given Mel and Becky loads of love, and we couldn't give her any more if we tried.

I said after Mel's stem cell transplant that I couldn't believe it would not work and we'd get to the Bone Marrow Stage. I couldn't believe that life could be so cruel as to put someone through all this and there not be a positive result at the end of it. How wrong was I? Life is unbelievably cruel!

I don't know what else to say.

Wednesday 2nd April

We were up early this morning in order to get to the hospital for half past nine. We arrived on time and we sat with Mel waiting for Dr. Haynes. Just after quarter past ten (you do a lot of clock watching in hospital) Maggie the ward sister came in and told us that he'd been caught up in clinic and would be with us later. Julie washed and dressed Mel, a major job in itself. I help her get up off the bed, lifting her legs round to the floor. Julie has to undress her, wash her and I pass and lift things. We spent the morning sat around the bed discussing all manner of things. Some meaningful, some stupid and most of which I can't remember. Mel was sore from the drain she had inserted yesterday.

In the middle of the afternoon Dr. Haynes visited us on the ward. He explained that the sample fluid they'd taken was analysed and an LDH test done. I don't know the details, but Dr. Haynes said the LDH count of a healthy person was 400. Mel's was 6400. He said that it would be pointless going ahead with the Bone Marrow Transplant, it would not have a lasting effect and it would be too dangerous. He went on to explain that we had now moved on to what they called Active Palliative Care. This meant they were trying to keep the disease at bay. For example, if the tumour started to grow again and got to the point where it was on the wind pipe, they may use Radiotherapy to stop its growth. It would be temporary, but it would keep it at bay. Ultimately, the disease would win and we'd then move on to Passive Palliative Care. It would no longer be possible to keep the disease at bay so they would just treat the symptoms. Pain relief would be at the forefront of this treatment. There may be times when Mel has to spend time in hospital and Doctor Haynes assured her that there would always be a bed for her at Nottingham if needed.

He also told us that initially the main thing was to get the lining around the lung sealed and that would be done tomorrow. Dr. Haynes explained that normally the success rate of this procedure is about 50%. With his guy doing it, the chances are nearer 80%. He will give Mel a local anaesthetic and then a form of sterile talcum powder (yes, talcum powder) is mixed into a liquid with water and poured down the drain in Mel's back and into the space between the lung and the membrane. If successful, this will stop fluid gathering in the future. That procedure is being done at nine o'clock in the morning.

He told us that Mel will have good and bad days. On the good days we may be able to go out and about, have days out etc. On bad days she would probably sleep. As time went on, the bad would overtake the good and eventually Mel would drift into unconsciousness and she would pass away. As he was telling her this we held her hands. She cried.

He told her it wasn't fair (I remember him saying that the first time we met him), he said they'd done all they could, there was nothing more that he or we could have done. He said there'd be feelings of anger and guilt. He then explained that we would be put in touch with the McMillan Nurses and they, along with our own District Nurse and GP would support us. He told us that he didn't know how long Mel has left. It could be weeks or months. Dr. Haynes delivered the worst news possible with such consideration and care. To tell a twenty year old girl they can do no more must be so hard, but he was kind, compassionate and as well as delivering the news also offered valuable advice.

After he'd gone there were more tears before Mel drifted off to sleep. A McMillan nurse came to see us and talked to us about their role. Mel tried to wake up to talk to her but couldn't so the nurse just talked to Julie, Becky and myself. One of their main roles is checking on the pain that Mel is in and then advising the doctors and nurses on pain relief.

After lunch, Julie and Becky went up to the ward whilst I updated Julie's sister and my mum and dad with the day's happenings. When I got back to the ward, Mel was awake and chatty. We discussed her coming home, food, football and the procedure that was going to take place tomorrow. Mel then ordered a tea and Julie drank it. It's a little scheme they have going between them and it saves Julie going over the other side of the hospital for a cuppa.

We left Mel watching Coronation Street and listening to Liverpool on the radio. It's incredible to think that less then twelve months ago, we were in Liverpool watching the reds play AC Milan on TV in a city centre bar. Dr. Haynes was right . . . it's not fair!

Thursday 3rd April

My day started by explaining the events of the last couple of days to Julie's work and Julie's mum. Julie's mum had been told before, but we wanted to go into more detail and fully explain what would happen over the coming months.

My next phone call will be to the university to tell them that Mel won't be returning and why. That's a job for tomorrow. Another job for tomorrow is to get Carol and the Nanny over to the hospital in Nottingham. In terms of the Nanny, I think it's important that she sees Mel. She probably imagines (and she's not alone) that she's somehow different. That she's turned green and has two heads. She's not. She's the same Mel that came into hospital a couple of weeks ago. Probably more drugged up. Falls asleep when doing things, slightly bloated on the legs, but other than that the same. She tells Becky off when she knocks the bed. She tells me off for rubbing her head without permission and Julie off for not sitting down and for constantly tidying up.

Mel slept for nearly eight hours last night, dropping off at half seven and waking up at half three in the morning. She was due to have the lung and membrane sealed this morning, but it didn't take place. There was concern that there was still fluid in the lung so they wanted to perform another ultrascan before going ahead.

Claire came to visit just after eleven and stayed until her car park ticket ran out at twenty past one. During that time, we left Mel and Claire to chat.

In the middle of the afternoon Mel went for her ultrasound scan. There was a little fluid left in the lung, but as Amy, the new doctor on the block, explained afterwards, there wasn't enough fluid there to stop the procedure going ahead. Mel was asleep when they brought her tea in and incredibly still asleep whilst eating it! Every now and then her fork would stick in the potato and I'd have to nudge her to eat some more. She half woke up and then insisted that Julie and I taste her cheese pie, saying that if she had to eat it, so should we. I couldn't. One sniff and I was two steps away from the sick bowl. Call me Mr. Picky, but I'll give that one a miss. Alison from the Stem Cell team came in to say hello.

Dr. Shaw came to see us at quarter to six. Becky and Julie nearly fainted. Apparently he was Premier League in the league of dishy doctors. He told us that this was one of four options and probably, taking in to account everything, the best for Mel. He explained the possible side effects of the procedure (infection etc) and the chances of it working. He explained how it wouldn't cure her breathing as the tumour, although inactive, is present and pressing on the lung. What it would hopefully do is help her breathing in terms of that particular issue (fluid build up). He put some taps into the drain line and then injected some anaesthetic into the drain. Whilst doing this he asked me about my rugby shirt. I explained about the pretty colours and told him that Mel and I were footy fans and he asked Mel who she supported. Up to this point things were ok, but Mel said Liverpool, he said he was an Arsenal fan and I wished I hadn't mentioned football! Becky decided that she'd stop with Mel for this particular procedure and it was nothing to do with the doctor being good looking!

After the anaesthetic had taken effect, he returned to us and carried out the procedure. The talcum powder was mixed and inserted down the line. The idea is that it causes irritation and inflammation and the lining of the membrane and the lung stick together. Mel can't have any anti-inflammatory tablets for a few days. We have to wait a couple of days and then the drain will be taken out. Dr. Shaw kept popping back for five to ten minutes to check Mel was ok. She was in a little pain, but the morphine sorted that out. He told her he hoped it would work and that he'd parked on double yellow lines to do this for Mel, but she was worth it. Becky swooned. We now wait to see if it works. As for Becky, she may take a while to recover!

In terms of Mel herself, she's been chatty today. Becky is considering her uni options and Mel called her a skiver, although I think secretly she's glad she's stopping at home at the moment. I don't think Mel has taken it all in. In a way it would be good if she never did. I imagine she's scared, but probably can't put into words what she feels. I don't think any of us can. I'm sure she knows that if she needs to talk we're there. What is going on in her head we can only imagine but I'm sure she knows she can tell us and we'll try to help.

THROUGH MELISSA'S EYES (Part Seventeen)

"How do I start? Last time I wrote things were looking up sort of, the tumur was down and we were going for bone marrow

stage. Not any more. Turns out the lymphoma is back in my system, they found out through some tests on the fluid that was around my lung which was causing my breathlessness and back pain. I've had a chest drain fitted to drain the fluid and it seems to have helped. I'm also having a procedure done in the morning (a few hours) to stick two parts of the lung together or something to stop the fluid building up again. I am dreading cos they use local anaesthetic and it fucking hurts!! Once that's done though they are looking at getting me home soon so that's good.

Anyway because the lymphoma is back it means I can't have the BMT and so now I am on Active Palliative care which means they are looking at controlling it with active treatment to keep it at bay. This might include radiotherapy or steroids, it all depends on how things progress. Eventually my disease will breakthrough and they will move onto just treating my stmptoms, making me comfortable and giving me pain relief. Hopefully I will be able to be at home for the majority of this but occasionally may have to go into hospital. I will be transferred back to Burton now also with my care as they can offer me everything there.

Needless to say I'm upset and shit scared but I have to be honest about things. They talked about how I'll start getting breathing problems and then slowly I'll sleep more and more until eventually I'll just pass away. Dr. Haynes talked about thinking about how I want and where I want this to happen. That's so scary. I don't want it to happen at all!! I thought a few months ago if they told me this I'd be prepared, I thought I was prepared for it but recently Ive started to believe things were gonna go right for us and now its gone the total opposite.

I cant write anymore at the min becos I haven't got my head round it. I can't take it all in. I'm so scared.

I'll try and update this more often I promise, I know I've been shit with it.

Mel xx"

Friday 4th April

Prior to leaving hospital last night, we sat talking to Mel about how she was feeling. She said she wasn't feeling as low mentally, than when she came into hospital and she feels like talking to friends more now. She said she was getting her interests back slowly but surely.

She had a stack load of morphine to help her over the pain of the procedure last night and that did the trick until this morning. Hiccupping hurts her back, but again pain relief controls that most of the time. Maggie the ward sister came in to tell Mel that they were going to remove her drain today.

This morning I phoned the university and the Willows Foundation. I explained to the university how Mel's condition had changed and there was now no chance of a cure. I hadn't spoken to the lady at the uni since August, so had to go through the whole scenario. At the end of it, I asked her if Mel would get any recognition for the work she'd completed and she said she would sort this out as soon as possible. It seems that she may get a Higher Education Diploma as she passed all the exams last year.

I called the Willows Foundation to inform them of the change too.

I went for some lunch at Fiveways and then drove home. I miss being at hospital. They were taking the drain out this afternoon and I wanted to be there. The McMillan Nurse was visiting and I wanted to be there. I know that it's important for Julie's mum to see Mel in order to come to terms with all that is happening, but I want to be at the hospital. I spent the afternoon at home, looking at how I may be able to get Mel tickets for a Liverpool game. Becky phoned at half past four to update me. I then picked up Carol and the Nanny to bring them over to see Mel.

When we got back to the hospital Mel hadn't had her chest drain removed. Becky had explained earlier that Dr. Haynes had been round to see Mel and check that the procedure was done ok. He said the line would be taken out later and that when Mel leaves hospital she will need oxygen and that needs to be sorted out. We're not sure whether we sort it out or the hospital. Either way, we'll deal with it. Dr. Haynes said Mel would probably be discharged on Monday or Tuesday.

At about quarter past six Maria (the German Doctor) entered the room to remove Mel's chest drain. Julie, her mum, Becky and Carol left the room and I sat with Mel whilst it was done. I held her hand as Maria asked her to sit on the edge of the bed. Although it's a chest drain it actually goes through the back of the chest. Mel asked her if it would hurt. Maria said no. She lied. Mel cried out in pain as the drain was tugged out. With the line removed, Maria left us. Mel and I hugged to try and make the pain go away. I'm not sure if the hug worked, but the second dose of morphine in ten minutes did! In time Mel worked herself back into her bed and I managed to convince her that she could get back on the bed and it wouldn't hurt. They give a local anaesthetic when they put it in. Why don't they do the same when they pull it out! The family returned and we started chatting again. I left to go to the loo and on my return saw Maria (the German Doctor) in the reception area. "Sorry about that" she said. I thought, it's not me you should be saying sorry to "me duck"!!

Mel's mood is pretty much the same as yesterday. I've not been at the hospital much, but when I have she's chatting about uni, food, hospitals and football. The last time I was on my own in the car driving home after bad news I cried. This time I didn't. I'm determined not to. I will in time. But not at the moment. If I cry this disease has beat me. I'll let it beat me when I'm good and ready. I find the worst time of day is when I go to bed at night.

Tomorrow Mel and I plan to watch the FA Cup game on the BBC. . . . oh, and stuff hospital food, we're all ordering in Domino's Pizza for dinner. We shall sit round Mel's bed, watch football and eat Pizza! We are rebels!

Saturday 5th April

Mel was asleep when we arrived at the hospital. After taking Julie's mum to see Mel last night we thought we should do the same for my mum and dad, so I rang them and told them I'd pick them up tomorrow and bring them over to see her. I don't want to be away from the hospital for too long, but I know the importance of the grandparents seeing Mel.

I picked up the Pizzas from the delivery guy and walked through the hospital holding the boxes. I walked onto the ward and the nurses drooled. Unfortunately, it was the pizzas making them drool and not me. Mel woke up when I walked in with the food and we sat and ate Pizza, chicken strippers and wedges. Every bit was eaten. Throughout the afternoon Mel kept saying how much she enjoyed it and that she could eat it again. It's the most she's eaten in two weeks. I know when we get her home she'll have plenty of home cooked food and will begin to eat well again. She's getting some of her taste back now. It's not back totally, but she can taste things for the first time in a long while.

This afternoon we listened to Five Live on the internet and watched the footy scores as they came in. Mel and I have been competing on Facebook's Premier Picks, where you predict the results of the weekends football matches. We did the same for the FA Cup. Mel won that one. I'm ahead in the Premier Picks by four points at the moment. It's a tough one to call!

During the afternoon, Mel's former roommate Lisa came in. They were letting her home this afternoon so she just came in to say goodbye. Her stem cell transplant is in May so hopefully she'll have four or five weeks "family time" before she comes back in.

Once Mel had woken up she was chatty. Her SATS were low at one point so she had to go onto oxygen for a while, but for most of the day she's been without it. I know that when we get her home, we'll have to have oxygen on standby. She may not need it all the time at first, but it needs to be there for when she does. Each time she needed the toilet she walked, the first time she's done that for a few weeks. On her return to her bed she needs to settle down and take in some oxygen,. Her back pain isn't the problem it was before, but her bum is numb through sitting on it all the time (mine's the same). The swelling in her legs has reduced somewhat, but the bottom of her legs are slightly swollen. She gets pain when she coughs. It's going to be tough when she comes home. At the moment she feels comfortable in the hospital. Any problems and a nurse is only a buzzer away. It will be different at home. Scary at first for all of us, but I'm sure we'll be ok and the care she'll have will be second to none.

Sunday 6th April

Mel was asleep when we went onto the ward. Shortly afterwards Mel woke up. She was in pain and had some morphine to ease it. She was taking in some oxygen and gradually woke up. She was able to walk to the toilet again today. Although, when I say walk, I don't mean with a spring in her step. Her steps are small and it's like she has to learn to walk all over again.

On the way home last night we discussed the house situation when Mel comes home. Our main aim is to make her as comfortable as possible. One of the main issues we face is Mel's ability to climb the stairs. With that in mind we took some measurements at home last night. We worked out that by getting rid of the furniture in the conservatory (something we were thinking of doing last autumn) and putting our table and chairs in its place, we could move a couple of other bits of furniture around and we'd have space to fit a single bed. We could then get a commode, Mel could sleep on the single bed downstairs, Julie and I could use the fold up bed at night and Mel wouldn't be on her own! Perfect! I rang Pauline and asked about getting a commode. After lunch I left the hospital and drove back to Burton to pick my mum and dad up. On my way home I stopped off at a bed shop and ordered a new bed for Mel. It will be delivered on Tuesday.

People keep asking how we're coping. It's tough, but we're concentrating on getting through one day at a time. Our main focus is Mel and Becky. We don't stop to think of the enormity of what's happening. There wouldn't be any point. It won't change anything. On our way home we always tend to have a discussion about the day and talk things through. We tend to focus on the day we've just had, but occasionally our thoughts turn to the future and what things are going to be like when Mel is no longer with us. The truth is we don't know. There'll be a huge void in our lives but she'll always be with us and there won't be a day goes by when we don't think of her. We'll miss her like you wouldn't believe, we'll cry, a lot at first, but we'll always have happy memories to turn to and even though she won't be there, she'll still be able to make us laugh and smile and that's what will help us through. It won't be easy.

Mel's back was hurting and she was suffering with pain and stiffness. She was coughing too and that caused pain. She spent a lot of time on the oxygen and had some morphine to take the edge off things.

Monday 7th April

Before we went into the hospital we went to update our parking ticket. Thankfully, we only pay £5 a month, due to Mel being on the Toghill Ward.

Mel was asleep when we went onto the ward. She sleeps a lot at the moment. I sat with her for a while holding her hand and within five minutes I'd nodded off too.

Julie had disappeared from the ward for what seemed like ages. Wendy was Mel's nurse today and she was explaining to us that they were looking to get Mel out of hospital on Tuesday or Wednesday. They were going to use an ambulance to transport her from Nottingham City Hospital to home. This is due mainly to her being comfortable and having the oxygen on tap. I gave Wendy the phone number of our district nurse Pauline. Several questions spring to mind, not least, who we call if Mel has a temperature.

We returned to the ward after lunch and Mel was drifting in and out of sleep. I sat by her and held her hand as she closed her eyes. Tears began to well up inside of them. I asked her to tell me if there was anything specific that was making her cry. She said it was "just everything". I asked her if she was scared. She nodded. I told her I was scared too. I think it's possible that all the events of the last week may be sinking in. I say by her side talking, trying to coax things out of her, but she couldn't talk about it. She said she wanted to come home. She went back to sleep.

Mid afternoon, Lindsey, the McMillan Nurse came to see us. She explained their role and that when we go home a local McMillan Nurse will be assigned to us. She also explained that Mel's care at home will be mixed between the Mac Nurses, the District Nurse and the GP. We enquired about what we do when Mel has a temperature spike and she explained that we would call the GP on call. We also chatted about the possibility of some aromatherapy for Mel, something she's had in the past that has helped.

Earlier, whilst I'd been sitting with Mel and holding her hand, Julie had been sorting out the logistics for when Mel comes home. Oxygen being delivered, District Nurses, GP's, McMillan Nurses, commodes, telephone numbers for contacts, beds being delivered . . . it all has to be arranged with a military like precision. Even the nanny was involved in the operations. Whilst she was sleeping Mel almost jumped out of the bed. It certainly made me jump. She was just twitching in her sleep. Whatever she was dreaming about, she'd just fallen off something I think. When she woke a little five minutes later, she was smiling about it. I held her hand and told her I'd make a deal with her. Next time she was scared, I'd tell her what was scaring me, if she'd tell me what was scaring her and she agreed.

Mel's nurse, Wendy phoned Pauline and sorted out everything for when we go home. It's going to be strange, but it will soon become the norm and we'll get our own routine. Mel woke up around tea time, but didn't talk much. We don't care. We just want to be with her as much as we can. As tea time approached Mel was getting hot. . so Becky sat with her and fanned her with a copy of this week's TV Quick! Only the arrival of morphine for Mel stopped Becky's fanning! After tea, Mel woke up and the three of us sat and chatted for a good hour and a half. Best of all we all laughed.

Our plan tonight is to leave the hospital around half past seven ish. Once home we have furniture to move around.

THROUGH MELISSA'S EYES (Part Eighteen)

"I know I'm crap at updating this these days but I just dont have the energy or motivation half the time. I dont really tonight. Just to let you all know I'm still in hospital but I'm coming home on Wednesday so thats good. I'm having a bed downstairs and a commode so I dont have to worry about going upstairs as I dont think my breathing could handle it right now.

I find myself sleeping alot of the time to shut out the thoughts of whats really happening but i think when i get home things will be better because i'll have more to do and more people to see. In here its just the same everyday and I can't handle it for much longer. Only one more day to go....

I appreciate all the messages of support even if I dont get back to you all. I'm scared of everything thats coming but I need to try and be strong and make the most of things.

279

Anyway I'm going to try and get some sleep.

Sorry this is so short but i really dont know what else i can say.

mel xxx"

Tuesday 8th April

Last night we commenced operation, "Get Mel Home". Just before and just after midnight I had a couple of texts from Mel asking for food to be taken in in the morning. A sure sign that she'd started on the steroids. Mel spent a lot of time on the Internet last night, updating her blog and posting on various sites. She also texted her friend Sooty and then texted Dan Robinson to tell him that the lady in the next bed was noisy.

As we walked into the Mel's room we were visited by the doctor who checked all was in order for her discharge tomorrow. Faith said a quick hello and then five minutes later Dr. Haynes came to see Mel. He tapped her back and commented that it sounded like the pleurodesis done by dishy Dr. Shaw had been a success. He also said that she looked a lot better than she had a few days ago. In terms of her steroids, she'll have four days on high dose dexamethasone and then ten days on a lower dose. He explained that he wanted to carry on the Clexane injections for the time being. He told us that if we had any problems he was only a phone call away. Before he left I thanked him for all he'd done for us. I said that even though things hadn't turned out how we'd hoped, we know we've had the best treatment possible and we couldn't have asked for more. The discharge nurse came to us and told us that everything was in place for Wednesday. Once Mel is ready to go, the ambulance will be called and Julie will travel with Mel whilst Becky and I drive home. I've always wanted to race something with blue flashing lights!

Whilst having our dinner, the Nanny called to tell us that the oxygen had been delivered. We have one machine that churns it out continuously, one large cylinder and one portable cylinder. All we have to do if we need anymore is ring the oxygen hotline and bingo, they deliver the next day! Back at the hospital, we spent the first part of the afternoon sat around Mel's bed chatting. She talked of people she'd spoken to the night before, some of the internet stories she'd read. Despite her own situation, she still takes time to help others. We talked about food (steroids again), bacon twists from schooldays and hot crumpets with melted cheese on them. It was great just to sit there and listen. Those of you who know Mel will know . . . . she loves to talk . . . and it's never sounded better!

Mel's nurse, Nerys, then came to check the oxygen. The machine we're having at home is set at number two, whereas in hospital, Mel is on number 4. Mel went on Number 2 for a while this afternoon and kept saying that she needed more. . . actually Julie hadn't switched it on, so she wasn't getting any! Whilst this was happening Becky and I went down to try and get Mel a magazine. We got into the lift, I pressed the button for the ground floor without looking and accidentally hit the panic alarm button. An intercom rang in the lift and then stopped. Then it rang again. Becky was in fits of giggles and no help at all so when we hit the ground floor, with the intercom still ringing, we left the lift. I'd taken about four paces out of the lift when I heard a voice say, "Lift control, hello . . .anybody there? Hello?". I dashed back into the lift and apologized for setting their panic alarm off and told them I wasn't trapped, I'd pressed it in error. The voice came back, "Are you sure you're ok?" "Yes, fine, sorry" . . . . and we went on our way. With our lift episode and Julie's oxygen issues, I do worry for Mel when we get her home!

At quarter past five we ordered Pizza again. The works. It's been a good day today. We've had loads of chat, lots of laughter and at the same time things have been sorted for Mel's homecoming. Her new bed arrived in the afternoon too. We're all set. We're stopping at the hospital later than usual this evening to watch the Liverpool and Arsenal game with her. We know the steroids are having an effect, they give her an appetite and lift her spirits, but if they continue to give us days like these we may all start taking them.

Wednesday 9th April

Yesterday evening we watched the Liverpool game and ate pizza. When Liverpool scored their first goal, Mel said that if she could have babies she would have Torres'. She then said never mind babies she'd just sleep with him. I commented that she'd need her oxygen afterwards, to which she replied she'd probably need it before, during and afterwards.

With ten minutes to go in the Liverpool game, Mel needed the toilet. She decided to wait as the game was on a knife edge. With five minutes to go she couldn't wait any longer and went to the ladies. Arsenal scored. I ran to the ladies, knocked on the door and whispered to Mel that Arsenal had knocked one in. I went back into the room to join Becky and no sooner had I sat down than Liverpool scored again. I ran back to the ladies and whispered through the door, "Mel, Liverpool have scored, Gerrard penalty". Back into the ward, Liverpool got another. I was backwards and forwards to the ladies, whispering through doors, God knows what they thought! Mel eventually walked slowly back into the ward and as ambled across to her bed, looked at me and said, "I missed three frickin goals. . three frickers!"

We couldn't help but laugh.. We said on the way home, we've laughed more in the last couple of days than we have in the seven months. It's bizarre.

We got over to the hospital this morning for 10am. Mel got dressed and while she did so I took some chocolates down to the day centre people as a thank you. We did the same for the Toghill Ward nurses too. We sat around in the hospital, doing crosswords, making a few phone calls and six hours later we left Toghill. Everything in hospital had been organised with a military precision. The District Nurses, McMillan Nurses, GP's etc had all been sorted, the transport too. Unfortunately, there weren't enough drivers to bring Mel home. So, Nottingham paid for a private ambulance company to take Mel home. Julie and Mel said the couple driving them were like Jack and Vera Duckworth. It took me and Becky forty minutes to get from Nottingham to Burton. It took Jack and Vera an hour and a half.

I have to say that throughout Mel's time at Nottingham, the staff have been brilliant. We couldn't have asked for better treatment, care and support. The only problem with the NHS is the pathetic support given to them by our government. Everything is paperwork and target driven. Even Mel's potential life saving Bone Marrow Transplant had to be costed and the funding applied for. It's pathetic. Why can't they let nurses nurse and doctors doctor. Maybe it's just too simple. Of course, it worked in years gone by. They didn't need a Ward Manager or a Discharge Co-ordinator. Matron's ruled the wards and it worked. It could still work, if only the government would take off their blinkers and realise they have a fantastic product, they just don't manage it very well.

We got home at about quarter to six, Mel and Julie arrived and Mel saw her new bed for the first time. After she'd settled, she sat on the sofa and I went to the chip shop for our tea. Pauline turned up and explained what she'd done already and what she was planning to do. She is brilliant. Our McMillan Nurse is visiting us tomorrow (Thursday), with Dr. Tansey (our GP) coming on Friday. After Pauline had gone, we settled down for the evening. Mel had her oxygen machine which gives a constant supply. We do have a couple of cylinders, one for back up in case of power cut, the other is portable for if we go out. Mel and Becky sat on the sofa talking about uni days, Julie packed away the stuff we'd brought home from hospital and we had a relaxing evening.

Thursday 10th April

We sat up watching TV yesterday till just before midnight. Julie and I slept downstairs on the fold up bed. I took a sleeping tablet and that helped me sleep until about 4am when Mel got up to use the commode. Julie didn't sleep much at all so at

4am I sent her upstairs to sleep in our bed. I sort of slept on and off till my alarm went off at 8am. Julie slept soundly. What kept us awake was the sound of the oxygen machine. The humming noise it makes isn't so bad, but every ten to twenty seconds there's like a drum beat as the pump kicks in and out. Mel woke up to use the loo again and then went back to bed. She complained of back pain at about half past eight, so I gave her some Oramorph to ease things. She came off her oxygen for a while and went to sleep.

Julie (District Nurse Sister) visited. As she chatted Mel was half asleep but chipped into the conversation every now and then. Mel decided that today would be a lazy day and she stopped in bed all morning. She took her tablets, all sixteen of them!! We spent the rest of the morning discussing food and what I could cook for her over the coming days.

Early afternoon we had a visit from our McMillan Nurse, only she wasn't a McMillan Nurse, she was from St. Giles Hospice. We all liked her. I went out just after two o'clock to get the headboard for Mel's new bed. When I got home the house was full. There was Mel, Becky, Julie, Julie's sister, Hannah and Sarah (Mel's cousins) and Gary (Sarah's dad). I'd been to pick up the ironing from Julie's mums and she was on her own, so I zipped back to her house, picked her up and brought her to join the party. Mel really enjoyed it.

After they'd all left we had our tea. Cheese and Potato pie. Whilst it was cooking we decided to remove the dressing from where Mel had had her drain removed. Mel had been complaining of a sore back all day. I removed the dressing and it revealed the cause of the pain. At the bottom of the dressing was a graze like mark, it looked sore. I gently covered the sore area and waited for the District Nurse to visit later for advice.

We had a visit from Anne, the aromatherapist. She spent about half an hour with Mel and left us her number so that when Mel wants another session, we can just call her. The District Nurse arrived just before 8pm to do Mel's Clexane injection. We also got her to take a look at the grazing wound on Mel's back. She checked it over and advised us. She said she was going to employ me as my re-dressing of the graze was very good.

Mel has been in good spirits today, she's currently on the high dose of steroids and her appetite reflects this. She's had a couple of doses of morphine. She got out of bed this morning and helped herself to a yogurt (something she wouldn't have done a week ago) and she's been off oxygen more than she's been on it today.

Friday 11th April

Our GP and Pauline, the district nurse visited today. They spent an hour or more with us, sorting medicines, offering advice and checking our welfare. Pauline brought Mel a "Snuggly Mattress". We fitted it this afternoon and it we all had a go, it is so comfy and the most important thing was that Mel liked it. Claire came round to see us, she'd been here about half an hour when Mel started to feel very sleepy. Claire left and Mel fell asleep for the best part of two hours. Whilst she slept, Julie sorted out our bedroom and Becky and I caught up on LOST. Mel had a bath before tea which she enjoyed, but she needed her oxygen after getting out of the bath.

She went on the internet during the evening. Someone on the MacMillan site asked a question about steroids and Mel replied ...

"Hi
I am on dexamethosone at the moment. im on a continuous dose of 4 days of 20mg and then 7 days of 4mg. Ive had them in the past and found they really helped with pain and appetitie though i did have a bit of trouble sleeping and also some issues with bloating and the mood face but generally ive found the benefits to outweigh the side effects. also find they keep your spirits up qite a bit and increase energy which i always find helpful!!
hope that helps."

I think that posting says so much about Melissa and the brilliant way in which she has dealt with this disease. Ten days after being told that they can do no more for her, she is on the MacMillan (www.macmillan.org.uk) site helping other people...I cannot put into words how proud I am of her.

Saturday 12th April

Mel received some lovely letters and gifts in the post today including a certificate from Aston University. It was a Certificate of Higher Education to recognise the work Mel had done in the first year of her Psychology course. There was a letter from the Willows Foundation. With Mel not being able to have the party she wanted, Willows asked if there was anything else she'd like. We looked at the football fixtures and noticed that Liverpool play Birmingham on 26 April. Birmingham is close by and although St. Andrews isn't Anfield, it would be a chance for Mel to see the Reds in action.

With Mel spending a lot of time in/on the bed, she wanted something to pass time. She thought about colouring yesterday, so today we bought her a couple of books and some pencil crayons. We arrived home and Becky and Mel sat together on the bed colouring. It was like turning the clock back about fifteen years. The two of them sat together, colouring in and Mel telling Becky where she was going wrong. Mid afternoon there was a knock at the door. It was Julie's sister. Shortly after, there were more visitors. This time it was Sarah and her boyfriend Nick and also arriving at the same time was my sister Karen, her husband Martin, and their two girls Abbie and Caley. We sat around talking for an hour or so when there was yet another knock at the door. It was Phil, Dan, Carly and Sooty!

At about half past four, with just Mel's uni friends left, we ordered pizzas for tea. Mel's friends left about half past six. She loves having friends and family visit and receiving messages of support. It means so much to her and us. You can't believe how good it is to just sit here and listen to her chatting away. Mel has always been the sociable one of the family. Whether it be visiting her Nannies or meeting up with school or university friends, she's always enjoyed having people around her. Thank you, it really does mean a lot to us all.

The visits do take it out of her. We watched the end of the football and whilst watching it, she talked endlessly about the visits this afternoon. By eight o'clock, she suddenly felt tired. She needed oxygen. The day had caught up with her and she fell asleep.

Sunday 13th April

After falling asleep at eight, she woke up a couple of hours later and for an hour or so we had a conversation that covered a range of topics in which she discussed leaving her body to science, burial v cremation and what to do with her ashes. Crazy isn't it?

I'm not sure how it started, but Mel began talking about donating her body to science, she didn't think she'd be able to donate individual organs as she thought she would be classed as "damaged goods", but she liked the thought of helping others so considered donating her body to science. We talked about the pros and cons and in the end she decided against it. She wanted to be cremated. She didn't want to be buried in case she was still alive.

The talk then turned to where she wanted her ashes scattering. Her first suggestion was Fernando Torres' back garden, but then we pointed out he may move and with the greatest respect, he probably wouldn't take Mel with him. She was adamant she didn't want to be scattered. Becky suggested scattering some at Aston and some at Burton, but Mel said she wasn't keen on having her boobs in Branston and her bum in Birmingham! She thought about being scattered in the lake at Aston University but I pointed out that on more than one occasion some of her friends had ended up in the there, and there was something a bit spooky about that. The conversation ended with her saying she would think about it. She then said she wanted a bench with her name on it. "I'd better get a bench" was her final comment before she fell back to sleep. It may sound strange to be talking about such stuff, but I'm glad we can. We can laugh about it with each other at the moment and that's important.

She had a good lie in this morning and was slow to get up. By the time I was serving up the dinner, she'd got washed and dressed with the help of Becky's nursing skills. Earlier this morning, whilst I was preparing dinner, Becky was giving Mel a back rub. She kept going until her hand was aching. During the back rub Mel kept warning Becky to stay away from her dressing . . . saying only dad was allowed near it!

Mel had a few pains in her back and chest this morning and coughed a few times. It is worrying when this happens, but we have to learn not to panic at the first cough or pain. Mel now has a patch on her back, similar to a nicotine patch, but it releases pain relief. It was offered by the district nurse and GP on Friday so we thought we'd give it a go. It can be used in conjunction with other pain relief and to be honest, anything that helps is welcome.

The district nurse came just after eight o'clock and was asking Mel about that afternoon's Liverpool game (trying to take her mind off the injection), Mel was telling the nurse who scored for Liverpool, "Torres, Voronin and . . errr Gerrard" . . ."Little prick" said the nurse. . . . I thought that was a bit harsh, but then realised she was warning Mel of the impending injection!

Another good day on the whole. A lot of visitors, plenty of football, and some laughs too.

Monday 14th April

I didn't sleep well last night. The sleeping tablet didn't work and I was restless. I woke up at quarter to seven and woke Becky up. She was off up to university today to sort out her plans over the coming months.

Mel was chatty today, a little back pain again, but the morphine is keeping that under control. Pauline visited to check that Mel was ok and to see if there was anything we needed. We discussed Mel's medication and told her that we'd had a call from someone who works at the local hospice who will come to speak to Mel and help with her psychological needs. Mel drops her steroid intake as from today. She has a high dose for four days and then a lower dose for ten.

With Pauline having left, Mel put her coat on, we put the wheelchair in the car along with a canister of oxygen and set off for town. Mel bought a DVD, a book, a new phone and a present for Becky. We went from The Carphone Warehouse to Phones 4U that many times we made tyre tracks in the shopping centre. She got home and we started sorting out her new phone. Mel's friends, Sophie and Matt came to visit. Sophie was the first person Mel met when she went to uni and I can remember that day so clearly. They chatted for a few hours and as with all visitors, it does Mel the world of good and we can't thank them enough.

Tuesday 15th April

We took Mel out for dinner today. We went to a pub with a carvery, just outside Stafford. On the way back we called in town to get Mel a case for her new phone. It was a good test run in preparation for our proposed trip to Liverpool on Thursday. We took the portable oxygen with us.

Faith called this morning. She was checking how Mel was. We told her that so far she was good. She had back pain, but she was probably as well as she had been since diagnosis. We told her it was a surreal situation. Here she was, feeling as well as she had done in months, but at the same time we were faced with the knowledge that the disease was now incurable. It's so hard to deal with. You can't believe that things aren't going to work out. It's why we continue to make the most of good days. We plan things a few days in advance but, as with the trip to Liverpool, we'll wake up on the day and if Mel feels like going, we'll go, if she doesn't, we'll stop at home. Last night I sat up with her till about half past midnight, just chatting.

We talked about her new phone, football, the trip to Liverpool, visits from her friends and just normal stuff.

On the way back from our lunch trip we had to call at the chemist to pick up some of Mel's medicines. We also had a big bag of old tablets, syringes, powders and potions to drop off. We now have to monitor how much morphine Mel is having, this is so they can balance things out with the pain relief patch she has.

In the middle of the afternoon my mum visited. Mel received a package in the post this morning. I've said before she loves receiving cards and letters in the post. The package this morning was full of goodies . . . but not just any goodies . . . Marks & Spencer goodies. I noticed there were ginger biscuits amongst the goodies. It's not the first time this has happened. I've mentioned on the blog some other things that Mel fancies and they either arrive in the post or people bring them when they visit. At times we've had more Maltesers in our house than Willy Wonka. All because that at one time I mentioned in my blog that Mel was keen on Maltesers. At this point I'd just like to point out that I have always been very impressed with the BMW 3 series!!!!

CHAPTER TWENTY FOUR
Special Days

Wednesday 16th April

I woke at five this morning, Mel had back ache and was coughing. Julie got up to sort her out with some linctus and morphine. I woke up at eight o'clock, Mel was asleep, she had the fan on and was on oxygen. She woke up and asked for morphine. I sorted her out with that and after having a bit of a chat, I went to Tesco. I bought Mel some Party Rings, Chocolate Fingers and Oreos amongst other things. Mel did a bit of colouring and then got changed. The postman delivered a package for her. This time is was a few quizzes to keep her occupied (thanks Nancy!).

Early in the afternoon I went to pick up Mel's friend Sooty from the station and when we got home we ordered pizza. Carol visited too so it was a busy house. Earlier in the morning Pauline called to see how things were. I explained to her that we wanted the morphine in the vials, not the bottles as they were easier to administer. Dr. Tansey is coming to see Mel on Friday. Mel's been in good spirits today, she's had friends visit her and she chatted for ages. Tomorrow, we plan to go to Liverpool. It was the trip we wanted to make back in August, but never made. Since day one, I've said to Mel that one day, we'd make that trip to Liverpool...tomorrow we aim to do it.

Thursday 17th April

Yesterday evening Mel and Becky sat up till 1am. They were chatting as Mel bonded with her new phone. I woke at quarter past seven this morning, came downstairs and gradually woke Mel up. She had a bad attack of back pain at one point and as a result we phoned the hospice nurse, who will visit tomorrow (Friday) and advise if her pain relief needs changing. The pain relief patches don't seem to be having a great deal of effect, but we'll go on the advice of the hospice nurse, the GP and the district nurse, all of whom are visiting tomorrow.

Getting ready to go out for the day is no longer the five minute task it used to be. We have to pack the wheelchair in the car, along with the cushions that Mel now requires to ease her back. We also need two cylinders of oxygen, one for whilst we travel around in the wheelchair and one for the back seat of the car in case Mel needs it whilst travelling. Then we have to sort out all the tablets she'll need whilst we're out along with the food/snacks she'll want. . . . and that's without getting ourselves sorted.

We set off for Liverpool just after 9am. As we left, Parcel Force came to the door and delivered a box addressed to Mel. We got to Liverpool at 11am, parked up at the Albert Dock and made our way to the dock. We had a wander round, I was responsible for pushing Mel around in the wheelchair. The last time I pushed her around it was in a pushchair.

Once in the city centre we headed for Nandos for our dinner. I noticed whilst wheeling Mel how we take things for granted when walking, such as being able to go from A to B without going via C, D and E. At one point we wanted to go into St. John's Shopping Centre, we got to the front of it and of course, you can't go up the steps, so you have to walk about thirty yards to the right, up the ramp and then thirty yards back. Don't get me wrong, it's not a great distance, but as I said, when walking, it's something you take for granted.

Mel was in her element as I wheeled her round and she ended up spending some of her money on Liverpool tops and shirts. The rest of the afternoon was spent shopping with Mel, Becky and Julie. I can't remember the last time I walked so far, but it was great to walk around the city. The memories came flooding back to the time Mel and I travelled up there on the night of the 2005 Champions League Final. Everything we do at the moment is bitter sweet. It's great that we were able to take Mel up to Liverpool as we promised, but it's tinged with an element of sadness as we remember how things used to be (and still should be). We have to make the most of what we have and enjoy these special days and moments and today was special.

When we got home we unpacked the car, got Mel settled on her bed and she opened the parcel that had arrived this morning. It was from a lovely person in America called Virginia. She'd sent Mel a box of goodies to cheer her up and a lovely letter too. There were t-shirts, pyjamas, jogging bottoms, sweets (candy), drinking glasses and plates with monkeys on them and a whole host of things that brought a smile to all our faces. Be it letters, cards, parcels or text messages, the stuff that Mel gets via the post and phone helps to keep her spirits up. So thank you again and again and again.

Finally, I checked our phone for any messages. There was one. It was the Willows Foundation. They've managed to get Mel, myself, Julie and Becky tickets for the Birmingham v Liverpool game at St. Andrews a week on Saturday. We'll have our seats in the ground, wheelchair place and parking space. So thank you Birmingham City and thank you Willows!

Friday 18th April

After our exertions of yesterday the plan today was to rest as much as possible. We didn't get up until just after nine o'clock and Mel woke not long after. She needed some morphine as the pain in her back was intensifying. Jane, the hospice arrived, we'd asked her to call and check Mel out with regards to the back pain. Our concern was that the tumour was pressing on a nerve. Part of Jane's role in all of this is to assess Mel's pain and offer advice to the GP as to which medication may help.

She wrote a letter for the attention of the GP who was due to be visiting later in the day. Mel attempted to have a bath later in the morning, but the pain got the better of her and she was only able to stay in the bath for a matter of minutes before she was crying with pain. We got her out of the bath and she lay on the bed. We were visited by Pauline and shortly after, Dr. Tansey. He takes time to explain things and that helps. We mentioned about Mel's back pain and he explained that if it were the tumour then chances are the pain would be permanent, whereas it seems to only occur whilst Mel is sitting up unsupported. He agreed with Jane's choice of drug and along with others, it was prescribed. He also enquired about Becky's health and asked how Julie and I were. The doctor and nurse left about three o'clock The Nanny popped round for an hour to see Mel and to look at the things she'd bought yesterday. Mel fell asleep during the latter part of the afternoon as the visit of doctors, nurses, nannies etc caught up with her.

Saturday 19th April

Whilst I was in the kitchen cooking dinner, Julie got Mel out of bed and washed and dressed her. The morning was littered with doses of morphine as Mel's back continues to ache.

This afternoon Mel had a few university friends visit and the house was full of girly chat.

Next week we have something planned pretty much everyday, so there's plenty to keep both Mel and ourselves occupied. A short blog today, probably the shortest since the blog began, but there's nothing much to say.

Sunday 20th April

Mel takes time to wake up in the morning and has probably had her oxygen on more than of late. Her back pain is causing her problems and if I'm honest, she's worse than she was, say a week ago. Only subtle things, but as Dr. Haynes told us before we left, there'll be good days and bad. On the whole though the days are good.

I went to Morrisons this morning to get the days supplies. I know it may seem strange that I go everyday and not on a weekly basis, but Mel's appetite is such that she fancies different things on different days and it's important for her to eat and keep her strength up. Therefore, it's easier to go every day and at least that way she has what she fancies that day rather than buying a trolley load of shopping and then wasting half of it. It also ensures that the food we get is fresh.

We had a house full of visitors this afternoon, Julie's sister Carol, Keith and Georgina, her brother Ray and his two children Katie and Lee all came to see Melissa. After they had left, Claire joined us for a couple of hours. Then as she left, Mel got a phone call from her friend, Amar. With Mel being as ill as she is, I often find myself asking the "Why" question. Why Mel? What has she done to deserve this?

Monday 21st April

Not a manic Monday, just a quiet one. Becky was in Durham and returns later this evening. This morning I went to Becky and Mel's (and my) old school. I wanted to update them on Mel's condition. I went in and was taken to the headmaster's office. The last time I was in there was about 30 years ago, I'd been sent there with a couple of mates. We'd been caught chair tossing! We had invented a great new game which involved standing about ten feet away from a particular desk and toss the chair with the aim being that it lands on the desk. Of course it was a crap game, the chairs just slid off the desks and onto the floor, well apart from the one that wrapped itself round this lad's leg. Who'd have thought then that thirty years later I'd be back in there telling the headmaster of the day that my daughter had an incurable disease?

After going to the school I took another certificate into work and spent a good three quarters of an hour in there. The usual emotions come to the fore. I should be there, working. My daughter should be at uni and not lying down on a bed under the stairs hooked up to oxygen. When I got home we all went a ride out to try and find a wig shop that we'd heard about. Mel sat in the car and unlike Thursday when we went to Liverpool, this time, she did need oxygen. We hooked up one of the portable cylinders in the car.

Whilst I'd been out this morning Jane, the McMillan Nurse called. The District Nurse also called to see how Mel was and how she'd been over the weekend. Today, Mel's cough is slightly worse, as is her breathing. It's noisy and I feel like I want to reach down and clear whatever it is that is causing this. The Hospice doctor is due to call on Wednesday and I'm sure we'll be able to voice any concerns we have.

Mel is due a visit from the aromatherapy Annie tomorrow and that always relaxes her.

Tuesday 22nd April
I stopped up with Mel last night until quarter past one in the morning. It's not easy keeping your eyes open when you've had a sleeping tablet, but I managed it . . . . just! She was on her computer, updating her blog. I stopped with her because when she'd finished she's unable to lift the laptop off her legs, so she needed help. I like reading Mel's blog, it gives us a partial insight into how she's coping with the situation and it brings home what she is feeling. I know I write on here everyday, accounting for what's happened and any changes in her condition etc, but nothing gets the message across better than listening and reading to Mel's own words. What follows below is an abridged version of how Mel is thinking about, and coping with this horrible disease.

"I know its been forever since I updated and I will try more to do it, its just I don't have the energy half the time and I don't know what to write the other half........I'm relativley ok, glad to be home and in my own surroundings........I have to use a wheelchair now everywhere I go which is strange and not particularly nice but it means I can get out ....I've been into town a couple of times................Its a big effort and it tires me out but at least it makes a change from the four indoor walls of the house............I've still got some pain in my back which isnt really improving despite all the painkillers I'm on but they are upping my dosage so I'm hoping that will make a difference

...............*They think its some kind of nerve pain..............I'm also more out of breath than I was a week ago and using more oxygen...............Things arent going to get better, though they may improve some days over others....................I'm feeling okish in myself, bit irritable at time, anger at the situation I guess and the unfairness of everything....................one minute I'll feel fine and motivated and want to talk to people......................... the next minute I wanna curl up in a ball and cry my eyes out though I havent actually done that yet................I'm having alot of visitors which is good.................some days I like to be more quiet and relaxed..................I hope to have a relaxing day finishing with a nice 1 or 2 nil victory over Chelsea in the Champions League (hey i can still dream!!)*

On Thursday I'm hoping to get into Birmingham for a few hours, have a meal and a drink in einies, at lunchtime on thursday i'm the one in the wheelchair with oxygen, say hello............ ....I look pretty different these days..................I'm wearing a red wig at the min and my face is quite bloated (as is my stomach - my jeans are soooo tight its scary!) dont worry if u dont quite recognise me........................I still feel a lot of the time like this isnt real and i'm watching my life from the outside ....I havent quite accepted yet that i wont actually get old and get a job and work again and have kids etc................sometimes if i try and think about the long term future it freaks me out too much.............I think i need more time yet................'i wish i was stressing about my placement essay.' ....I would give anything to be stressing out in the library right now.............i love hearing about uni stuf and everything but sometimes when i sit down and think about it, i'm so jealous of everyone............That's not to say I dont want you to talk about it cos i do, thats the stuff i wanna talk about, normal stuff...........im just saying its hard when i think about it so im trying not to right now.

I'm feeling a lot more tired the last few days...............my breathing is worse.....its not compressing or restrciting me like it has in the past so i know the tumour isnt pressing on any major veins at the moment................I'm officially no longer a student at Aston (though im keeping my student card to get into einies lol) but they did give me a certificate of higher education for completingmy first year of psychology which is great cos at least i got some recognition.................I dont think people understand what its like for me now living with this. If you've visiited you have an idea................I live downstairs, i can't get upstairs becasue it takes me too long and my breathing is too bad................my bed is in the living room with a commode (yes a commode, embarrasing but it has to be done)................I get upstairs about once a day at the min and i have to have a wash at the bedside becasue my back pain is so intense................i cant sit in the bath without support behind me. Getting dressed in the morning is a huge effort and my mum has to help me alot ....I have a district nurse come in every night to give me an injection to prevent clotting and yes these do sting and they bruise your stomach!................................I'm pretty used to them now................My life revolves around drugs and tablets and what nurses and doctors are coming in when and what for ....I'm on high dose steroids which makes my appetite go crazy.

I'm into most foods but I cant drink tea, the look of it makes me feel ill! Also not into cadburys chocolate - like dairy milk and stuff i wont eat though i do like chocolate fingers................I love biscuits though, chocolate biscuits are great, as are oreos, triple and rocky bars and ginger biscuits............I also love chocolate mousse yogurts, ham sandwiches, cheese and onion crisps, sausage rolls and tuna sandwiches.............Not so into cheese as i was though i can eat it...............I love chicken still and also chip shop chips.........I also love domino's pizza and cooked breakfasts (hence the trip to einies for a big breakfast on thurs!)....................Drinks wise i'm addicted to capri sun and apple and pear squash!

To keep myself busy i've been watching alot of TV, I bought Take That in concert but i havent watched it yet...............Been watching loads of football which is great..............Dunno what I'm gonna do when the season ends..............I'm also into colouring books, childish as it sounds!! they are really theraputic and it takes up some good time..........We had to cancel my Willows Party .... i wont be strong enough to do something like that again ....Instead the willows got us some match tickets for Brum v Lfc this weekend with wheelchair seats so we are going to that and then after the game we are going out for a meal in Burton at the Golf Club

Becky has half sorted out uni now so shes taking some time out to spend at home with us and just visiting her friends as and when this term............. I feel bad becos shes missing out ....but in a selfish way i'm glad cos i want her here with us really and I miss her when she goes now and shes extra company in the day...............I also bought a new phone randomly...................I'm also on the lookout for a new wig but i'm having issues finding a shop in burton.

My hair should be growing back but its being stubborn this time and not doing so i need something to cover it and with going out more i like my wigs again now...............I wear a bright red one at the min though and i want a normal plain one as an option...............If anyone wants to visit me, they're welcome, just leave me a message first on Facebook."

For everything she's going through, she's handling it amazingly well. It doesn't matter if she cries from now till Christmas, she's handling it brilliantly. So often when I tell people how she's doing they say, "I'd like to think that if I was faced with something like this, I'd face it with the same bravery as Mel is doing" There's no better testament to her courage than that.

It's Champions League semi final night tonight and I can't make up my mind if I want Liverpool to win. Not because I'm a sad Everton fan who begrudges them success, it's because I remember the last few finals they've got to. Mel and I went up to Liverpool and had a fantastic time, drinking in the atmosphere during the build up, watching the game in The Blob, walking the streets with other fans after the game. Mel always said that the first trip to Liverpool, when they beat AC Milan on penalties, was the best day of her life. I'm sad because I'll never have the opportunity to try and better that. So, I'll have mixed feelings,

She seems better today. Her breathing is not as noisy and for a good half hour or more this morning she sat on the sofa with Becky. She has been on morphine a fair bit and this morning we noticed we were running short so we made a quick call to the doctor's surgery and within fifteen minutes they rang back to say the prescription was ready for collection. We also had a call from Debbie at the Queen's Hospital in Burton. It was just a follow up call to see how we were all coping. After lunch Mel had her session of aromatherapy. The session lasted an hour and she benefited from it greatly. Annie, the lady who comes to do the aromatherapy, is really good. We'll book another for Mel next week.

Becky is great at making us smile and she did it again this evening. One of the lovely gifts sent by Virginia from America was a magnetic doodle pad. It's a bit like Etch a Sketch and you can write messages on it. Becky wrote "Nil by Mouth" on it and put it by Mel's bed!!

Wednesday 23rd April

After watching the Liverpool game we watched a bit more telly and I spent some time looking through one of Mel's old photo albums. There were pictures I'd taken of her over the last few years at various football matches. Pictures of her holding trophies, pictures of her watching games, pictures with players. She loves football and these pictures show how much. We had the best of times at some of those matches. We can sit and talk, think of a town or city and chances are we'll have a football story to tell. Treasured memories. Mel and Becky stopped up till the early hours talking. Well, Becky talked and for the majority of the time Mel listened. It used to be the other way round. I woke up about two o'clock in the morning as I couldn't sleep so I went downstairs, made myself a coffee, chatted to Mel for half an hour and went back to bed.

Last night Burton Albion qualified for the end of season play offs and after a discussion with Mel, we decided we'd like to go to one of the play off games. So, bright and early this morning I was at the ground to ask if it were possible. It is, so next Thursday or Friday, all things being equal, myself, Mel, Julie and Becky will be guests of the club for the play off semi final game. If they win the play off, the final is at Wembley and Mel and I have already pencilled that in!!

Mel's friend Laura came round this afternoon and as she left, Jane arrived. Dr. Grove (Hospice Doctor) followed. We explained Mel's issues over the last few days, the breathing difficulties, the back pain, the bloating and the sweats. Basically, the new tablets she had last week haven't made any difference. After listening to her issues, Dr. Grove decided that it is the steroids that are making the difference. When she was on the high dose, she felt a lot better whereas, when she switched to the lower dose, there was a gradual decline. Therefore, they're not prescribing any different tablets. She's sticking to the steroids. Acupuncture was suggested as a treatment for the sweats, but there may be a problem with bleeding so, that's a "wait and see".

As I was serving up dinner, Mel was struggling to stay awake. She ate it and then fell asleep as she was taking her tablets. The visitors kept coming, this time it was Julie's sister, she'd brought some washing from her mums and also an envelope for Julie. Julie worked at Burton library for over twenty years and they'd had a collection for us. It was a lovely thought, totally unexpected and very much appreciated.

Thursday 24th April

It was quarter to one when we went to bed last night after we spent a while talking with Mel. Mel was due to visit Birmingham today and have an Einies breakfast with Becky, but she decided last night that she wasn't up to it. Her energy levels are low at the moment as she comes to the end of her low dose steroids. It will be interesting to see how the second pulse of steroids effect her. She texted her friends to explain she wouldn't be there.

When I returned home from picking Julie up Mel was awake and taking her tablets. There were eighteen this morning. Not eighteen today. Just eighteen this morning. Mel is back on the high dose of steroids and over the next couple of days should start to feel the benefit. As well all those tablets we had to change her pain relief patch and give her some codeine linctus for her cough. Our main aim at present is to make sure Mel is comfortable and well enough to see Liverpool on Saturday. This afternoon Kirsty from the Willows rang to confirm all was in place for Saturday. As well as the football, we're going for a meal afterwards at the Branston Golf and Country Club and that is all booked too.

This afternoon we ordered in pizza for our dinner/tea and watched Mel's new Take That DVD. As that was coming to a close we had a wig trying on session. Well, Mel, Julie and Becky did. I abstained and took some photos.

This evening will be a quiet one. We're saving our energies for Saturday.

THROUGH MELISSA'S EYES (Part Nineteen)

"Hey everyone
Just thought I'd write a quick blog entry while I felt like it. Was gonna go Brum today to meet with some friends but the last few days I've felt exhausted what with visitors and going out and just thought it would be a bit too much so decided to have

a coupla days just chilling at home and resting to prepare for Saturday when I go and see Liverpool play Birmingham at St. Andrews which should be really good. Its what the Willows Foundation have organised for us instead of my party which I was gonna have cos now that will be too much.

Anyway the right decision was made I think. I enjoy my visitors but some days I need a break where I can just take it easy and fall asleep as and when etc etc which I have done today.
Also watched my Take That DVD which was very good and also tried my new wig on (you can see it in my photo) which I'm warming too more each time I wear it. Trouble is the steroids are making me so fat in the face I'm not very happy with any wigs or looking in the mirror at all to be fair plus I've got a rash, thanks again to steroids so I'm a bit self concious about my looks at the min :(

But I bought a long wig anyway and I love the colour! If you go on my facebook page then there's loads more pics.
Aside form that I've not done much really. My breathing is worse than it was a week or so ago but we're hoping cos i'm going on high dose steroids again it will improve as well everything else including this bloody back pain which is doing my head in!!
We saw the hospice doctor yesterday and the St. Giles Hospice nurse and they are sorting out a TENS machine which can help with nerve pain, also mentioned about acupuncture but I'm not sure I like the idea of that!

My little mini bedroom downstairs is working out well anyway, I have everything I need down here and dont need to go upstairs at all really though I can if I really need too.
I had a really insensitive text from someone the other day which I wont go into detail about but to be fair to them they weren't fully aware of the situation but it just reminded me how difficult it is for people to understand or come close to realsiing what life is really like now.

Aside from that I feel okish in myself, again like i'm living my life from someone elses perspective, it doesnt seem real really half the time and I can't describe how I even feel. I think I need to talk to the psychologist who is coming next week. I think she will help alot to be fair to get my head straight cos its a bit all over the place at the min. One min I'm all motivated and others I'm irritable and angryor upset. Its all a bit bizarre!

Anyways I think thats enough for now....and hey I updated pretty quick this time!! I had pizza today for dinner - was very very nice!! and I'm addicted to mini oreos!!!
Mel xxx"

Friday 25th April

After staying up late last night we didn't get up till 9am. Mel had been on Life Site for a while. It helps her so much and I know some of the people she chats to read this blog so can I say thank you for all the help and support you give to Mel. The Post Office delivered a parcel first thing, a lovely package of goodies for Mel. From 11am onwards the phone seemed to be permanently ringing throughout the day.

We had calls from district nurses, hospice nurses, parents, the willows foundation, the reception at the doctor's surgery and of course the obligatory twat trying to sell us a product that we don't want. The other calls were just general calls about Mel or medicines. Just after lunch Pauline came to visit. She stopped for an hour or so, chatted to Mel and asked us how we all were. Mel is to have a TENS machine to help with her pain. TENS machines deliver small electrical pulses to the body via electrodes placed on the skin. This is to help ease pain. They are also looking at changing Mel's dosage of steroids. They're keeping the high dose the same, but increasing the low dose a little. This is because it seems obvious that Mel is better on the high dose than the lower. The dosage has to be balanced out against the possible side effects. They are changing the way the morphine is given. She will have two tablets a day constantly and then she can have the liquid form to keep on top of it. They say the reason they do this is because the liquid form gives peaks and troughs of relief when it's working. The tablet will provide consistent relief. It was decided to try this after we phoned up again today requesting more morphine and the receptionist checked our records and saw we'd only had a bottle earlier in the week. She must have thought Mel was swigging it back like gin and reported it to the doctor who, having thought about things prescribed the tablets.

Mel is looking forward to the game tomorrow and the meal afterwards. Mel has expressed a wish to go and see a match at the new Wembley so I've written to the Football League and also to Wembley itself to try and arrange some tickets for the end of season play offs. Of course, if Burton Albion get to the Conference play offs we'll go there too.

Mel ordered a new Liverpool shirt this morning off the internet.

Saturday 26th April

Mel woke up and had her usual breakfast of ham sandwiches and sausage rolls. After breakfast it took nearly two hours to get her ready to go to the match. Whilst Julie washed and dressed her, I sorted out the oxygen for the day. We have three portable canisters that last about three hours each. I fitted them all with nasal tubes and put them in the car.

We left for Birmingham at quarter past twelve. We had a walk around the ground and Mel bought a programme. We picked up our tickets and took some pictures. We had to go in through the visitor's entrance, which was brilliant as it meant we were sat in the away end surrounded by Liverpool fans. We watched the Liverpool team warm up in front of us, Stevie G was literally only yards away from Mel when he walked out onto the pitch. Mel had a hot dog and I took photos.

The game itself was good. Liverpool rested a few of their better players and the only down side to the day was that Mel didn't see Fernando Torres, but that apart it was perfect. Mel joined in with the Liverpool fans as best she could as they went through their repertoire of terrace songs. She left her oxygen off for the second half of the game. Liverpool went 2-0 down but fought back to draw 2-2. The game finished and we made our way back to the car.

We got Mel home, got changed and then she sat in her wheelchair and we made our way round to the golf club for our meal. It's only five minutes away and it was easier to push Mel in the chair than load up the car with the chair etc. Our table was waiting for us and on it were a massive bouquet of flowers from the staff at the Branston Golf Club. Mel worked at the club before her illness and the flowers were beautiful. The meal was fantastic. The service was first class and at the moment I don't think I'll ever eat again!!

So that was it, Willows did a fantastic job of organising it all for us. From start to finish it was exactly how we would have wanted it to be. There was a bitter sweet side to things of course, there always is. Mel should have been sat in the middle of the Liverpool fans singing her head off and not sat in the wheelchair on oxygen. If nothing else though it reminded me of how much I love watching football with her and taking her to games. It's what we do. It's what we'll do again too, hopefully this Friday at Burton Albion. Whilst Mel and I have been to hundreds of matches, this was Julie and Becky's first experience of a big game and they enjoyed it.

I stopped up with Mel until about 1am last night. We watched Match of the Day and then discussed football until we were both too tired to talk. We went through all the divisions, including Conference, looking at who would go up and who would stay down!

Thank you to Warwick Horton for organizing the tickets, thank you to Willows, thank you to Branston Golf & Country Club. You gave Mel (and ourselves) a day to remember!

Sunday 27th April

When Mel woke up this morning she was in agony. Her back pain was severe and she had several doses of morphine to take the edge off the pain. The exertions of going to see Liverpool had taken it out of her and not only was she in pain, she was tired. I made her sandwiches and sausage rolls but when it came to, she couldn't eat them. She says that it takes a long time for food to go down and she feels as though she needs to burp to clear it, but can't. Consequently, eating takes ages and at times the food goes cold before she finishes it. This is something that had been happening before, but has worsened over the last few days.

I went to Tesco this morning to get supplies. My mind was all over the place. So many thoughts. What I wouldn't give to be able to go and watch football properly with Mel. To take her and Becky to Alton Towers like we used to. I want us to visit Barmouth and go swimming in the sea in the late evening. I have so many brilliant memories, but I'm greedy. I want to do them all again. Would I appreciate them more? At times like this you realise how much you take for granted. Whilst walking round Tesco I saw a chap with his son. They were laughing and joking about things and I wondered how many times I'd done that with Mel and Bex, but never truly appreciated it. I'd never realised how special going to the supermarket with my children was. Maybe subconsciously I did appreciate it. Who knows?

Mel's tiredness continued throughout the day. Five of her uni friends visited this afternoon and she enjoyed that. The advantage of there being so many is that Mel didn't have to do a lot of talking. So thank you girls . . . and the guy too!! They left just after four o'clock. Mel fell asleep.

Today was what Mel and I refer to as "Three Match Sunday". Three footy matches on TV back to back. After the football she slept again for a while and then we ordered Pizzas. Throughout the day we kept giving her morphine in order to keep the pain at bay. She has oxygen on permanently now and

I think that during the coming weeks we'll have to increase her dose and that will mean another machine.

Monday 28th April

I stayed up last night till 3am. Mel hadn't been too good in the evening and her condition deteriorated throughout the evening. She had morphine to ease the pain, but it was such that it didn't do much good. She woke up this morning feeling uncomfortable with pain in her back and she was struggling with her breathing. Debbie from Burton Hospital called and told us that the psychologist, Holly, was ill and wouldn't be able to see Mel this week. I sat down with Mel and explained to her and said that if she felt she needed to talk and there were things she wanted to talk about, no matter how difficult, try me.

I had cause to nip to the hospital this morning and whilst there memories of Mel in the early days of her illness flooded into my mind. I remember walking down the corridors at two o'clock in the morning when Mel had pneumonia. I thought about the first day we went in thinking she'd got a bad chest infection. Here we were eight months later and things are very different. When I got home Mel was relaxing in bed, she'd had trouble with her breathing after sitting on the commode. Her breathing is poor at the moment and getting out of bed and onto the commode is a major effort. It affects her breathing so much that she panics and this makes it worse. We have to get her onto the bed, get her settled and then calm her down. It can take up to half an hour or more to do this.

Just after lunch time Pauline called round followed by Dr. Tansey. In the short time that Pauline had been in the room with Mel she'd noticed the same deterioration as ourselves and we discussed the situation. Dr. Tansey then went in to see Mel. He stayed for over an hour. He could see the difficulty she was having and decided on a course of action. Firstly, he prescribed a slow release morphine pain killer. The idea of this is to keep the pain relief constant. At the moment, we're reacting to the pain with the oral morphine. We will now be pre-empting it and if it gets worse we can top up with the morphine. In the early stages we have to be careful not to give her too much as the tablets kick in. He also decided to increase her level of oxygen to number four and put a humidifier on it. She will also have an inhaler, again to assist with breathing difficulties.

Before prescribing everything he talked it through with us and also, more importantly, with Mel. He then talked to her about other possible options. Radiotherapy was discussed in the early days, but we've been worried recently about whether the trauma of travelling to Derby for this would be more detrimental than the effectiveness of the treatment. Dr. Tansey discussed this with Mel and she agreed that she didn't want radiotherapy. With the disease now seemingly taking a bigger hold, it is debatable as to whether it would do any good. He also discussed with her the possibility of resuscitation. Should things get to that stage would she want to be resuscitated? She said she would. The other item under discussion was the Clexane injections. Mel's belly is a mass of bruises and the doctor gave her the option of withdrawing from those injections. Of course, in doing so the risk of an embolism is increased. It's like playing Russian roulette. All of Mel's medication is now optional. It's up to her. If there's something she doesn't want, she doesn't' have to it. It brought home to us the sudden change in her condition. She decided to have the injections, only they will be given in her leg for a while in order to give her belly time to recover.

My mum, dad, aunty and cousin visited this afternoon for a couple of hours. Whilst they were here the phone was constantly ringing. Willows rang to see how our day went on Saturday. The hospice rang to say they were going to deliver the TENS machine later and we also had a call from the Burton Mail wanting to run a story on this blog. I don't want them to run a story on the blog. If we were to do it, it would be to give awareness to the disease and the possible financial implications for someone so young having this illness. We'll decide what we're going to do in the next couple of days. At the moment we have other things on our minds.

After tea, Mel needed the loo. Up until today she'd been slightly constipated, today the opposite occurred. She has dia... dio.... the runs! That is Julie's department. I can deal with the needles and surgical procedures, but show me a bucket of sick or poo and my stomach reacts. I'd like to think that if I had to deal with it, I would, but you don't ask a reserve to do a first teamer's job. As Julie finished off sorting out the commode contents upstairs, I sat with Mel and held her hand for a while. I could sense she wanted to talk. I asked her what was wrong. "Everything" came the reply. I asked her to tell me. I wanted her to talk to me, to get it off her chest. She told me she was scared. A silly question I know, but I asked her what of.

"The obvious."

"Dying?"

"Yes."

I told her I couldn't tell her what it was like, but I'd read up on people who had had "near death experiences" and they'd all said they felt peaceful and not scared. It was the best I could do. She continued to talk. She was angry because there is so much she wanted to do. She wanted it to be her carrying on at university, doing placements, passing exams, going on nights out. She talked about her friends that visited on Sunday and that she was sad that she might never see them again. There were certain people she wanted to see before she died. She said it was so unfair. She cried as she explained how she knew that Saturday may well be the last live football match she ever sees. Sad that she may not live to see next football season. She was scared of the pain getting worse and becoming unbearable. Again, I tried to calm her fears and explained that the pain relief would be given to match the pain and as time goes on she'll be sleeping through it.

As she talked I told her to try and remember all the things she had done. I couldn't say anything else. I couldn't say, don't worry you'll do this and that. Chances are she won't. But

I told her to concentrate on the things we'd done. The football matches we'd been to. The trips to Alton Towers. I told her to remember the great times she had at uni and I reminded her that she'd probably packed more into her two years than most students do in four. I reminded her of her constant enthusiasm for everything and explained to her that, as hard as it may be, to try and remain enthusiastic about each day. To look forward to Liverpool's game on Wednesday and then Sunday's match. Just enjoy and get the most out of each day as possible. I told her that I'll stay up with her again tonight. She can sleep or we can talk, but we're all there for her for as long as she needs us.

This evening we watched football on the TV and chatted. Mel's breathing is poor, the pain is being controlled at the moment. It's been a tough day, they will get tougher.

Tuesday 29th April

I sat up with Mel until she finally fell asleep at 3am this morning. Julie went to bed around midnight as did Becky. Becky returned downstairs a short time later as she couldn't sleep. The three of us sat up until 3am talking. We talked about my old girlfriends and Mel's boyfriends, listened to music and generally kept Mel company. Becky went to bed around three ish. Mel and I talked a little more before she fell asleep and I went up to bed at 4am. I was awoken at five to six by the sound of Mel shouting for me. She was struggling with her breathing and was scared. She thought I was still downstairs. I jumped up out of bed, ran downstairs and tried to calm her down. It must be horrible for her when she gets this feeling. It frightens her and it takes all our efforts to relax her. We hold her hand. We talk to her. Reassure her. Calm her down. Julie came downstairs a short while after and between us we settled her down and got her into a relaxed state. It took the best part of an hour.

Becky had a hair appointment at 9 this morning so after dropping her off I went into town. Mel wanted some photographic prints of the pictures we'd taken on Saturday. I visited the Burton Mail. I mentioned yesterday they'd been in touch regarding doing a story on the blog. To be honest, I don't find the blog exciting and worthy of a story. I've said before, originally the purpose of the blog was to provide an outlet for me to get down on paper (well, 21st century paper) about what was happening and help me understand things. Events were moving at such a pace in the early days I needed to talk it out. I did so via the blog. As Mel's condition failed to respond to treatment, more and more people were asking after her. The blog then became a useful tool to keep people informed. It saved endless phone calls and having to go over details again and again. At the end of a long tiring day in hospital, with the best will in the world, you don't want to come home to a host of phone calls. Over the past months the blog has done the job of keeping friends and family up to date with our lives and has provided an outlet for myself. I have asked the Burton Mail to respect our privacy at the moment, but at some point in the future I will talk to them. It was nice to see some familiar faces in the Mail office. As I left, I said goodbye to our football buddy, Bob and told him I'd see him at the Albion next season . . . . but I'd be alone.

Pauline visited this morning and then again in the afternoon to check on Mel. The purpose of the afternoon visit was to explain to us how we used the inhaler. Mel had a go, but her breathing was so bad she was unable to do it. We've now opted for a nebuliser, which will assist her breathing. Whilst calming Mel down for a second time this morning she confessed that didn't realise she would deteriorate so quickly. She knows that her condition has declined a little in the last three or four days and along with other things that is scaring her. Hopefully in the next few days the pain relief will take effect and she'll be comfortable. At the moment, she cannot get a decent level of comfort and the pain is excruciating for her. With her tablets and the morphine kicking in, she should start to feel the benefit.

We've decided that as from tonight, I will stop downstairs with Mel. She gets more scared at night and as last night proved, she needs us there. Julie caters for Mel's hygiene needs during the day and therefore needs a good night's sleep. I can have naps during the day and be there for Mel throughout the night if she needs me. She is prone to waking up panicking at the moment and it's important to have someone there. We are trying to do all we can to make her comfortable. She is wearing my t-shirts at the moment as they are large and baggy and she doesn't perspire so much in them as she does in her own tighter clothes. I went over to Stretton late afternoon to pick up another prescription. This time it was for some stuff to put in the nebuliser. Mel had the nebuliser and went into a deep sleep.

I made Mel her favourite tea this evening, cheese and potato pie. The Nanny visited and had a portion too.

I had a phone call this evening from Burton Albion. I'd rang them earlier today to say we wouldn't be able to attend the match on Friday, but they asked if Mel would like to have a couple of players visit her tomorrow. I asked her and she decided she would. So, that's something for her to look forward to tomorrow. Eight months on, we're still going one day at a time. It's the only way.

Wednesday 30th April

We watched the football last night, then an old episode of The Bill. Julie and Becky went to bed around midnight. They're not big fans of The Bill, it's a Mooch and Dad thing! At around 1am we switched off the lights and settled down. As I mentioned yesterday I am now sleeping downstairs with Mel. I didn't set up the fold up bed. I know that if I lay down on that, it would be much harder to wake up. Waking up and getting off a couple of sofa cushions is easier. I lay on the cushions in the dark, the hum of the oxygen machine and Mel's coughing breaking the silence. As I lay there I listened to her coughing. She seemed to be taking between twenty - thirty breaths and then coughing. This continued throughout the night. . . .

At four o'clock in the morning Mel woke up. She had an attack of the munchies and needed Mini Oreos. She needed the toilet so I helped her off the bed and she used the commode. I helped her back onto the bed. It took three hours to calm her down, get her relaxed and ready to sleep again. In that time she had four small doses of morphine. She was in so much pain and couldn't get comfortable. She drank four cartons of Capri-Sun. At ten to seven I lay back down on the sofa and closed my eyes. Mel's coughing started again. This time though it was a constant cough. No sessions of breathing in between, just constant coughing. I asked her several times if she was ok and she replied, saying that she just had to clear her throat.

I got up at ten o'clock. I can't say I hadn't slept all night, but it had been a very light sleep. I can remember Mel coughing. The sound of the oxygen machine didn't keep me awake at all. At ten o'clock this morning I went upstairs for a shower and woke Julie. She came downstairs and got Mel's breakfast. The postman called and there were two packages for Mel and a couple of letters for me. Mel received a card signed by all her old teachers from Paulet School. Becky woke up and came downstairs. She's decided not to go and visit uni next week. She wants to stay at home with us.

Pauline arrived late morning and I went through the night's events with her. She rang the GP and it was decided to up Mel's dose of MST (Painkiller) to 90mg a day with top ups of morphine should the pain break through. They're also considering upping her oxygen levels from four to five, but a decision on that will be made on Friday. It's a measure of how Mel's condition has deteriorated in the last week. This time last week the oxygen levels were on two. Today they were upped to four and they're looking at increasing them further still. The guy who came to up the levels also added a humidifier. This will take some of the dryness away from the oxygen. He also shortened the tube. Mel can no longer get upstairs and only goes from her bed to the commode. A couple of Burton Albion players were coming to see Mel this afternoon after training but we had to cancel. She wasn't well enough and didn't have the strength.

Sooty visited this afternoon and later on, Pauline returned with more tablets for Mel. This time it was Valium. Only a small dose to try and assist her breathing and lower her panic levels when she has breathless moments. I managed to grab an hour's sleep, and after I'd woken up we all had Pizza for our tea. Mel is finding it increasingly difficult to eat, which considering she is on steroids, is a bit of a bugger. She keeps saying she's the slowest eater in the world!

I drove Sooty back to the station just after half past six. It's when I'm on my own that my mind goes into overdrive and thoughts push themselves into my mind. Like the fact that Mel will probably never go out of the house again. The last time she went out was to see Liverpool. I can't see her going out again now. The doctor's are controlling the pain. They're making her comfortable. They're not making her better. She sits on her bed in the lounge, her bedroom is barely six feet above her head, but she'll never see it again. It's hard to imagine being in a house, but never setting foot upstairs. It's so wrong. I sit here watching football with her and I can hear the noise of the oxygen machine, the bubbling of the humidifier and above all this, Mel constantly coughing.

CHAPTER TWENTY FIVE

As Bad As It Gets

Thursday 1st May

Throughout the eight months or so of Mel's illness, the law of sod has reared its ugly head on several occasions. So, it's no surprise that at a time when Mel can no longer leave the house and struggles to get on the commode she receives offers of tickets to see Liverpool on Sunday and England v USA at Wembley in June! The guy who organised the Wembley tickets is Theo Walcott's (Arsenal and England) agent. He texted me but I had to tell him it wouldn't be possible. Becky wanted me to text him and tell him she was 18, pretty and would Theo be interested!!!! A work colleague got the Liverpool tickets and, although we won't be able to go, we appreciate his efforts.

We watched Liverpool v Chelsea last night and it was a strange experience. At the start of the game I wanted Liverpool to score, but when they did, I immediately wanted Chelsea to hit back and this continued with each goal. Part of me wanted Livepool to win for Mel, but another part of me wanted Chelsea to win . . . also for Mel. This time there'd have been no chance of a trip to Liverpool to watch the final and that would have been so sad! Mel was disappointed Liverpool lost, but not as disappointed as she would have been, had she not been ill.

Julie and Becky went to bed about half past twelve and Mel and I watched three episodes of The Bill. After that we talked well into the night. We talked about all sorts of things. We chatted for an hour about football, reminiscing on some of the games we went to over the years, the experiences we had. Mel just wasn't tired, and I sat up with her all night, finally lying down on the sofa cushions at quarter past six this morning.

I woke Julie at eight o'clock, she climbed out of bed, I climbed in. Julie went downstairs and got Mel's breakfast ready, helping her on and off the commode, she tidied up her bed and attended to all her hygiene needs. I slept till half past ten. I came downstairs and waited for Pauline to arrive. She checked on how Mel had been overnight, made her notes and left. Whilst I'd been asleep the postman had been delivering an array of letters and parcels. Mel's friend Carly had ordered her some sweets from a website called www.aquarterof.co.uk We'd also ordered some for ourselves and they both arrived today. . . the packages contained such delights as Jelly Tots, Banana Mojos, Kola Cubes, Rock Sweets, Fizzers, Refreshers and a load of others goodies. We now have enough sweets to open a corner shop.

Mel bought herself a Nintendo DS and a Brain Train game. It's something she's been thinking of for a while and it's a good sign that despite the fact she's bedridden she still wants to do things. Whilst Becky and I were out, Annie the aromatherapirst arrived. We returned home from shopping just as she was finishing off. She'd given Mel a head and foot massage and the effect on Mel was good. It calmed her down to such an extent that she slept for the best part of three hours. There was no coughing, her breathing was totally relaxed and she slept soundly. At about half past two I went upstairs and lay on the bed and drifted off, waking a couple of hours later. Mel listens to a relaxation CD and on this CD it asks her to imagine she's walking to a meadow....he woke up this afternoon complaining that she never gets as far as the meadow...

On the whole, Mel is stable today, her cough is an issue, but it's been in the background, rather than at the forefront. The pain is being managed. As well as her weekly sessions of aromatherapy, managing the pain requires Mel taking 36 tablets a day, an average of ten shots of morphine, four shots of codeine linctus and an injection. She finds the radio very therapeutic at the moment and listens to TalkSport throughout the day. The background talking helps her relax and gives her something to focus on.

Friday 2nd May

We finally settled down at quarter past five this morning. As with the previous day I then slept until around 8.15 and then went to bed for a couple of hours. My sleep at the moment is in two to three hour sessions as and when I can. It's obvious from the past couple of days that Mel's sleep patterns have changed and she prefers to stay awake most of the night. It's plain to see she feels more comfortable having someone down stairs with her for company. When I go to bed, Julie comes down and takes over. Today, I've managed a couple of hours in the morning and then a couple more in the afternoon.

Becky and I did the supply run to Tesco this morning and nipped into town to get Mel some games for her Nintendo. Dr. Tansey and Pauline arrived and discussed Mel's current condition, her medication and any other concerns/worries we may have. Mel and I discussed in the night about having her oxygen turned up to level five. She doesn't need it on that level at the moment, but should the time come to turn it up, particularly over the weekend, we didn't want to have to wait around for prescriptions, faxes and deliveries. We also needed more morphine and some codeine linctus. With the introduction of the MST tablet, the need for morphine has dropped over the past 48 hours, but she is using a fair amount and again, as with all her medicines, we're trying to be pre-emptive as opposed to reactive. This seems to be keeping Mel calmer and as a result she feels more comfortable.

Earlier in the day I took the wheelchair back to her nanny's house. We won't need it anymore. Annie called again to administer aromatherapy to Mel. This form of therapy has an extremely positive effect on her. It relaxes her and we appreciate Annie's visits. Monica from the St. Giles Hospice called round, she was delivering some relaxation tapes to Mel. She asked Julie how we all were and told us that everyone says we're doing brilliantly. It's nice to hear. There are no text books for this sort of thing, you can't go on courses or plan. You just have to do your best and what you think is right. That is what we're doing and it seems to be working. After her aromatherapy session with Annie, Mel went into a deep sleep. Her breathing was very rattly, but she slept well.

This evening, we're going to have a late tea and then watch Burton Albion's play off game against Cambridge United. We should have been going.

Saturday 3rd May

Mel updated her blog last night. As usual it was frank and honest. She talked about how she looked, how long she thinks she has left to live ("weeks rather than months") and she mentioned how it "scares the shit out of her". It scares the shit out of us all. We can't imagine life without her. We know how poorly she is. We don't want her to suffer, but we don't want to lose her. We don't know what is going to happen in the coming weeks. I sit and wonder what life will be like without Mel. I try to remember how she used to be before this horrible disease took over. She may look different, but I know that the same Melissa is there. There won't be a day that goes by when we won't think of her. I'll talk to her. I'll listen to her too. I'll wonder what life would have been like if all this had never happened.

I think of how we'll cope when Mel passes away. I know we will, but it will be so hard. Not just in the days afterwards, but in the weeks, months and years to follow. The anniversaries we'll have to get through, particularly in the early years. We'll have a funeral to arrange. Mel's made it easier for us by telling us what she wants, but it will be tough. I worry about stupid things too. For twenty years I've been there for her. I don't want her to be scared. I don't want her to feel alone and frightened. We all love her so much and I know if she keeps that love with her she'll be ok. I wish someone would tell me she'll be ok. I can't imagine going through the rest of my life and never seeing her again. How do you cope with that? I worry about not being here when she needs me. What if I'm out at the shops and something happens. I know that I can't be there 24/7, but I want to be.

There are so many things I want to tell her, but if I do, I'll break down. I want to tell her how proud we are of her for the way she's battled this disease. The immense pride we have in her school years. Both Mel and Becky were phenomenal at school and they made parenting easy. Both Julie and I love them so much and I'm sure they know that. I promised myself I wouldn't look to the future, that I'd just concentrate on the present and deal with one day at a time, but her deterioration over the last week is a reminder that this state of affairs isn't going to last forever. When Mel was diagnosed with this disease I wasn't frightened of the future but as time has gone on it scares me more and more.

Mel didn't sleep last night . . . at all. It was ten to eight this morning when she closed her eyes. I went upstairs for a nap and Julie came downstairs to sit with her. Mel and I had spent the night watching The Bill and then episode after episode of Friends. Becky joined us at one stage and stayed downstairs for an hour or so. Just after half past six we started talking. Mel says she finds it easier to talk about the "scary" stuff at night. There are no nurses or doctors, no phone calls and she can talk without fear of interruption. We talked about funerals and we talked again about how she wants some of her possessions giving away. Over the next few days we're going to write a list and then after she's passed away we can carry out her wishes.

Today has been a mixture of sleep and football, plus a visit from one of her closest uni friends, Hammad. He'd driven up from Wycombe this afternoon and there was a visible lift in Mel's spirits when he arrived. I also managed to track down one of her old school friends that she'd lost contact with and hopefully she'll be coming to visit her sometime soon. We watched TV this evening. Mel's breathing was a little rattly earlier on, but a shot of Oromorph eased it. Pauline called earlier in the day and we discussed Mel's difficulty in taking the tablets. She continues to struggle to digest things and tablets need to be taken. Pauline suggested taking them with ice cream, so we'll give that a go. If it gets to the stage where she can't take them then they will look at using a drive, which is through a "butterfly" needle into the arm. Pretty much the same as the syringe driver she had in hospital during the stem cell transplant.

So that was Saturday, I haven't slept much today, I managed a couple of hours this morning, but that's about it. I've grabbed forty winks here and there. Mel hasn't slept much either, maybe she'll sleep tonight or maybe we'll be up watching Friends and talking...I don't care either way!

THROUGH MELISSA'S EYES (The Final Part)

"Just an update to let you all know the current situation. As you all know my condition is now terminal and im not getting any better. I no longer have treatment at hospital and all my care is based at home. I have a bed and a commode downstairs and no longer go upstairs for anything.i have doctors and nurses in most days to check on me and monitor medication. Im constantly on oyxygen and pain relief for pains in my back and chesr and can move out of bed as far as the commode before getting out of breath. it can take me half an hour to get out of bed, go to the toilet, get back in again and be settled becos i have to do things so slowly. Im very bloated due to steroids which is very uncomfortable on my stomahc and means even though i want to eat loads im trying to space things out and eat slowly. I look very different to how you would all remember me. I'm bald and failry chubby with a rash on my face and i do look quite strange!! I sleep alot during the day at the moment and so when visitors come sometimes i can difrt in and out and it is why at the moment visiotrs are pretty limited and when they do come an hour is usually enough before i need to rest. I have no idea how long i have left, i would imagine weeks rather than months though i guess you never know. i just keep going but i never expected to deteriote this quickly if im honest and it scares me, i just hope now we have things under control so i will remain at this level for awhile without getting dramaticlaly worse again over the next week.

A week ago i went to the football in the wheelchair as you all saw and i think people think i can still do that now, now that wud be impossible. Realistically i will never leave this house again, i wont leave this room again. i dont have the energy or the physical ability. I use relaxation CDs to help me sleep and i have regular aromatherapy sessions which really help relax me but means i sleep alot after them but i need that at the moment. I have had to start thinking about life after ive gone, things i want people to have, funeral wishes etc etc which is really hard and scares me and i dont always want to think about it but i have too. If i say to you i dont want you to come visit at the moment its not personal its just cos i need my rest. im not sleepin at night very well but i am during the day and i have to just go with that at the moment. But that is what its like now so please dont be unrealsitic about things, this thing will beat me, and in a week i have deteorited a fair amount. I wont ever leave the house again i know that. i wont be going to einies or uni again, thats all over now. its the way it is and there are things i will want to say to certain people but the time isnt here yet but i will do, some people i have talked to briefly already. But yeh sometimes i dont want to sit on the phone and a have chat, i just dont have the energy and its hard for me to know what to talk about sometimes. im making the most of what i can do. im watching the football, i bought a nintendo to play on and im keeping going at the minute but people need to understand how it really is for us now. Theres no doubt my tumur is growing back and the lymphoma is active and doing whatever it does.

My dad has to sleep downstairs with me in the living room as im too ill to sleep on my own and i get too panicky breathing wise if im left on my own. i feel like i cant breathe and that is the scariest things. i have to take things so slowly and i also use the radio as something to focus on to help my breathing. i have a bad cough which is difficult but not too troublesome though it doesnt help me in terms of breathing. wen i wake up i always struggle to get back into a routine. once im settled im ok though i can find it very hard to talk as i get out of breath. I cant swallow food very well at all so everything im eating is soft and even that is hard. Im very bloated cos of steroids and am not ever entirely comfrotbale though the pain relief im on is helping to a certain extent and it maintaining control.

but yeh theres not alot else i can say really. ive sent this as a message as well becos i want everyone to realsie what its really like now for me. im on palliative care and im not getting better. i just want as long as possible but neither i nor anyone else knows how long that will be and thats sometthing i have to live with...

i know people will want to come and visit and at some point you will but dont be offended if its only for an hour or so, 2 hours is too much now, flying visits are more what i need and be prepared that i may cancel if im too tired or need rest.

thats about all i can say and im sorry if ive been blunt but its the only way i can be.

Mel xxxx"

Sunday 4th May

My body clock has gone tits up. I want breakfast when I should be eating dinner, dinner when I should be eating tea and don't even mention sausage rolls at two o'clock in the morning. I managed about four hours sleep in total last night, split into a three and one hour session. I don't feel particularly tired. Mel and I went through a marathon Friends session last night. She was in a lot of pain around four o'clock in the morning, but we controlled it with morphine and the TENS machine. By the time we went to sleep we must have watched about eight episodes of Friends and when I did get to sleep all I could hear in my head were conversions between Mel, myself, Becky, Monica, Ross, Joey, Rachel, Chandler and Phoebe!

Midway through our Friends marathon Mel needed the commode and that meant a wake up call for Julie. Becky, who goes to bed and then gets up again to join us in the middle of the night, takes delight in giving Julie a wake up call in the early hours to tell her the commode needs emptying. Again, I've mentioned before, we each have our own particular skills. Mine is injections and medical procedures. Julie excels in the poop and sick department.

I bought Mel a new fan this morning. We've set it up at the end of her bed and it is a big improvement on the previous one. With this disease comes night sweats and add to that the heat that the oxygen machines belt out and it does tend to get a bit warm in the lounge. Julie helped Mel get changed whilst I set up the fan. After I'd set it up there was a piece left over. There always is. I'm crap at stuff like that. I'm surprised that there wasn't a bit left over when Mel and Becky had been born. It wasn't an important bit and the fan works perfectly. Mel was changed, the fan set up, we changed the water in the humidifier, changed the bed sheets and got Mel dressed. The whole process took over an hour.

As Julie was washing Mel we noticed that her right leg had started to bleed. She's been having the Clexane injections in her legs to give her stomach a rest and they must have scabbed and the scab been rubbed. We put a couple of plasters on Mel's leg. We were just finishing off washing and changing Mel when Carol, Georgina, Hannah and the Nanny arrived to visit. During the visit we loaded up Georgina with some of the sweets we'd been given. Every time she comes she visits the sweetie jar...I'm sure she thinks that in a previous life I was Willy Wonka!

Whilst Mel had been napping her bleeding leg had bled a lot and it had gone through her pyjamas, onto the sheets and the duvet. It meant another bed change and confirmed to us that Mel would go back to having her Clexane injections in her belly. We put another dressing on top of the previous one and waited for the District Nurse to arrive to give her verdict on it.

Monday 5th May

The bloody leg I mentioned yesterday continued to bleed. It wasn't gushing, just oozing a little and at 4am this morning I had to change the dressing. Mel and I carried on watching Friends. We eventually fell asleep, sometime after seven o'clock this morning and woke around quarter past nine. I went upstairs, climbed into bed and slept for an hour or so before Julie woke me. Mel wasn't too good. She needed her oxygen mask and Julie was having trouble changing it. I could tell when I went downstairs that even in the space of three short hours Mel's condition had deteriorated once more.

She was in constant pain. She had got onto the commode, but been in agony. Across her stomach, across her back, it was crippling her. Julie had phoned the District Nurse and we awaited her call back. In the meantime it was obvious that the visitors would have to be cancelled so I made the necessary phone calls. As Mel lay in pain, I sat with her and again, I wondered, why is she being put through this? What has she done to deserve this? Becky, Julie and I took it in turns to sit with her and hold her hand to comfort her. The District Nurse arrived and checked her over. She changed the dressing I'd put on Mel's leg in the night. It was soaked with blood and her leg was still oozing. She called the on-call doctor. By now, Mel was way behind with her tablets, but she was in such pain there was no way she could take them. We'd ask her, she'd say five more minutes and then she'd close her eyes again.

The doctor came and checked her over. The bloating in Mel's stomach was causing much discomfort and I held her hand as the doctor examined her. She cried out in pain as he felt, prodded and poked his way round her battered and bruised body. He decided that for the time being we should increase the morphine, trebling its dosage. He thought the pain in her stomach was constipation, but he ruled this out and pointed to the tumour and fluid as the cause. The doctor prescribed stronger pain relief, which we can fall back on if the morphine doesn't do the trick. Becky and I went to the pharmacy at Asda to get it.

No sooner had we walked back in the door and Mel's condition had worsened. Mel slept for the majority of the afternoon. My mum and dad visited for a short while and just after six o'clock I went to catch up with some sleep. I slept for an hour and then just lay on the bed listening to music. I'm relaxing if nothing else. Karen and Abbie are hoping to visit next week. She called last night and we spoke for half an hour. She was coming later in the month, but such is Mel's condition she is bringing her visit forward.

When Karen last visited in February, she returned to my mum's house and my mum asked how Mel was. Mel had just come out of hospital and so Karen remarked that Mel wasn't too bad considering and that being at home and my home cooking will make her feel better. Karen thought nothing of what she'd said until she visited an old school friend. Her friend enquired about Mel and Karen said she wasn't too bad and she'd been to see her. Her friend asked Abbie if she'd seen Mel and Abbie told her, "She's poorly, but Uncle Ian's cooking is going to make her better"...if only it were as simple as my cooking!

I found a video of Mel on my computer. It was taken a few years ago when she'd been out with Claire for New Year's Eve. She'd come home plastered and it was the first time we'd seen her drunk. I love that video. It is so precious. As the pain killer kicked in, Mel's pain eased and she woke up. She dozed off during dinner and then attempted to take her tablets. We feel today that we've moved to another level. The increase in pain. The subsequent increase in pain relief. With that Mel becomes more tired. This evening she fell asleep whilst eating some Chocolate Fudge Ice Cream. I had visions of her falling head first into the tub of Ben & Jerry's. She can fall asleep doing anything. We sit rubbing her back. We rub her feet. She listens to TalkSport. All these things contribute to her feeling comfortable and relaxed.

Tuesday 6th May
Mel slept well last night. After settling her down and sorting out her tablets Julie went to bed at about 1.30am.

Mel fell asleep soon after and I lay down on the sofa cushions and closed my eyes . . . . Tick follows tock, follows tick follows tock . . . . . . I'm asleep, but I'm awake. I'm asleep, but I can hear Mel's breathing. I'm asleep, but I'm aware of Mel coughing and all the time . . . . tick follows tock, follows tick, follows tock . . . . There's no daytime and no nighttimes anymore, just time. Mel slept till about half past four and then stayed awake for an hour or so before falling asleep again. She was very drowsy.

Mel wanted a Cheese and Potato Pie for dinner today. We'd discussed this at about half past five this morning. At about one o'clock this afternoon Pauline came and was soon followed by our GP, Dr. Tansey. They had been made aware that yesterday was a tough one and we discussed the way forward. It was decided that some of her medication that was in tablet form could be transferred to syrup. She has trouble with digestion at times and this will help her with medication at least.

The increase in medication has made her drowsy today and she drifts in and out of sleep. It is all about being comfortable and controlling the pain. Her condition has worsened since a week ago, but that's irrelevant now. It's all about controlling the pain. I mentioned the other day about the amount of tablets Mel has to take. Thirty six in total. Julie does a great job in remembering them all. If I'm on my own with Mel I know what she has and when, but that's due mainly to the list Julie's created.

The hospital rang this morning and told us that Holly, the psychologist, was available and would come and see Mel at home later today. We spoke to Mel and she decided not to see her. Partly because she was tired, but Mel also explained that she felt at the moment she was ok with things and if she needed to talk about anything she could talk to me or Julie. I know she feels more prone to talk about the "deep" stuff at night and I feel so happy that she can discuss her thoughts and fears with us. We discussed visitors too. Mel wants to see her friends, but such is her condition we can't say yes or no until the day of any particular visit. We don't know how well she is going to be. Visits need to be limited to half an hour . . An hour at most.

Whilst Becky and I went to get a prescription, Mel and Julie had a chat, discussing such things as resuscitation and dying at home. Our GP broached the subject a couple of weeks ago and Mel said then that if the paramedics had to be called and the situation arose, she would want to be resuscitated. Now she's not so sure. It's another of those situations where you have to weigh up the possible scenarios. We have our own opinions, but it's a decision only she can make. Mel said she wanted to pass away at home and didn't want to be resuscitated. She didn't want to die in hospital and we will do everything we can to ensure that things happen the way she wants them to. The aromatherapist called just after six o'clock and Mel had a session to relax her. It wasn't Annie this time, it was Jody and, like Annie, she was really good.

We sat watching Burton Albion v Cambridge this evening on Setanta. Under normal circumstances we'd have been there. Normal isn't what it used to be and now I have to settle for watching it on TV with Mel sat in her bed, drifting in and out of sleep. It's not bloody fair!

Wednesday 7th May

Mel drifted in and out of sleep during the football and when she woke, she spent time organising her social diary . . . or getting Becky to organise her social diary! She has a few visitors planned over the next few days and we all appreciate the efforts people make. Due to the deterioration in her condition and the subsequent increase in medication, she is very drowsy at times, but as she keeps reminding us, she likes to just sit there and listening to people talking. The other change in circumstances is that she no longer has the energy to take phone calls. She likes the texts, but a phone call takes it out of her so much, chances are she is likely to fall asleep during the call.

Mel fell asleep at half past one. She woke twenty minutes later asking for the old fan. I put it near her and with two fans blowing on her face she fell back to sleep. She woke up again at about 3am. She was struggling with her breathing and was getting agitated. I sat with her, holding her hand, talking to her and trying to calm her. I gave her some morphine and it was then I noticed the temperature in the room was 32 degrees so I set about opening the patio doors, the conservatory windows, the kitchen door and within about twenty minutes we'd knocked four degrees off the temperature. The temperature in the house is raised due, in no small part, to the two oxygen machines that sit side by side next to her bed. They throw out a lot of heat. As the doors and windows opened, the temperature dropped and Mel's breathing calmed. Following a back rub we sat talking for another couple of hours. She told me how Becky was an expert at foot rubs and she was going to ask her for another tomorrow.

She confirmed what she had spoken to Julie about earlier in the day, saying that she has now decided that if the situation arose, she wouldn't want to be resuscitated. She wants to die at home with her family around her. Julie had related these wishes to Pauline and she had informed Dr. Tansey.

Amongst the other things we discussed in the early hours was religion. Mel said she had beliefs, but over recent months they'd been tested to the limit and she wasn't sure at the moment. I told her I could understand. I feel the same. We both said we believed that this life was a "passing through" and it wasn't the end. Our middle of the night conversations are a mixture of the sad, the serious and at times the downright silly. I told her last night how proud I was of her, not just for the way she's dealing with this but the way she's lived life. I'm not sure if she'll remember, but I wanted to tell her.

Mel did say that at sometime, maybe in the future, she may want to speak to a vicar or someone from the church. She didn't at the moment, but it's something she has thought about. I reassured her that if she did, we would sort it out for her. We've had a few instances of well-meaning people trying to push their religion on us, and with the greatest respect, it's not what we need at the moment. After talking to Mel for a while last night I came to the conclusion that she does have beliefs, they are being tested, but she needs to re-discover her faith for herself, I'm sure she will and that will be without being preached to.

She fell back to sleep about six o'clock in the morning and I lay back on the cushions. Julie came down just before eight and took over the care duties. I went back to bed and slept till ten o'clock. After showering and getting dressed I drove over to Tamworth to see some of my work colleagues. They'd asked me to go over and I was glad of the drive out. As I drove through the lanes outside Alrewas it took me back a year to when I used to drive Mel to the train station at Tamworth. She'd spend the weekend at home and in order to stay as long as possible, she'd get up early in the morning, drive with me over to Tamworth and catch the train to Birmingham from there. It seems a lifetime away now.

At Tamworth I talked (probably too much) about what had happened over the last few days. and how we were coping. Unbeknown to me, my work colleagues from across the force had made a collection and they presented me with an amount of money that left me speechless! I've said it before on here and I'll say it again, Staffordshire Police, my employers, have been fantastic. My colleagues, old and new, have been brilliant and without their support getting through this would have been so much more difficult than it is. Thank you doesn't do it justice, but I just want you all to know how much Julie, Becky, Mel and myself appreciate your support and it's helping us through a very tough time that in the next few weeks will get even tougher. I brought the collection home, told Mel and she too was speechless. She kept saying she felt guilty because she hadn't done anything!!

Mel has drifted in and out of sleep today. The extra morphine is now beginning to kick in and as a consequence she sleeps. This time last week she was on 180mg tablets and

70mg of oral morphine. She's now on 240mg and the same 70mg a day. This is designed to keep the pain away. She's said to me many times that she's constantly in pain, it never goes away. The tablets just keep the edge off it. I've noticed too that her feet are swelling slightly and this is something we'll mention to Pauline in the morning. Getting onto the commode is becoming increasingly difficult for her. An average trip to the commode (Less than two feet from the bed) takes about forty minutes. She has to sit up (rest for 10 mins), get onto the commode (rest for 10 mins), do what she needs to do (rest for 10 mins) and then get back on the edge of the bed (another 10 minute rest). But she is adamant she wants to keep trying. Also, her hair has started sprouting. Not a great deal, , , , less than Pepe Reina, , , more than Homer Simpson ,.but there are signs of movement on the head. I tried to take a picture on my phone to show Mel what it was like, but the flash reflected off her head. They're great mobile phones are for medical matters. You wouldn't believe it. Mel has a bed sore on her right bum cheek. She wanted to see it. Mirrors were a complicated possibility, but ...yep, you've guessed it, out with the Nokia and two minutes later she was viewing her own bedsore. . . . not the most artistic picture I've ever taken, but then it was never meant to be a competition entry!

Mel had some aromatherapy. This is giving her so much help and it relaxes her. After the aromatherapist had gone, Mel dozed off to sleep as Becky gave her the foot massage she'd wanted at four o'clock the previous morning!

Mel posted an entry on Facebook today, it read . . .

"Mel Leech is having a rough coupla days and visitors are restricted at the min . . . its not personal. . . I just need to recover and sort my meds out"

Thursday 8th May

Mel and I sat up till half past six. We watched two episodes of The Bill and then what seemed like two dozen episodes of Friends. She fell asleep and I lay down on the sofa, I couldn't be bothered to get the cushions on the floor. I went upstairs at 8:30 and Julie took over. I slept for an hour and a half and then got dressed and went downstairs. Mel was on the commode and her condition had deteriorated further. Her breathing was erratic and there was a visible decline. She had wet the bed. Julie and I discussed her condition, the deterioration and we both agreed we needed help. It wasn't far away.

Julie had spoken to Jane, the Hospice Nurse, earlier this morning and as Mel wasn't too bad at that point, arranged for her to come out later. We rang the doctor's surgery and were told the doctor would visit and the district nurses would be round as soon as possible. They arrived within minutes.

The doctor examined Mel and was concerned by the breathing. He felt round her bloated stomach. He was joined by district nurses, Jenny and Rachel (Pauline was on holiday). The doctor suggested to us that Mel would be better off with a syringe driver. This device allows the drugs (morphine, etc) to be administered gradually on a timer. I'd talked to Mel about it earlier and after the doctor had mentioned it she agreed to have it done. She struggled to get on and off the commode, so they suggested a catheter may help. As always, and in spite of her drug induced state, Mel asked questions about it and after getting the answers she agreed to the procedure. The doctor ordered a shed load of oxygen for Mel as her requirement levels had shot from 5 to 8 litres. He explained to us that Mel's lungs were not good and he thought this was the beginning of the end. Tears welled up but I didn't want Mel to see me crying. I looked at her this morning and for the first time throughout this whole illness, I wanted it to be over. I don't want her to suffer and this morning I felt she was suffering.

Mel continues to listen to TalkSport throughout the day. It gives her comfort and she likes listening to the football arguments. At one point the doctor asked to have the radio turned off and Mel came as close as she could to putting up a fight! Over the next couple of hours the district nurses came and went, the oxygen delivery man came and went and the doctor went. When they returned the nurses explained what they would be doing and they set about making her as comfortable as possible. They helped Mel onto the commode, changed her bed, washed and changed her and then sat her back on the bed. I held Mel's hand as they put the syringe driver in and then stayed with her as they sorted out the catheter. Julie was sorting out her clothes, her bedding and during all this the oxygen man arrived with 8 cylinders of oxygen.

Eventually it was all sorted and we all took turns to sit with Mel and keep her calm. The doctor stopped some of the medication she'd been having. Penicillin, Anti-biotics, Norathisterone were all stopped as they no longer serve any purpose. They decided to stop the Clexane injections. Mel drifted in and out of sleep. At one point Jane, the hospice nurse, called me into the conservatory, where the nurses had set up camp. She asked if I knew what to do when Mel passed away. Some of it I did, some I didn't.

Eventually all the medical people left and shortly after they did so, Mel needed the loo for a poo. She decided again to use the commode so we helped her off the bed and onto the commode. Again, this is where Julie comes into her own and Becky and I run for the hills. Smelly poo on an empty stomach isn't a good combination. I shall award Julie a medal in due course. After she'd finished Mel climbed back on the bed but sat on the edge again with the bean bag supporting her. She put her legs on top of the commode and although she looked a bit uncomfortable, she assured us she wasn't. Pauline (who was off duty) called round to see Mel.

Just after 6pm the doctor from the surgery came back to check on her comfort levels. He agreed she seemed more comfortable than this morning. He checked her sats again and despite the 8 litres of oxygen they were down again, this time to

86. He asked her if she was in pain, she replied no. He asked if she was comfortable, she replied yes. The drugs are working. It's now 8pm. She's sat on the edge of the bed. Her breathing is erratic; she wakes up every now and then to check we're still here. She mentions now and then that she can't breathe properly, but on the whole she just sleeps. She's not eaten all day and has survived on about a two dozen sips of Capri Sun. I said that Monday was a tough day . . . today was the toughest so far.

Friday 9th May
The best we can say today is that Mel is comfortable and as far as we can tell, relatively pain free. The pain relief being fed through the syringe driver, along with the steroids is keeping it at bay. She remained on the edge of the bed with her feet on the commode all night. She drifted in and out of sleep throughout the night. We all stayed up with her, taking ten - twenty minutes sleep as and when it overcame us. I've slept for about five hours in the last forty eight. The District Nurses visited us around 9pm last night. They asked if we'd like a visit from the night time staff. We said yes at first, but then decided against it. We thought that if a nurse turned up at 2am Mel may think things were serious. Of course, they are, but we want to protect her for as long as possible. Mel listened to the radio and then asked us to put Friends on the DVD. We watched it till about 7am. It's an easy watch and it helps to relax Mel.

Yesterday she switched to cylinders of oxygen. We had 8 delivered. It wasn't long before she upped the oxygen requirement from 8 litres to 15. Double what she'd been on and seven times the amount she'd been on a couple of weeks ago. Just after lunchtime Julie (District Nurse) arrived. She administered more pain relief through the syringe driver and Julie (my Julie) and Julie (the district nurse) washed and changed Mel and got her back into bed. A short sentence doesn't do that job justice. There is a lot involved, moving Mel, undressing her, washing her and all the time treating her like a china doll as the slightest movement in the wrong place can cause intense pain. Whilst the two Julies were doing this I was on my mission to get the cylinders of oxygen changed to the machines. This task was achieved and this evening the little guy from the oxygen place arrived with two eight litre machines. We kept three cylinders as back up in case of a power cut. Julie (district nurse) checked Mel's catheter too. They'd struggled a bit yesterday when they'd inserted it, the reason being there was a blockage which they said could be a tumour. The disease has a hold of her body. District Nurse Julie explained that as the disease intensified, they would administer more pain killer to counteract it. Dr. Haynes had said last month that Mel would drift into sleep and unconsciousness and the district nurse confirmed this.

My sister and niece visited this afternoon as did Julie's sister Carol. They stopped till around tea time and Mel said she enjoyed listening to the conversation, even though she couldn't take part. Mel can hardly speak now, she gets too breathless. In the care package sent by Virginia from the USA there was a scribble board. It's a bit like an Etch a Sketch. Mel uses that to communicate with us. She hasn't eaten for nearly 48 hours and takes a few sips of water. She uses the lollipop sponges to moisten her mouth. These are small pink sponges on lolly sticks, we dip them in water for her and she rubs them around her mouth to keep it moist.

We have to stop visits from friends. We've asked Mel, and as much as she'd love to, she is simply too tired to receive any visitors. I'd like to think this situation may change, but if I'm honest I doubt it will. I know she's appreciated all the visits she's had whilst she's been ill and so have Julie, Becky and myself. Her friends mean so much to her and although you can't visit, please text her. If she can't read the texts I'll read them to her.

It's now ten to seven. . . . Mel has sat up for a while. Her breathing is still rattly, her stomach bloated and she's beyond tired. She sits up, watches a few minutes of TV and falls asleep.

We're hungry but can't eat, tired but can't sleep. I want to shout, scream and cry my eyes out, but I can't. I don't want her to be in pain anymore. This is the cruellest thing. No-one should have to watch their children die. It's so so wrong. I'm coping, but feel as though I shouldn't be. No one should cope with this, because no one should have to. It's now seven o'clock and I've just nodded off. I awoke suddenly and thought I'd forgotten to change Mel's oxygen cylinder and then realised she was now on a machine. I call it old age. Mel would call it chemo brain!

Saturday 10th May

The days are getting harder. Julie and I stayed up all night with Mel, snatching sleep as and when it got the better of us. Julie curled up on the sofa, me in the armchair and latterly on the floor. The medication kept Mel's pain at bay and she woke up a couple of times. Julie Becky and myself were watching TV when all of a sudden Mel called me over. "Dad, we haven't watched The Bill."

It was totally random. I asked her if she wanted to watch it and she sleepily replied "In five minutes". I put it on and we watched it. She kept drifting off, but every now and then she'd wake up and try her hardest to focus on the TV. I took the opportunity at one point to tell her how much we loved her. I wanted to tell her at least one more time before the medication took over. We watched three episodes of The Bill in all, Mel watched as much as she could before falling asleep again.

She has no energy and can't talk properly. Her voice is just a forced whisper. She's stopped eating, she drinks just sips of water and she's dying before our eyes . . . but then again I suppose she has been since August. The difference is, it wasn't a reality then, it is now. Every day is worse than the last. We no longer live one day at a time; it's now one hour at a time. Her breathing is erratic and she now just wants close family around her. I felt awful when I had to cancel Emma, one of her best friends from school. They'd not seen each other for a couple of years and Mel had said she wanted to see her. I managed to track her down, but unfortunately we had to cancel the planned visit. Maybe it's better Emma remembers her as a chatty teenager full of life and with an incredible enthusiasm for everything.

I sit and wonder what is going through Mel's mind. I wonder if she realises she's as poorly as she is. I think of the things we've done and also the things we'll never do again. In the middle of the night, earlier this week we picked our Premier Picks on Facebook for the final matches of the season. If it weren't for this horrible situation we'd be sat together watching it, or she'd be at uni with her friends watching the final games. She phone in the evening and relay all that had happened and when she'd told me, she'd tell Julie. I'm sure she's dreaming, she woke up startled yesterday and asked for reassurance that I wasn't going anywhere. I told her, none of us were going anywhere. We would be with her all the time. I haven't left the house since Thursday. I know Mel would understand when I say I have "pissing at the footy syndrome". When you're at the football, nine times out of ten, if you go for a pee during the game, there's a goal scored or a major incident. I'm scared that if I nip to the shop or something, she'll pass away whilst I'm out.

Her right arm is swollen. Her right foot is too. Again it's her right hand side. She lies slumped on the bed, her head forward and whilst her breathing has stopped being noisy, she struggles for each and every breath. She tried to cough this morning, but it was weak effort, she couldn't get the air in her lungs and her pain was visible as she tried. This morning she was in pain again and we called the doctor and the district nurse. They upped the dose of pain killers. All other medication has now been withdrawn. There's no point. No more Clexane, no more steroids, anti biotics, anti sickness. No more penicillin ...just pain relief.

The increase in pain relief meant a trip to the pharmacy which Karen kindly did for us. Carol brought round some ironed washing from the Nanny and my mum and dad visited late afternoon. Another bout of pain hit her this afternoon. She tried to move and I helped her to sit up to ease the pressure. She sat at right angles across the bed again and put her feet on me. I held her hand and talked to her. Becky sat with us whilst Julie and the doctor sorted out the pain relief. As I've said previously, the idea is to relax her and make her comfortable. She keeps fighting, but this disease is getting the better of her and we know that in the next few days we're going to lose her and life will never be as good again.

Sunday 11th May

Mel passed away at 1.35 this morning.

The District Nurse looked in around eightish and after seeing she was comfortable and asleep, she left soon after. After watching TV we put Mel's Take That concert on the DVD. We knew that even if she was sedated, she could still hear. Whilst the concert played, Becky and I looked at some family photographs. We were laughing. Every now and then Mel would tap the side of her bed. She needed help sitting up. She was in a bit of discomfort. We told her we were looking at silly photos of Becky and she smiled back at us. It was her last smile. I asked her if she was in pain and she nodded so I asked Julie to ring the on call district nurses. They arrived just after 1:15. As they arrived I was telling Mel that I thought two of her uni friends (Carly and Dan) were now an item. (Apologies to Carly and Dan if you're not an item). Mel was sedated but could still understand us. The nurses had been with us for about five minutes, Julie, Becky and I were around the bed, I was holding her hand, Becky was stroking her arm and Julie had her arm round her shoulder.

As we sat there with her, she slipped away peacefully, with her family around her just as she had wanted.

When Dr. Haynes told us they could do no more, we promised her we'd be with her all the time. When she got frightened and didn't want to be on her own at night, I promised her I would stop up with her every night. We never broke our promises. She lost the physical battle, but in terms of the mental battle, she kicked its arse big time! She never gave up and kept fighting it till the very end.

After the nurses had washed and dressed her we sat with her until the undertakers arrived. Her battle is over. She fought it to the very end with courage and dignity. The lymphoma can't hurt her any more and she's at peace. The last eight and a half months have been hell and in some ways that hell continues. We knew a while ago we weren't going to win and defeat is hard to take, but through it all we've been there, not just for Mel, but for each other and we'll continue to do so. She's had fantastic support from family and friends and she passed away knowing she was loved so much by so many people.

Today will be a day of family visits, sorting out a few things and facing the loss of our beautiful daughter and as I said last night, life will never be as good again...

Monday 12th May

As predicted, yesterday was a procession of visitors. The afternoon was quiet and in the evening we all went for a walk. I rang everyone that Mel wanted me to in the morning and when I'd finished a whole load of emotion came pouring out and I cried and cried and cried.

I'm trying to keep busy. If I stop and think, I start crying again. I started to watch the football yesterday, but couldn't get into it (sorry Mel) and I turned it off before the end. It's only been a few hours and I miss her so much. I keep expecting a text message, but I know it will never come. I want to keep her phone, she loved it so much and it gave her so much pleasure. The messages she received on it helped her cope in the darkest times. I'm keeping her mobile charged at the moment; I want to keep it on. I feel that if her phone is charged she may ring me. I want another hug. When I tried to move her last night she put her arms around me and tried to hug me. I want another hug, just one more.

Today we've had plenty of things to do. Informing people of the funeral, sorting out certificates, organising our own flowers.

We took back all the tablets she had and also the commode and bath chair. We also visited the Queen's Hospital in Burton to thank all the staff who had dealt with Melissa. They have all been brilliant and we wanted to tell them. This morning we took down her Liverpool pictures from where the bed used to be. We thought last night it was quite ironic that she was diagnosed a week into the football season and passed away on the final day.

The funeral directors came round in the evening and we discussed the arrangements for the funeral. As per Mel's wishes, she'll be cremated and she'll be dressed in her Liverpool (8 Gerrard) shirt. We spoke to Mel about what she wanted and she was adamant that she'd prefer everyone to wear either football shirts, scarves or bright colours. Only Julie, Becky and myself are sending flowers. Mel wanted some good to come out of all this and liked the idea of helping others. With this in mind, we would like donations made in Mel's name to The Willow Foundation. Mel's last day out was organised by the Willow and they help people in her situation have great days out. The funeral will be held at Bretby Crematorium on Friday 16th May at 3pm (I suppose I should say with a three o'clock kick off) and everyone is welcome. Afterward the service , we would like as many of you as possible to join us at Burton Albion's Pirelli Stadium to enjoy a drink, a few nibbles and to reminisce about Mel. We want the funeral to be a celebration of her life and we'd like as many people there as possible

Tuesday 13th May

We had visitors last night. We talked about Mel and looked at some photographs of her before she was diagnosed in August. We can do that now. It's almost like her spirit has been set free and we can begin to remember her as the beautiful young girl she was. We also have a few videos too and if ever we want to hear her voice it's there...even if one of the videos was of her in a drunken state!

I went to book a hair appointment for tomorrow morning and then went into the newsagent to pick up a Burton Mail.

Mel's death notice was in the paper. It made me cry. It brought home the reality of it all and upset me. I returned home and within half an hour Pauline came to visit us. She has been wonderful over the last few weeks and months and we feel we've gained a real friend. Whilst she was here, the local paper rang wanting to do a story on Mel and we all agreed it would be nice so they're coming round in the morning. We've also got the vicar coming to see us too.

After Pauline's visit we drove over to Nottingham to say thank you to the doctors, nurses and consultants who treated Mel during her time there. They are all wonderful people and we know that thanks to them Mel had the best treatment possible. Nothing was too much trouble and everything possible was done.

We saw Faith and Dr. Haynes. Mel thought the world of both of them and had complete trust and confidence in them. We all did. We cannot thank them enough for all they did for Mel and we felt it was important to go and thank them personally. We guessed that Dr. Haynes knew Mel had only a matter of weeks left, but the fact he said weeks or months made the time left much easier. Dr. Haynes told us that Mel was one of the most "together" young people he'd ever met and the way she dealt with the disease was amazing.

After speaking to Dr. Haynes and Faith we went up to Toghill Ward and thanked the people on there. No disrespect to Fletcher Ward, but Mel's favourite was Toghill and she had a special fondness for Kaz and American nurse Melissa. We saw Sister Maggie and some of the other nurses and again they received our heartfelt thanks for all they did. Finally, we went up to Fletcher Ward to see another of Mel's "roommates", Lisa. She is due to have a bone marrow transplant tomorrow, so we went to wish her well and tell her that Mel had passed away. We wondered if we were doing the right thing, but Lisa had been asking after Mel and was so grateful that we'd been to see her.

So that was it, goodbye Nottingham City Hospital...You were fantastic!

I have one more request for the funeral on Friday. Whenever she watched football and there was a tribute, she always told Becky and I that she didn't like the minute's silence. She preferred the minute's appreciation with supporters clapping. With that in mind, if you are attending the funeral on Friday, when we arrive at the crematorium, until we sit down in the chapel we would like to you give Mel a generous round of applause, if nothing else, for the courageous and dignified way she handled the this cruel disease.

Wednesday 14th May

People keep asking how we are and considering what's happened, we're ok. We have photographs to look at and Facebook messages to read and that is helping at the moment. Individual things tend to "set us off", but we talk them through and carry on.

Yesterday evening, Becky and Julie were in the conservatory talking and I was sat on the sofa watching the Championship play off game. It was how it used to be, but with someone missing. One minute I was ok, the next I was crying buckets. There I was sat on my own watching the football. In that moment I missed Mel so much and the emotion came pouring out of me. I wanted her back on that sofa, watching it with me, I wanted to talk to her about it but I can't and I have to try and get used to that. I try to imagine she's there with me, but I can't even do that.

We'd been playing Premier Picks on Facebook since Christmas and up until last week I'd been winning. Last Tuesday at "stupid o'clock" in the morning we both did our picks for the final games on Sunday. She got five points and I got three and she beat me by one point! It's horrible to think we won't be doing that next season or any season. We had a stream of visitors today including Tim Fletcher from the Burton Mail and as he left, Julie, the vicaress arrived and we spent nearly two hours talking to her about the service and the funeral in general on Friday. Two of Julie's friends from work called to see us and the final visitor of the afternoon was the oxygen cylinder man. He came to collect Mel's oxygen machines and the remaining cylinders. That last visible reminder of Mel's illness has left the house.

After he'd left we went out for a drive just for a change of scenery. We've decided today that we are going to keep Mel's Facebook open for ever. Mel loved Facebook and it proved invaluable to her whilst in hospital. She always seemed to find a way to access it, even if at times it was only by phone. With that in mind, we think that wherever she is now, she'll be able to access it and read it. So if ever you want to send her a message, wish her Happy Birthday or Christmas or laugh at her because Liverpool have lost, you can...

Thursday 15th May

Last night we sat for an hour or two looking through photographs of Mel. It's something we've not felt able to do over the last eight months, but now we can and we looked through loads. They brought back so many happy memories.

I woke early this morning, I couldn't sleep properly and I went round to the shop and bought a Burton Mail. The article on Mel was excellent.

I was thinking today about Mel's new Liverpool shirt that is due to arrive on May 22nd. I don't want it to just sit on a shelf. I rang up Liverpool and explained that Mel had passed away and that I wanted to change the size of the shirt to a larger size and to replace the "Torres 9" with "Mel 20". Despite being an Everton fan I would be proud to wear Mel's shirt.

Friday 16th May

Thursday was a bad day for lots of reasons. I couldn't even think about Mel without crying. In the evening I went on the Lymphoma Life Site chat room where Mel spent a lot of time chatting to some wonderful people. I was made so welcome and they talked of Mel being brave, courageous and an inspiration. It gives me a certain amount of satisfaction that throughout her illness, as well as her family and friends, she had wonderful support from people who truly knew what she was going through. We can never thank them enough.

I woke up this morning just after eight o'clock. Despite the sleeping tablet I didn't sleep brilliantly and neither did Julie. We spent part of the morning at The Pirelli Stadium sorting out a few last minute things. We returned home to a load of post, cards mainly. Becky had the results of one of her exams she'd taken and had got a first, which considering all she's been going through is incredible. We all said that we could imagine Mel being with us and saying, "I don't know what all the fuss is about, I knew she'd get a first."

One of the letters we received was from Aston University. It said it had been an honour for them to have Melanie as a student at Aston . . . . . This made us laugh and I'm sure her university friends will understand why.

After reading the rest of the post we did some more reminiscing and got ready. We felt ok. No tears, just calmness. We felt we'd said our goodbyes in the early hours of Sunday morning and today was as much about Mel's friends and other family saying their farewells. That may sound strange, but having seen her in so much pain over the last few months and in particular the last few days, her death, as sad as it was, was a release from all that pain and the saying "at peace" could not have been more appropriate. We all said we felt ok and that over the last nine months we'd had tougher days. . .

Julie wore one of Mel's Liverpool necklaces, Becky the other and I pinned a Liverpool FC badge to my Everton top. We then waited for the cortege to arrive. It duly arrived and we drove up to the Crematorium, passing Mel's old school, Paulet, on the way. Some teachers and prefects stood at the side of the school gates in tribute and for the first time tears appeared.

We reached the crematorium and walked in behind Mel. As we entered the chapel the applause rang out and the tears welled up in my eyes. The place was packed full of Mel's friends and family and the service that followed was a fitting tribute to our wonderful, beautiful daughter. . . . .

Following the hymn All things bright and Beautiful (in which The Nanny sang the wrong verse...she was in the "Cold wind in the Winter", when she should have been up the "Purple Headed Mountain") we said prayers and I gave my tribute to Mel...it read as follows...

"Wow, a full house of family and friends, a three o'clock kick off and You'll Never Walk Alone ringing out from the terraces...exactly as Mel planned.

She may have only been with us for twenty years, but she crammed so much into the time she had.

We all have our favourite memories of Mel and I'm sure over the coming weeks, months and years we'll be reliving them over and over again just as Mel used to share stories of her life with us all...over and over and over again...

Hour after hour, most nights, Julie would hear school stories, nursery stories and latterly university stories as Mel related the day's events in minute detail. If Julie was lucky she would only get to hear each story once, but at times there'd be no stopping Mel. Becky and I would have to intervene and rescue her. . If Mel thought Julie hadn't been listening she'd slip in a sneaky question about what she'd been talking about and woe betide Julie if she didn't know the answer...Mel would have to go through it all again!

Becky and Mel had such a close relationship and they were the best of friends. Becky's formative years were spent listening to her sister and having her life organised in the most loving way. It was Becky who christened her Mooch and that nickname stuck in the home and eventually travelled to uni with her.

As the numbers here today show, she is loved by everyone whose life she touched and she loved life...well, with one or two exceptions...On her Facebook profile in the "Things I don't like" section it lists....Cancer, Non-Hodgkin's Lymphoma and when Man United win!

It's hard to believe that as an eight year old her school report read, "Melissa is a quiet, somewhat shy girl."

As she grew older the shyness disappeared and her confidence blossomed. She became Deputy Head Girl at Paulet and achieved all 'A's in her GSCE's and two A's and a 'B' in her 'A' levels. She developed an enthusiasm for school, study and life that knew no bounds and thankfully stayed with her until she passed away...

As well as her enthusiasm for life, she was also a kind, considerate person who influenced the life of so many who met her...I remember getting an email from a friend of Mel's back in February and it summed up the type of person she was in one simple paragraph. It read...

"Mel, I remember back in my first lesson in psychology when I came into your year for the first time and we were all put into groups. I was so nervous, but you just made a comment that made me laugh, and I just felt strength, and then I felt ok. Another time, when I was giving a presentation and I felt so nervous and jittery and I started, and people weren't paying attention as I was so nervous, but you just smiled at me and paid attention and it just inspired me and I remember how I just got so much confidence that by the end of the presentation, everyone was paying attention."

Melissa was a very open person who would befriend anyone. She rarely judged people and was always very honest. She said what she thought and stood by her own opinions. You always knew where you stood with Mel.

Family and friends apart, Mel had one other love...Liverpool Football Club. As a father I like to think I got most things right, but unfortunately, try as I might I could never convert her to the blue side of the Mersey. Her devotion to Liverpool was down to one man. I've always said, I can compete with most things, but unfortunately the boyish good looks of a young Michael Owen wasn't one of them.

Mel's love of football started in January of 2001. Becky had gone to her cousin Sarah's for the day and Mel, in typical teenage mode, kept saying she was bored. I suggested she come with me to see Burton Albion, I was the club photographer at the time and I explained to her that if she didn't like the football she could go and sit and talk to her Nan, who worked in the boardroom. After mooching around for twenty minutes or more she reluctantly decided to come with me.

Burton played well, won 2-0, there was a bit of fighting on the pitch. Even more off it and she found other young people to talk to. From that moment she was hooked. It wasn't long before she attended her first away game, travelling down to Folkestone, and for the next five years we travelled up and down the country, her watching and me photographing Burton Albion. We had the most fantastic times and I could talk for ever about some of the adventures we had.

Mel always said that the best day of her life was when I took her to Liverpool to watch the 2005 Champions League Final in a bar in the city. Being an Everton fan and a keen photographer I took pictures of her and other reds fans. It gave me an excuse not to cheer. I ended up taking nearly two hundred pictures and six weeks later a book was published which was in essence a record of our trip. Only Melissa Alice Leech could get an Everton fan to travel to Liverpool and sit and endure one of their greatest ever triumphs! But she could, because her enthusiasm made me want to do it.

We went back in Liverpool the following year to watch the FA Cup Final against West Ham in the city centre. As her Uni friends will testify, Mel was fond of singing. She couldn't sing a note, but she was still quite fond of singing. Becky and Leanne came with us, back to the city to watch the game. We got out of the car in Liverpool and for some reason, known only to Mel she burst into song and treated us to a rousing rendition of...I'm forever blowing bubbles...West Ham's anthem! She'd had the song in her head and started singing it without thinking!

We returned again last May to the same pub and as usual her eyes sparkled and her smile lit up the room. Just before half past seven a load of lads poured into the pub, and within minutes they'd got their arms round Mel, hugging her and shouting, "It's Mel, we knew you'd be back, we just knew it." They'd been at the pub two years before and they'd remembered her. She made an impression on everyone she met.

Sadly, three months later she was diagnosed with Non Hodgkin's Lymphoma and life changed for all of us. Despite a series of devastating setbacks, Mel's personality shone through, she never changed, she was always herself and that endeared her to all the doctors and nurses who came into contact with her. Her enthusiasm even transferred to the disease as she sought to know all about it, not just to help herself, but also to help others. Regardless of the horrible treatment she endured she fought the disease with courage, bravery and dignity. She worried less about herself and more about how family and friends were coping. That was Melissa. The best daughter, sister and friend that anyone could ever hope to have."

That was followed by a song by Josh Groban called You're Still You. The service finished with Angels by Robbie Williams and as we left the chapel I gave her one last wave goodbye. .

A big thank you to Rev Julie Coates who conducted the service, she did a brilliant job.

We went out of the chapel and saw so many people who'd come to pay their respects. There were family, teachers, old school friends, uni friends, you name it, they were there.

We went back to the Pirelli Stadium afterwards and so many people joined us, The Nanny got a bit tipsy and ended up tidying away people's glasses (even when they weren't empty) and we left the stadium just after half past seven. The whole service and reception was just as Mel had wanted and we cannot thank everyone enough.

***

I started this blog on November 1st. The intention six months down the line wasn't to be talking about Mel's funeral. We should have been talking about her going back to university, watching the "England Free" Euros, working in Branston Golf Club and buying season tickets for Burton Albion. Those were just some of the plans we'd made. Tomorrow marks the start of another chapter. It's going to take time to get over all we've been through during the last nine months. We've had such wonderful messages of support and I will always treasure the support you've given us all.

I want to thank some people. First and foremost, Melissa for showing courage and making looking after her a lot easier than it could have been, our family, particularly Carol and Keith and The Nanny (and for her ironing duties which we hope if we don't say anything will continue), my sister Karen for her help during the worst time when Julie and I were full of cold, my Mum and Dad for their help. Also to Sarah and Hannah for their support of Mel, which although sometimes from afar, helped keep her spirits up. A big thank you to all her friends for the visits they made, the texts they sent and the friendship they gave. Claire, Sooty, Hammad, Rachel, Phil, Dan, Carly, Gemma, Sophie, Matt, Steve, Dave, Kirsty, Ria, Samantha and others too numerous to mention who kept visiting her, she loved you so much and so do we. We hope you keep in touch.

We are forever indebted to Dr. Adrian Smith, Dr. Zai, Dr. Ahmed, Pat Holland, Wendy the Cannula Queen and the rest of the fantastic staff at Burton's Queens Hospital, Dr. Nik at Leicester, Allan at Derby, Maria who treated Mel at Derby and latterly at Nottingham City Hospital. Ah yes, Nottingham . . . Again our most heartfelt thanks to the incredible and wonderful Dr. Haynes, to Faith the lymphoma nurse. Thanks too to Alison and Maxine in the Stem Cell Unit, to Jenny, Angela and the rest of the staff in the Day case centre. Thanks to all the staff on Toghill Ward, particularly Kaz, Melissa, Hannah the trainee nurse, Sian and Wendy and of course Sister Maggie. Thanks too to those staff on Fletcher Ward and all the health care assistants who do an incredible job.

Many thanks to the Lymphoma Association (www. lymphomas.org.uk) and the members of Lifesite chat room who supported Mel during some of her toughest times and also her online friends from Webmagic and MacMillan (www.macmillan.org.uk) .

Finally, big thanks to Pauline, Julie, Dr. Tansey and the rest of the District Nurses who were unbelievable and who helped make Mel's time at home so comfortable. Thanks to Jane and Alison from the St. Giles Hospice Team and to everyone else who helped us whilst we cared for Mel at home. A special thank you too to Annie Sheldon and Josie Brown the aromatherapists, I am forever converted to your methods.

I'm sorry if you're not mentioned in person, there are so many people and I know I'll read this at a later date and think, crap, I should have mentioned so and so...anyway, so and so, thank you too!!!

Julie and I need some time to relax and take stock of things. We've both talked about returning to work, but we need a few weeks first to work our way through all we've been through. We hope people will understand. For nine months we've cared for and looked after our beautiful daughter, we've travelled thousands of miles to see her in hospital, spent countless hours at her bed side being with her and looking after her. We'd do it all again if we had to. She was worth it a million times over. I said yesterday that I felt lost. It seemed strange having nothing to do. No sausage rolls to cook, no cheese and potato pie to make, no drinks to fetch, no TV to watch with her. It's a strange feeling. Part of us is glad she's out of pain; another part of us just yearns for her to ask one more time for a Capri Sun out of the fridge. All these emotions that have been with us for nine months will take time to ease. We will get back to work; we will start to live a new "normal". We have Mel's strength and courage to help us through this. I've thought about re-writing her story. I've kept all my blog notes, some of which I didn't publish due to varying reasons. Maybe I can get Mel's story published and we can boost the coffers of a few more charities. Who knows, but it's something positive for the future.

We'll start to live again, because ultimately, that is what Melissa would want us to do. There won't be a day we don't think of her and we'll carry her in our hearts wherever we go... always.

You get one shot at life...Don't Miss.

Mel didn't, she hit the bullseye every time!

CHAPTER TWENTY SIX

Carrying on...One Day at a Time

In the weeks and months that followed we tried to make sense of all that had happened during the previous year. We still keep ourselves occupied and even now expect Mel to arrive home asking what all the fuss was about. Julie busied herself in the garden and we created a quiet space that the family contribute to with plants and ornaments. It's Mel's garden. Becky had missed her exams in May and studied hard throughout the summer, took them in August and passed them all. A remarkable achievement considering all that she had to deal with during her first year at university.

I quickly discovered the only way I could get through the days was to keep busy and the first thing I wanted to do was to get a memorial bench for Mel at Aston University. With the help of her friend Sophie, Sophie's dad and the university we granted one of Mel's final wishes and on Tuesday 19th August, on what would have been Mel's 21st birthday, over fifty friends and relatives attending the unveiling of Mel's bench. It was situated by the lake and the inscriptions of "Friend to many, inspiration to all" and "You'll always be my Brightside, YNWA" were chosen by three of her closest friends at university, Rachel, Hammad and Sooty.

As I mentioned in one of the blog entries, our district nurse, Pauline became a close friend. It was Pauline who first planted the seed in our minds about having a dog. Julie and I love walking and the thought of a dog appealed as it would get us out of the house and provide a distraction. Alfie certainly does that, although during the first week of him being at home we could have easily sent him back. We struggled to find the energy to deal with all that an eight week old puppy brings. We worked through it though and now Julie, Becky and I wouldn't be without him. We find that we talk more when we're out walking and Alfie gives us a reason to get out.

Throughout Mel's illness and beyond, the question we are asked more than any other is "How do you cope?" Some days we cope better than others. Grief is strange. It's there all the time, bubbling under and then suddenly it will surface and a tidal wave of emotion will envelop us. The best way I can describe it, is that we can allow ourselves to see the headlines, but we can't read the story. We have a distinct lack of energy that on days leaves us feeling unbelievably tired. The realisation that Melissa had cancer was a life changing moment. We knew there would be no going back. It was as though in an instant an impenetrable barrier had come down, separating the past from the "new" present. The past now seeming like an ideal world to which we could never return. Coping with the loss is like becoming emotionally paralysed. We can think about Mel, the illness and her death as we can easily talk about them, sometimes with tears, sometimes without. There is a switch in our heads that most of the time is in the off position, leaving us numb and giving the impression to most people that we are strong and coping well. The reality is we don't even try to deal with our loss most of the time. We look on our life with detachment, it's the only way to function on a day to day basis. Appearances can be deceptive, behind the smiles we live with unfathomable depths of grief and hurt which we are constantly aware of, but don't allow ourselves to become immersed in very often. When we do it saps all of our energy. Our lives will be forever changed, the clock can never go back and therein lies the terrible heartstopping awareness that "this is it", Melissa has gone forever and only in our own dying can we ever hope to be re-united with our daughter.

"Time will heal". It is said to us often and with the best will in the world, it doesn't. Cuts heal, broken bones heal. Losing your daughter (or in Becky's case sister) to cancer will be as horrible in twenty years as it is now. Nothing will make it better. Time may give us the ability to manage our grief, but it will not heal. I had a dream the other night. I was arriving home from somewhere and Mel was waiting for me at the door. She was about 7-8 years old. She shouted "Daddy", ran toward me and hugged me tightly. Although it was a dream I felt the hug like it was real. I woke up and I could remember it so clearly, I could still feel her arms around me. Within seconds I had tears streaming down my face as the reality hit home. The only way I was ever going to get a hug from Melissa again was in my dreams, of which I have no control over. It may be next week or next month. It may be never. If I get through the day without a tear then I feel I've coped. Most days I don't cope. I want to tell her I love her once more, I want a hug, I want a water fight in the garden, I want to sit with her and enjoy three match Sunday, I want a text to say Everton are crap, I want to send her one to say Liverpool aren't much better . . . I just want her back so much.

As I mentioned earlier in this chapter, I need to keep busy and I took the decision to do all I could to raise awareness of Lymphoma. I began working closely with the Lymphoma Association (www.lymphomas.org.uk). Had Mel recovered she would have done the same. The Lymphoma Association were a great help to Mel during her illness and have been a fantastic support to Julie, Becky and I. In September of 2008 I was awarded a Special Commendation at the Lymphoma Association's Beacon of Hope awards. As I sat there in the auditorium afterwards, all I wanted to do was to speak to Mel. I just wanted to say to her, "Look at what we've done Mel".

Speaking of awards, we donated an award to Paulet School in memory of Mel. It was presented to the pupil who had inspired others or displayed enthusiasm in a particular subject or project. We attended the awards evening as guests of the school in November and a fitting winner was chosen. It is something we will continue to support.

The fight with the government goes on. I've had letters from other people who were in the same situation as Mel, receiving no financial support because they are students. We've got the government to admit there is a problem and we are now waiting for the funding to be sorted and the rules on how students with long term illnesses are treated can be changed.

I have signed up to cycle from London to Paris to raise awareness and funds for the association in June 2009 and also will be cycling the Lymphoma Association's own annual cycle ride a week later. Thanks to Mel's friends at uni and our own friends we've smashed the target for both rides. In 2008 we emailed over 150 universities with an article I'd written asking them to put it in their university newspapers, again helping to raise awareness. We've had articles in local and national newspapers and I have also spoken on local and national radio. One of my proudest achievements was the introduction of a "Friends, family and Carers" section on the Lymphoma Association website message board (www.lymphomas.org.uk). This was something I felt there was a need for, I suggested it and it was done. We set up a website www.mad4mel.co.uk the mad part standing for Making a Difference because that is what we want to do. Be it by raising awareness or raising funds, we want to make a difference. I have received some tremendously uplifting emails from people across the world who have been inspired by our blogs and it is so satisfying to know that even though Mel is no longer alive, she continues to help and inspire others.

***

Life can be terribly cruel. Nothing could have prepared us for Melissa's illness. As a parent you think you can fix everything for your children. You're their superhero. We cared for Melissa as best we could by making life as "normal" as possible in the circumstances, but ultimately we could do nothing and life was, and still is, anything but normal. We had to watch helplessly as this disease took our beautiful daughter. Sometimes we want to talk, other times we want to be silent. We get through the days and nights as best we can. We visit past times, some we wish we could live all over again, others we want to obliterate from our mind forever. We're surrounded with memories of how life has changed and how good it used to be. I have dreams that I never want to wake up from and nightmares that shake me and I wake in tears.

There was no parenting manual, no course to attend, we relied on love and pure instinct. Nothing could have prepared us for sitting with our child and telling her that nothing more could be done and in a matter of weeks or months she would pass away. No-one should have to sit with their child whilst they're told how they are going to die. We were with Melissa when she breathed her first breath in this world and we sat holding her hand as she breathed her last. We think of Mel all the time, imagining what she'd be saying and remembering all the happy times we shared over the years and it is those memories that help us through each day. We're lucky in as much as we have photos and videos of Melissa and her voice is never far away. Certain dates now take on more significance and we weren't prepared for the double anniversaries during the first year without Mel. What we didn't realise as we inevitably cast our minds back twelve months is that you get two shots at every event. Mel was diagnosed on the 20th August 2007, a Monday. In 2008 20th August was a Wednesday, so you end up reminiscing on the day and the date and that makes things twice as hard, although that is something that in time will cease to happen and it will be just dates that are remembered. August 20th – Diagnosis. Christmas Eve – When the rules changed and her chances of a cure diminished. April 1st – We were told it was incurable. May 11th – The day she passed away. There are many others, but these stick in the memory. What also sticks in my memory is the last hug, the last smile, the moment she passed away and the moment the undertakers took her away. Four images that don't seem to want to move from my mind. Four images that no parent should ever have to deal with.

Life will never be as good again, we're a three now and we should be a four. As the future unfolds, there'll always be someone missing. How Mel's life would have panned out had she not died, is something we can only dream about as we continue to live our lives...one day at a time.

A Letter to Mooch

I want to tell you I cried today
And the reasons why, I just want to say,
It's nothing you did, or didn't do
It's just that I was thinking of you
Remembering times we all had together
They'll stay in my heart, just like you . . . . forever,
Your smile, your tears, the sound of your laughter
Why couldn't we all live like, happy ever after?
I remember your chats with mum each night
Each story ending with "You're listening, right?"
Playing Barbie's with Becky there was Skipper and Todd
Talk of no-neck Barbies sounded so odd
Days out I'll cherish, I could talk for hours
Of Barmouth, London and Alton Towers
No fancy holidays and weeks in the sun
Just family days out where we had so much fun
Football trips, I remember so well
Bob and Bill, Me and Mel
Watching football, at weekends we'd be out
The best of times...never in doubt,
Champions League day, I know you adore
One Night in the City Mooch...Need I say more?
When you came home from uni, the house came to life
Food cupboards were full and hog feasts were rife
Loved by your family and adored by your friends
Two great years at uni, then the saddest of ends
You fought to the last, now the tears just fall
No chats on the phone, no text and no call
I miss you so much and things just aren't right
But when I climb into bed, I still say goodnight
You're here in my heart and it makes me so sad
I miss you Mooch, much love from your dad

x